'Stop in the ♡ name of pants!'

Fab ⭐New Confessions of

Georgia Nicolson

Louise Rennison ♥

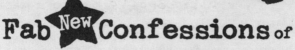

HarperCollins *Children's Books*

Find out more about Georgia at www.georgianicolson.com

First published in Great Britain in hardback by HarperCollins *Children's Books* 2008
First published in Great Britain in paperback by HarperCollins *Children's Books* 2009
HarperCollins *Children's Books* is a division of HarperCollins*Publishers* Ltd,
77-85 Fulham Palace Road, Hammersmith, London W6 8JB

This production 2013

ISBN-13 978-0-00-793479-9

Printed and bound in England by
Clays Ltd, St Ives plc

To my groovy and fabby and marvy family and mates (including my extended family at HarperCollins and Aitken Alexander).

'Stop in the name of pants!' – my latest work of geniosity – is dedicated especially to absent mates. Who have selfishly gone off to have fun. (Yes, you know who you are, Jeddbox and Elton.)

And also to absent mates who aren't really absent but lurking about somewhere pretending to be absent.

A Note from Georgia

Dear chums, chumettes and, er... chummly wummlies,

I write to you from my bed of pain. Once again I have exhausted myself with creativitosity writing 'Stop in the Name of Pants!' I am having to lie down with a cup of tea and a Curly Wurly. But that is how vair vair much I care about you all, my little pallies. I am a fool to myself, I know.

I ask only one thing in return and that is this. All of you must dance the Viking disco hornpipe extravaganza in classrooms and recreation facilities throughout the world. It doesn't matter if there are only two or three of you, just stand up proudly, get your horns and paddles out (oo-er) and dance!!!

Loads and loads of deep luuurve,

Georgia
xxx

p.s. Some of you don't know what the Viking disco hornpipe extravaganza is, do you?

p.p.s. Please don't tell me you didn't know that Vikings had discos.

p.p.p.s. Or that they shouted "Hooooorrrn!!!"

p.p.p.p.s. For those of you who haven't bothered to keep up with my diaries because you are just TOO BUSY, I have put instructions for the dance at the back near the glossary.

p.p.p.p.p.s. What have you been TOO BUSY doing?

p.p.p.p.p.p.s. I suppose you have been TOO BUSY to even know what the having-the-hump scale is as well.

p(x7).s. So I have included that at the back too. My so-called friend Jas (who has the hump pretty much all of the time) would be at number four with you by now (cold-shoulderosity work).

p(x8).s. I really luuurve you and do not mind that you are lazy minxes. That is your special charm. Pip pip. X

Deep in the forest of red-bottomosity

Saturday July 30th
Camping fiasco
11:30 p.m.
In my tent of shame.

Again.

The rest of my so-called pals are still out in the woods with the lads and I have crept back to the campsite aloney. I can hear snoring from Miss Wilson's tent and also Herr Kamyer's. I bet there will be a deputation of voles coming along shortly to complain that they can't get any sleep because of the racket.

11:32 p.m.

I'm going to forget about everything and just go to sleep in my lovely sleeping bag. On the lovely soft ground. Not. It's like sleeping on an ironing board. And I do know what that is like actually.

11:33 p.m.

I said coming on this school camping trip would be a fiasco of a sham and I was not wrong.

11:34 p.m.

I was right.

11:35 p.m.

I wonder what the others are doing?

11:36 p.m.

Anyway, the main thing is that I am now, officially, the girlfriend of a Luuurve God. And therefore I have put my red bottom behind me with a firm hand. I will never again be found wandering lonely as a clud into the cakeshop of luuurve. Or picking up some other éclair or tart or fondant fancy. Ditto Eccles cakes and Spotty dick or... shut up, brain.

11:37 p.m.

So, speaking as the official girlfriend of a Luuurve God who has put my red bottom behind me with a firm hand and who will never be wandering around looking for extra cakes, can someone tell me this...

How in the name of God's pantyhose have I ended up snogging Dave the Laugh?

Also known as Dave the Tart.

Two minutes later

Oh goddy god god. And let us face facts. It wasn't just a matey type snog. You know, not a – "It's all right, mate, I'm just a mate accidentally snogging another mate" – sort of snog.

It was, frankly and to get to the point and not beat around the whatsit, a "phwoooaar" snogging situation.

Thirty seconds later

In fact, it was deffo number four and about to be number five.

Four seconds later

Anyway, shut up, brain, I must think. Now is not the time for a rambling trip to Ramble Land. Now is the time to put my foot down with a firm hand and stop snogging my not-boyfriend Dave the Laugh.

One minute later

I mean, I am practically married to Masimo the Luuurve God.

Ten seconds later

Well, give or take him actually asking me to marry him.

Five seconds later

And the fact that he has gone off to Pizza-a-gogo land on holiday and left me here in Merrie but dangerous England to fend for myself. Being made to go on stupid school camping trips with madmen (Miss Wilson and Herr Kamyer).

He has left me here, wandering around defenceless in the wilderness near Ramsgate, miles away from the nearest TopShop.

Three seconds later

And how can I help it if Dave the Laugh burrows into my tent?

Because that is more or less what happened. That is *le* fact.

I was snuggling down under some bit of old raincoat (or sleeping bag, as Jas would say in her annoying *oooh isn't it fun outdoors* sort of way). Anyway, where was I? Oh yes, I was snuggling down earlier tonight after an action-packed day of newt drawing when there was a *tap-tap-tapping* on the side of the tent. I thought it might have been an owl attack but it was Dave the Laugh and his Barmy Army (Tom, Declan, Sven and Edward) enticing us into their tent with promises of snacks and light entertainment.

Four seconds later

I blame Dave entirely for this. He and I are just mates and I have a boyfriend and he has a girlfriend and that is that, end of story. Not. Because then he comes to the countryside looking for me and waving his Horn about.

We were frolicking around in the lads' tent, and Dave and me went off for an innocent walk in the woods. You know, like old matey-type mates do. But then I put my foot down a bloody badger hole or something and fell backwards into the river. Anyway, Dave was laughing like a loon for a bit before he reached down and put his arms around me to lift me up the riverbank and I said, "I think I may have broken my bottom."

And he was really smiling and then he said, "Oh bugger it, it has to be done."

And he snogged me.

When he stopped I pushed him backwards and looked at him. I was giving him my worst look.

He said, "What?"

I said, "You know what. Don't just say 'what' like that."

"Like what?"

I said, with enormous dignitosity, "Look, you enticed me with your shenanigans and, erm, puckering stuff."

He said, "Erm, I think you will find that you agreed to come to my tent in the middle of the night to steal me from my girlfriend."

I said, "It was you that snogged me."

He looked at me and then he sighed. "Yeah, I know. I don't feel very good about this. I'm not so... well, you're used to it."

My head nearly exploded. "I'm USED to what??"

He looked quite angry, which felt horrible. I'd seen him angry with me before and I didn't usually like what he had to say. He went on: "You started all this sounding the Horn business ages ago, using me like a decoy duck and then going out with Robbie, then messing about with me and then going out with Masimo. And then telling me that you felt mixed up."

I just looked at him. I felt a bit weepy actually. I might as well be wet at both ends.

My eyes filled with tears and I blinked them away and he just kept on looking at me. I couldn't tell what he was thinking. Maybe he had had enough of me and he really hated me.

Then he just walked away and I was left alone. Alone to face the dark woods of my shamenosity and the tutting of Baby Jesus.

Ten seconds later

And I didn't even know which way the tent was.

The trees looked scary and there was all sorts of snuffling going on. Maybe it was rogue pigs. Pigs who had had enough of the farm life, fed up with just bits of old potato peelings to eat and nowhere to poo in privacy. Maybe these ones wanted a change of menu and had made a bid for freedom by scaling the pigpen fence late at night. Or perhaps they were like the prisoners of war in that old film that Vati's always rambling on about. *The Great Escape.* When the prisoners dug a tunnel under the prison fence.

That's what these pigs must have done. Tunnelled out of the farm to freedom.

There was more snuffling.

Yes, but now they were hungry. Runaways from the farm just waiting to pounce on some food. If they found me, they would think of me like I thought of them. As some chops. Some chops in a skirt. In sopping knickers in my case. Out here in the Wild Woods the trotter was on the other foot.

I could climb up a tree.

Could they climb trees?

Could I climb trees?

Oh God, not death by pig!!!

The scuffling got nearer and then a little black thing scampered out of the undergrowth. It was a vole. How much noise can one stupid little mousey thing make? A LOT is the answer.

I should make friends with it really, because with my luck I will be kidnapped by voles and raised as one of their own. On the plus side, I would never have to face the shame of my red-bottomosity, just spend my years digging and licking my fur and being all aloney on my owney.

Like I am now.

Dave appeared out of the darkness in front of me. I ran over to him and burst into tears. He put his arm around me.

"OK, Kittykat, I'm sorry. Come on, it's all right. Stop blubbing. Your nose will get all swollen up and you'll collapse under the weight of your nungas and I can't carry all of you home."

It was nice in the forest now. I could see the moon through the trees. And my hiccups had almost gone. As we walked along he smiled at me and stroked my hair. Oooh, he was nice.

He said, "We haven't done this luuurve business before, so we are bound to be crap at it. I do feel bad about Emma, but that is not your fault. That is my fault. We can put away our Horns and be matey-type mates again. Come on. Cheer up. Be nasty to me again, it's more normal. I like you and I always have and I always will."

I sniffed a bit and gave him a brave, quivering but attractive smile. I kept my nostrils fully under control so that they didn't spread all over my face. As we walked along I could hear little squelching noises coming from the knicker department. With a bit of luck you couldn't hear it above the noise of rustling voles (also known as my nearly adopted family).

Dave said, "Is that your pants squelching, Gee? You should change them when we get back. You don't want to get pneumonia of the bum-oley on top of everything else."

We walked back through the trees in the light of the jolly old big shiny yellow thing, and no, I do not mean an illuminated banana had just appeared, although that would have been good.

Then everything went horrible again; there were some hideous noises coming from the left of us...

"Tom, Tom. over here. I think I've found an owl dropping."

Oh brilliant – Jas, Wild Woman of the Forest, was in the vicinity. Dave took his arm away from my shoulder. I looked up at him, he looked down at me and bent over and kissed me on the mouth really gently.

"Ah well, the end of the line, Kittykat. You go off with your Italian lesbian boyfriend and see how it goes and I'll try and be a good mate to you. Don't tell me too much about you and him because I won't like it – but other than that, let's keep the accidental outburst of red-bottomosity to ourselves."

I smiled at him. "Dave, I...".

"Yes?"

"I think I can feel something moving in my undercrackers."

Midnight

And that is when I scampered off back to Loony Headquarters. That is, our school campsite. To change my nick-nacks.

Ten past midnight

I said to Baby Jesus, "I know I have done wrong and I am sorry times a million, but at least you have been kind enough not to send a plague of tadpoles into my pantaloonies."

Sunday July 31st

11:00 a.m.

I must say, it was a lot easier getting our tent down than up. I pulled all the peg-type things out of the ground, Rosie and Jools kicked the pole over, and though it wouldn't go in its stupid bag thing, we made a nice bundle of it in about three minutes flat.

Jas and her woodland mates and Herr Kamyer and Miss

Wilson were folding and sorting and putting things in little pockets and so on for about a million years.

Ten minutes later

Rosie, Jools and me stashed our tent bundle in the suitcase holder thing at the side of the coach and got on board past Mr Attwood. The only reason we got on without some sort of Nazi investigation and body search was because he was slumped at the wheel with his cap pulled down over his face.

Rosie said, "That's how he drives."

And she is not wrong if the nightmare journey home was anything to go by.

Twenty minutes later

We were having a little zizz on the back seat under a pile of our coats when Jas, patron saint of the Rambling On Society, came on board. I knew that because she came to the back of the coach and shook my shoulder quite violently. I peered at her. She was tremendously red-faced.

I said, "Jas, I am trying to sleep."

"You didn't pack your tent up properly."

I said, "Oh, I'm sorry, are the tent police here?"

She said, "You have just made a big mess of yours in the boot. We had to take it out and pack it up so that we could get ours in!"

"Yes, well, Jas, as you can see, I am very, very busy."

"You are soooo selfish and lax and that is why you have a million boyfriends, none of whom will stay with you."

She stormed off to sit at the front near her besties Miss Wilson and Herr Kamyer.

God, she is annoying, but luckily no one else heard her rambling on about the million boyfriends scenario. I wonder if the boys are home yet?

Five minutes later

Herr Kamyer stood up at the front of the bus and said, "Can I haff your attention, girls." Everyone carried on talking, so he started clapping his hands together.

Mr Attwood jerked to life and said, "It's time to go."

Herr Kamyer said, "*Ja, ja, danke schön, Herr Driver*, but first I vill count zat ve are all pre—"

At which point Mr Attwood put his foot down and Herr Kamyer fell backwards into Miss Wilson's lap.

Quite, quite horrific.

We just watched the young lovers as they got redder and redder. Like red things at a red party.

Herr Kamyer tried to get off her lap, but the coach was being driven so violently by Mr Mad that he kept falling back again, saying, "*Ach*, I am *sehr* sorry I..."

And Miss Wilson was saying, "No, no, it's quite all right. I mean I..."

Eventually, when Mr Attwood was forced to stop at the lights, Herr Kamyer got into his own seat and pretended to be inspecting his moth collection. Miss Wilson got out her knitting but kept looking over at him.

I said to Rosie, "Just remember this – he was there when Nauseating P. Green did her famous falling into the shower tent fiasco and Miss Wilson was exposed to the world having a shower. He has seen Miss Wilson in the nuddy-pants."

I was just thinking about popping back to Snoozeland when Ellen dithered into life.

"Er, Georgia... you know when Jas said... well, when she said that you had... like a million boyfriends or something, I mean have you or something?"

Rosie said, "Ellen, gadzooks and lackaday, OF COURSE Georgia hasn't got a million boyfriends. She would be covered in them if she had."

Ellen said, "Well, I know but, well, I mean, she's only got Masimo, and that is like... well..."

Mabs said, "Yeah, Masimo... and the rest."

I said to Mabs, "Who rattled your cage?"

And Mabs said, "I'm just remarking on the Dave the Laugh factor."

Ellen sat up then. "What Dave the Laugh factor?"

Oh Blimey O'Reilly's nose massager! Here we go again, once more into the bakery of love. I am going to have to nip this Dave the Laugh thing in the bud.

I said, "Ellen, did you snog Declan and, if so, what number did you get up to?"

Ellen looked like she had swallowed a sock full of vole poo, which is not a good look.

"Well, I... well, you know, I, well, do you think I did or something?"

I said, "A yes or no any time this side of the grave would be fab, Ellen."

Ellen said she had to get her cardi from Jas's rucky and

tottered off to sit next to her. Hahahahaha. I am without doubtosity top girlie at red-herringnosity.

4:00 p.m.

Dropped off at the bottom of my road. By some miracle we have arrived home not maimed and crippled by our coach "driver" and school caretaker Elvis Attwood. He hates girls.

I don't think he has a driving licence. When I politely asked to see it after a near-death experience at a roundabout, he suggested I remove myself before his hand made contact with my arse. Which is unnecessary talk in a man who fought for his country in the Viking invasions. I said to him, "You are only letting yourself down by that kind of talk, Mr Attwood."

Two minutes later

Walked up the drive to Chez Bonkers. Opened the door and yelled, "Hello, everyone, you can get out the fatted hamster, I am home!!!"

Two minutes later

No one in.

Typico.

I don't know why they ramble on so much about where I'm going and what time I will be in, when they so clearly don't give two short flying mopeds.

Kitchen
I'm starving.

Nothing in the fridge of course.

Unless you like out-of-date bean sprouts.

Four minutes later
Slightly mouldy toast, mmmmm. I think I am getting scurvy from lack of vitamin C, my hair feels tired. Perhaps Italian Luuurve Gods like the patchy-hair look in a girlfriend.

I wonder if he has left a message on the phone for me?

Five minutes later
I really wish I hadn't listened to the messages – it is a terrifying insight into the "life" I lead.

First it was some giggling pal of Mum's saying that she had met a bloke at a speed-dating night and had got to number six with him. How does she know about the snogging scale? My mum is obviously part crap mother and part seeing-ear dog.

The next message was from Josh's mum, saying, "After Josh came home with a Mohican haircut I don't think it is a good idea that he comes round to play with Libby again. I am frankly puzzled as to why she had bread knives and scissors in her bedroom. Also I cannot get the blue make-up off his eyes. I suspect it is indelible ink, which means the word BUM on his forehead will take many hours to get off."

There was a bit more rambling and moaning, but the gist is that Josh is banned from playing with my little sister Libby.

Dear *Gott in Himmel.*

And that was it. No message from the Luuurve God. It's been a week now. I wonder why he hasn't called? Has he gone off me?

Maybe I did something wrong when we last saw each other.

One minute later
But it was so vair vair gorgey porgey.

One minute later
He said, "We like each other. It will be good, Miss Georgia."

One minute later

What he didn't say was, "I will call you as soon as I get there."

One minute later

Or "I will pay your airfare to Rome, you entrancing Sex Kitty."

Ten minutes later

God, I am so bored. And my bottom still hurts from my falling-in-the-river fiasco. So I can't even sit down properly.

One minute later

I wonder if Dave the Laugh will tell Emma about our accidental number four episode. Probably not. After all, it didn't mean anything and, as he said, we are mates in a matey way. And what goes on in the woods stays in the woods.

Thirty seconds later

Hmmm. He also said in the woods that he has always really liked me. Maybe he meant that in a matey-type mate way.

One minute later

Will I tell Masimo?

One minute later

If he doesn't ring me, I won't have to make the decision. Anyway, it was only an accidental number four, verging on the number five. It could happen to anyone.

One minute later

It could happen to Masimo and his ex-girlfriend. What was her name? Gina. Yes, it might happen if, for instance, she happened to be in Rome.

One minute later

Even if she is not there, I bet he and his mates will be roaring round Rome on their scooters smiling at all the girls in their red bikinis or whatever it is they wear there.

Probably nothing. They probably go to work in the nuddy-pants because they are wild and free Pizza-a-gogo types. They don't have inhibitions like us, they just thrust their nungas forward proudly and untamed. Probably.

In my bedroom looking in the mirror

The only thing that is really thrusting itself forward proudly is my nose. Even Dave mentioned it.

One minute later

Perhaps it has grown bigger and bigger in Masimo's imagination in the week he has been away. He hasn't even got a photo of me to remind him that I am more than just a nose on legs.

Five minutes later

Perhaps because he is foreign he is a bit psychic. Perhaps he has a touch of the Mystic Meg about him and he knows about the Dave the Laugh incident.

One minute later

Jas has probably sent a message via an owl to let him know. Just because she has got the hump with me. AGAIN. About the stupid tent business.

Lying on my bed of pain
8:00 p.m.

And I mean that quite literally because my cat Angus (also known as a killing machine) is pretending my foot is a rabbit. In a sock. If I even move it slightly, he leaps on it and starts biting it.

Also, ouch and double ouch. I can't get into a comfy

position to take the pressure off my bum-oley. I think I may have actually broken something in my bottom. I don't know what there is to break, but I may have broken it. I wonder if it is swollen up?

Then I heard the *phut phut* of the mighty throbbing engine that is my vati's crap car. Carefully easing my broken bottom off the bed and slapping at Angus, I went downstairs. Angus was still clinging to my sock-rabbit-foot even though his head was bonking against the stairs.

As I got to the hall I heard the front door being kicked. Oh good, it was my delightful little sister.

"Gingey, Gingey, let me in!!! Let me in, poo sister."

Then there was squealing, like a pig was being pushed through the letter box.

Thirty seconds later

It wasn't a pig being pushed through the letter box, it was Gordy, cross-eyed son of Angus. I could see his ginger ears poking through.

Oh, bloody hell.

I said, "Libby, don't put Gordy though the letter box. I'm opening the door."

She yelled, "He laaikes it."

When I got the door open, it was to find Libby in Wellington boots and a bikini. Gordy was struggling and yowling in her little fat arms and finally squirmed free and leaped off into the garden sneezing and shaking.

Libby was laughing. "Funny pussy. *Hnk hnk.*" Then she came up to me and started hugging my knees and kissing them. In between snogging, Libby was murmuring, "I lobe my Gingey."

Mutti came up the steps in a really short dress, very tight round the nungas. So very sad. She gave me a hug, which can be quite frightening seeing her enormous basoomas looming towards your head. She said, "Hello, Gee, did you have a larf camping?"

I said, "Oh yes, it was brillopads. We made instruments out of dried beans and Herr Kamyer did impressions of crap stuff with his hands that no one could get except Jas. And, as a *pièce de résistance*, I fell in a pond and was attacked by great toasted newts."

She wasn't even listening as usual, off in her own Muttiland.

"We went to see Uncle Eddie's gig at The Ambassador last night. It was like an orgy; one of the women got so carried away she stole his feather codpiece."

Is that really the sort of thing a growing, sensitive girl should have to listen to? It was like earporn.

one minute later

I watched her bustling about making our delicious supper (i.e. opening a tin of tomato soup). She was so full of herself burbling on and on.

"Honestly, you should have been there, it was a hoot."

I said, "Oooooooh yeah, it would have been great to have been there. Really great." But she didn't get it.

Libby was still kissing my knees and giggling. She had forgotten that they were my knees; they were now just her replacement friends for Josh. But then she had a lovers' tiff with her knee-friends, biffed me on the knee quite hard and went off into the garden, yelling for Gordy.

I said, "Mum, you didn't take Libby with you to the baldy-o-gram fiasco, did you?"

"Don't be silly, Georgia, I'm not a complete fool."

I said, "Well, actually, you are as it happens."

She said, "Don't be so rude."

I said, "Where's Dad? Have you managed to shake him off at last?"

And then Vati came in. In his leather trousers. Oh, I might be sick. Not content with the horrificnosity of the trousers, he kissed me on my hair. Urgh, he had touched my hair; now I would have to wash it.

He was grinning like a loon and taking his jacket off.

"Hello, no camping injuries then. No vole bites. You didn't slip into a newt pond or anything?"

I looked at him suspiciously. I hoped he wasn't turning into Mystic Meg as well in his old age. I said, "Dad, are you wearing a woman's blouse?"

He went completely ballisticisimus. "Don't be so bloody cheeky! This is an original sixties Mod shirt. I will probably wear it when I go clubbing. Any gigs coming up?"

Mum said, "Have you heard anything from the Italian Stallion?"

Dad had his head in the fridge and I could see his enormous leather-clad bum leering at me. I had an overwhelming urge to kick it, but I wasn't whelmed because I knew he would probably ban me from going out for life.

I gave Mum my worst look and nodded over at the fridge. I needn't have worried, though, because Dad had found a Popsicle in the freezer and was as thrilled as it is possible for a fat bloke in constraining leather trousers to be. He went chomping off into the front room.

Mum was adjusting her over-the-shoulder-boulder-holder and looking at me.

I said, "What?"

And she said, "So... have you heard anything?"

I don't know why I told her, but it just came tumbling out.

"Mum, why do boys do that 'see you later' thing and then just not see you later? Even though you don't even know when later is."

"He hasn't got in touch then?"

"No."

She sat down and looked thoughtful, which was a bit alarming. She said slowly, "Hmm – well, I think it's because – they're like sort of nervous gazelles in trousers, aren't they?"

I looked at her. "Mum, are you saying that Masimo is a leaping furry animal who also plays in a band and rides a scooter? And snogs?"

She said, "He snogs, does he?"

Damn, drat, damnity dratty damn. And also *merde*. I had broken my rule about never speaking about snognosity questions with old mad people.

I said quickly, "Anyway, what do you mean about the gazelle business?"

"Well, I think that boys are more nervous than you think. He wants to make sure that you like him before he makes a big deal about it. How many days is it since he went?"

"I don't know. I haven't been counting the days actually, I'm not that sad."

She looked at me. "How many hours then?"

"One hundred and forty."

We were interrupted by Gordy and Angus both trying to get through the cat flap at once. Quickly followed by Libby.

In my bedroom
8:45 p.m.

I can hear Mum and Dad arguing downstairs because he hasn't taken the rubbish out. And never does. On and on.

I will never behave like this when I am married. Mind you, I will not be marrying a loon in tight trousers who thinks Rolf Harris is a really good artist.

Who will I be marrying at this rate? I haven't been out of my room for years and the phone hasn't rung since it was invented.

Why is no one phoning me? Not even the Ace Gang. I've been home for hours and hours. Don't they care?

The trouble with today is that everyone is so obsessed with themselves. They just have no time for me.

Five minutes later

At last, a bit of peace to contemplate my broken bum. Oh no, here they go again. They are so childish. Mum shouted out, "Bob, you know that sort of wooden thing in the bedroom, in the corner? Well, it's called a set of drawers and some people, people who are grown up and no longer have their mummy wiping their botties, well those sort of people put their clothes in the drawers. So that other people don't have to spend their precious time falling over knickers and so on."

Uh-oh. Fight, fight!!

Then I could hear him shambling into their bedroom and singing, "One little sock in the drawer, two socks in the drawer and two pairs of attractive undercrackers on the head then into the drawer, yesssss!!"

How amazing. I shouted down, "Mum, is Dad on some kind of medication? Or have his trousers cut off the circulation to his head?"

That did it. Vati hit number seven on the losing it scale (complete ditherspaz). He yelled up, "Georgia... this isn't anything to do with you!"

I said, "Oh, that's nice. I thought we were supposed to be a lovely family and do stuff together."

He just said, "Anyway, where is your sister? Is she up there with you?"

Why am I Libby's so-called nanny? Haven't I got enough trouble with my own life? I am not my sister's keeper, as Baby Jesus said. Or was it Robin Hood? I don't know. Some bloke in a skirt anyway.

I said, "No. Have you tried the airing cupboard or the cat basket?"

Five minutes later

Things have got worse. While Mum went hunting for Bibbsy, Dad unfortunately decided to check the phone messages. He heard Mum's mate's message. I could hear him tutting. And then it was Josh's mum's message.

He had the nervy spaz of all nervy spazzes, shouting and carrying on. "What is it with this family??? Why did Libby have a bread knife in her bedroom? Probably because you are too busy pratting around with your so-called mates to bother looking after your children!"

That did it for Mum. She shouted back, "How dare you! They're MY children, are they? If you took some notice of them, that would be a miracle. You care more about that ridiculous bloody three-wheeled clown car."

Mum had called his car a clown car. Tee-hee.

Dad had really lost it. "That car is an antique."

I shouted, "It's not the only one."

Mum laughed, but Dad said, "Right, that's it, I'm off. Don't wait up."

Mum shouted, "Don't worry, I won't." The door slammed and there was silence.

Then there was the sound of the clown car being driven off at high speed (two miles an hour) down the driveway.

And silence again as it whirred away into the distance.

Then a little voice said, "Mummy, my bottom is stuck in the bucket."

9:30 p.m.
Dear God, what a nightmare. This has taken my mind off the oven of luuurve situation.

Libby has wedged herself into the outdoor metal bucket. We pulled her and wiggled her about but we can't get it off.

Mum said, "Go and get me some butter from the fridge. We can smear it on her and sort of slide her out."

Of course, we didn't have any butter; we had about a teaspoon of cottage cheese but Mum said it wasn't the same.

Twenty-five minutes later

In the end Mum made me go across the road and ask Mr Across the Road if we could borrow some butter. She said I could lie better.

Mr Across the Road was wearing a short nightshirt and I kept not looking anywhere below his chin. He was all nosey about the late-night butter scenario though.

"Doing a bit of baking, are you?"

I said, "Er... yes."

"It's a bit late to start, isn't it?"

I said, "Er, well, it's emergency baking. It has to be done by tomorrow."

He said, "Oh, what are you making?"

How the hell did I know? I was lying. And also the only kind of confectionery I knew were the cakes I had got from the bakery of love. The Robbie éclair, the Masimo cream horn and then I remembered the Dave the Tart scenario and quickly said, "Erm, we're making tarts. For the deaf. It's for charity."

He said, "Tarts for the deaf? That's a new one on me. I'll have to go down to the storeroom for some packets." And he ambled off.

And that is when Junior Blunder Boy and full-time twit came in. Oscar.

He looked at me and said, "Yo, wa'appen, bitch?"

What was he talking about and also what was he wearing? He had massive jeans on about fifty sizes too big for him. He had to sort of waddle about like a useless duck to keep them from falling down. And pull them up every five seconds. How spectacularly naff and sad he was. I just looked at him as he waddled over to the kitchen counter. He reached up to get a can of Coca-Cola from a shelf and momentarily forgot about his elephant jeans. They fell to his ankles. Leaving him standing there in his Thomas the Tank Engine undercrackers.

I said to him, "Oscar, you are wearing Thomas the Tank Engine undercrackers. I know this because, believe it or not, your trousers have fallen off."

He said, "Yes man, me mean to do that. Be cool, it is righteous." And he shuffled off, still with the trousers round his ankles.

I will never, ever tire of the sheer bonkerosity of boydom.

11:00 p.m.

It took us nearly half an hour to get Mr Bucket off Libby. We greased as much of her bottom as we could reach, like a little suckling pig. Eventually we cut through the top of her panties and managed to make a bit of leeway and free the bum-oley.

For some toddlers, being greased up and pulled by brute force out of a metal bucket might have been a traumatic experience. But then not all toddlers are insane. Libby laughed and sang through the whole episode, amusing herself by gobbling stray bits of butter and smearing other bits on my head. Oh, how I joined in the merry times. Not.

In addition, Gordy and Angus lolloped in to lick at the leftover butter on her botty. Soooo disgusting. Libby was shouting, "They is ticklin me!!! Heggy heggy ho!!!"

Back in bed

It is like the botty casualty department in here. My bottom, which I have had no time to attend to, is being supported by Libby's swimming ring and I have a buttered-up child rammed in next to me.

Also, have I got a boyfriend or not?

Midnight

And I am still thinking about the Dave the Laugh accidental snogging in the forest incident.

12:10 a.m.

Perhaps this is God's little way of saying, "She who lives by the red bottom gets to lie in a rubber ring."

once more into the huffmobile

Monday August 1st
8:00 a.m.
Oww oww and double owww!! I think my botty has taken a turn for the worse. I wonder if it is swollen up?

Looking in the mirror
It does look a bit on the swollen side. Oh marvellous. I will have to ask Jas if I can borrow some of her enormous winter pants. She will have got them out of her winter store by now. She starts ironing her school pants about a month before we are forced back to Stalag 14. Which reminds me, we only

have about four weeks of holiday left. *Sacré bleu* and *merde*.

Libby has already scarpered off to get ready for nursery, so I can just have a little dolly daydream about snogging the Luuurve God. If I make a mental picture of us snogging, I might attract him to me through the psychic ethery stuff.

Ten minutes later

I can hear the postman coming up the drive. Ah, the postie. It's a lovely job being a postie; you see it in all ye olde films that ye olde parents watch. Mr Postie coming up the drive with a cheery whistle and a handful of exciting letters for the family. A "Good morning, ma'am" to the mistress of the house and then—

"I've got a bloody stick, you furry freak, and I'm not afraid to use it!!!"

Charming. Utterly, utterly charming.

I looked out of the window. Angus was sitting on the dustbin showing off to Naomi, his mad Burmese girlfriend and slag, by taunting the postie – hissing and doing pretend biffing, sticking his claws in and out. The postie had to get by the dustbin to get to the door and he was waving a big stick about in Angus's direction. Angus loves a stick. The larger the better. He lay down and started purring so loudly I could hear it in my bedroom. I don't know why he loves sticks so much, but he does. Almost as much as he loves cars.

He thinks cars are like giant stupid mice on wheels. That he can chase after.

He brought a stick home the other day that was so big, it took him half an hour to figure out how to get it through the cat flap. He did it, though, because he is top cat.

Two minutes later

It was the same with the ginormous dead pigeon. Angus backed his way through the cat flap dragging the feet first, and then Gordy heave-hoed the head bit through.

It was an amazing double act. Father and son were very impressed with themselves. Although slightly covered in feathers. They even arranged the pigeon so that it was looking towards the door and propped up so Mum could get the full benefit when she came in.

She did get the full benefit and went ballistic, jumping on a chair and screaming etc. Angus and Gordy and the dead pigeon all looked at her.

"Bloody murdering furry thugs!!!" she yelled.

I said, "Look, you are really hurting their feelings."

And then she threw the washing-up bowl at me. That is the kind of mothering I have to put up with.

One minute later

The postie has bravely got past Angus and disappeared from view as he posts our letters through the letter box. Angus has disappeared as well. Oh, I know what he is doing!

He is doing his vair vair amusing trick of lurking in the top of the hedge to leap down on the postie's head as he passes by. Tee-hee. Happy days. I wish I was a cat. At least I would get fed now and again.

I wouldn't be quite so keen on all the bum-oley licking. Although as mine is so swollen now, it would probably be easier to reach.

Mum yelled up, "Gee, come down and have brekkie and say goodbye to your family."

I said, "Have I still got one? I thought that Father had left us and would never be back. That is what he promised."

Dad yelled up, "You think you are so bloody funny, but you won't when I don't give you your ten-quid pocket money. Nothing to spend on your eyeliner or nit cream or whatever else it is that you plaster yourself with."

Nit cream? Has he finally snapped?

Mum said, "Stop it, you two. Oooh look, here is a foreign postcard addressed to Georgia – I wonder who it's from?"

Oh my giddy god's pyjamas!!! I leaped downstairs, putting the pain of my bottom behind me. Tee-hee. Oh brilliant, my brain has gone into hysterical clown mode.

Thirty seconds later

Dad had the postcard in his hand and was reading it!!! Noooooo!

He was saying in a really crap Pizza-a-gogo accent, "*Ciao*, Georgia, it is smee."

I tried to get the postcard from him. "Dad, that is private property addressed to me. If it doesn't say 'to some mad fat bloke', it isn't yours."

Dad just went on reading it. "I am, how you say, hair in Roma wive my family."

Finally I ripped it out of his hand and took it upstairs.

Mum said, "You are mean, Bob. You know what she is like."

Dad said, "Yes, I do. She's insane like all the other bloody women in this family. Hang on a minute... what the hell happened to my car-washing bucket?"

Mum said, "We had to hit it with a hammer in the end. Libby got her bottom stuck in it."

Dad said, "I rest my case."

In my room

Oh God, I am sooooo excited, my eyes have gone cross-eyed. What does it say?

Twenty seconds later

> Ciao, Georgia,
>
> It is smee. I am, how you say, hair in Roma wive my family. I am hot. (You don't have to tell me that, mate.) I am playing fun. Are you playing fun? I miss I you me.
>
> I call on the telefono on Tuesday for you.
>
> Ciao, bellissima, Masimo xxx

An hour later

After about three thousand years and a half, the Swiss Family Mad all crashed off to ruin other people's lives and I could get on the old blower.

I nearly dialled Wise Woman of the Forest before I remembered that she had practically called me the Whore of Babylon. She is so full of suspicionosity. And annoyingnosity. How dare she suggest in front of everyone that I had been up to hanky-panky and rudey-dudeys with Dave the Laugh? She knows very well that I am going out with a Luuurve God. Who is a) hot and b) playing fun.

What in the name of arse does "playing fun" mean?

I must consult with my gang.

But not her.

I am *ignorez-vous*ing her with a firm hand and it serves her right. I hope she realises that I am *ignorez-vous*ing her, otherwise it's all a bit pointless.

Two minutes later

I may have to call her and let her know I am *ignorez-vous*ing her, as she can be a bit on the dense side.

Phoned Jas.

Her mum answered. "Hello, Georgia. Gosh, you had a fabulous time camping, didn't you? Jas said you sang and played games till all hours."

I said, "Er yes..."

"You had a great time, I bet."

"Er yes, it was very, erm, campey."

"Good. I'll just call Jas, dear. I think she's in her bedroom dusting and rearranging her owls and so on."

You couldn't really write it, could you? If I wrote a book and I said: "I've got a mate who dusts her collection of stuffed owls and follows greater toasted newts about," people would say: "I'm not reading that sort of stupid exaggeration. Next thing you know, someone will say they went to a party dressed as a stuffed olive. Or accidentally snogged three boyfriends at once." Hang on a minute, everything has gone a bit *déjà vu*-ish.

Jas came on the phone. "Yes."

"Jas, it is me, the Whore of Babylon, but I am preparing myself to forgive you."

"What are you forgiving me for?"

"Because you are a naughty pally saying things about me being selfish and lax and having a million boyfriends."

Jas said, "It's up to you how many boyfriends you have. I am not my brother's keeper."

"Jas, I know you aren't. You haven't got a brother."

"I mean you."

"I haven't got a brother either, thank the Lord. I do,

however, have an insane sister, who by the way is now probably going to be done for TBH."

"You mean GBH – grievous bodily harm."

"No, I mean TBH. Toddler bodily harm. Josh's mum has complained about her and she is suspended from nursery school. She is staying with Grandfarty and he is looking after her. She is the first person in our family to get a restraining order besides Grandad."

Jas was not what you would call full of sympatheticnosity.

"I don't think she will be the last person in your family to get a restraining order, Georgia. I am a bit busy actually."

"Jas, please don't have Mrs Hump with me. I need you, my dearest little pally wally. Pleasey please, be frendy wendys. Double please with knobs. And a tiny little knoblet. And—"

"All right, all right, stop going on."

She deffo had the minor hump, but it was only four on the having-the-hump scale. (cold-shoulderosity work).

"Jas, come on. Remember the laugh we had when we all snuck off to the boys' tent? And I came and told you that Tom was there, didn't I? Even though you were singing 'Ging Gang Gooly'."

"Well, yes, but—"

"I displayed magnanimosity, which isn't something everyone can say. But I did it because I luuurve you. A LOT."

"OK, don't go on."

"You are not ashamed of our luuurve, are you, Jas?"

"Look, shut up. People might hear."

"What do you mean, the people who live in the telephone?"

"NO, I mean, anyway, what's happened?"

"I've got a postcard from Masimo and we have to call an extraordinary general meeting of the Ace Gang."

"Oh no."

"Oh yes."

In the park
2:00 p.m.

Naaaice and sunny. I wore my denim miniskirt and halter neck and some groovy sandals. I will have to do something with my legs, though, because they give me the droop, they are so pale. Rosie had some eye-catching shorts on; they had pictures of Viking helmets all over them. She said, "Sven had them specially printed in my honour. Groovy, aren't they?"

I said, "That is one word for them."

Rosie said, "Sven has got his first dj-ing job next weekend and I am going to be his groupie. You all have to come."

Ten minutes later

We settled down in the shade underneath the big chestnut tree by the swings. The bees were singing and the birds a-buzzing, dogs scampering around, people eating ice creams, toddlers sticking ice creams in their eyes by mistake etc. A lovely, lovely summer afternoon, ideal to sort out the game of luuurve.

We had just passed round the chuddie and decided for Ellen where she should sit after about eight minutes of: "Well, erm, I should sit in the shade really, don't you think, because of the ultraviolet, but, erm, what about, erm, not like getting the sun and then like maybe not getting enough vitamin D because that would be, like, not great. Or something."

Finally she sat with her top part in the shade and her legs sticking in the sun because we told her no one had ever got cancer of the knees. Which might or might not be true, but sometimes (in fact, very often, in my experience) lying is the best policy. Especially if you can't be arsed talking about something boring any more.

One minute later

I don't know why I bother lying because Ellen has gone off to the loos to run her wrists under cold water so she doesn't get sunstroke of the arms.

Jas still hasn't turned up. I wonder if she has progressed to number six on the hump scale and is doing pretend deafnosity?

Thirty seconds later

The Ace Gang started talking about the camping trip and sneaking out to see the lads at night.

Mabs said, "I had a go at snogging with Edward."

Jools said, "What was it like?"

Mabs chewed and popped and said, "Quite groovy. We did four and then a spot of five."

I said, "Oh, so *you* missed out four and a half as well. I said I thought it was a WUBBISH idea that Mrs Newt Knickers came up with. Who apart from her and Tom would do hand snogging?"

Mabs said, "What do you mean 'as well'?"

I said, "What do you mean 'What do you mean as well'?"

Mabs put her face really close to mine. "Georgia, you said,

and forgive me if I'm right, 'Oh, so you missed out four and a half as well.' Which means, 'Oh, so you missed out four and a half as well AS ME.' Meaning you must have missed out four and a half with someone. The only someone around was Dave the Laugh."

Uh-oh, my red-herringnosity skills were letting me down.

Mabs was going on and on like Jas's little helper. "So what did you get up to with Dave the Laugh by the river?"

I said in a casualosity-at-all-times sort of way, "Ah well, I'm glad you asked me that. Because suspicionosity is the enemy of friendshipnosity. The simple truth is that Dave and I were playing, erm, tig. Yes, and I accidentally fell in a stream and then I went back to my tent because I was, er, wet."

Rosie said, "You and Dave were playing tig. I see. One moment. I must give this some serious thought. Luckily I have my pipe."

Oh no.

Two minutes later

Good Lord, I am being interrogated by Inspector Bonkers of the Yard.

The inspector (i.e. Rosie with her pipe and beard on)

continued, "You expect us to believe that you and Dave the Laugh gambolled around the woods playing a little game of tig?"

I said, "Yes."

Rosie said, "You are, it has to be said, my little chumlet, even dimmer than you look."

Ellen came back then, just in the knickers of time. I smiled at her and said in a lighthearted but menacing way, "You haven't told us about Declan. It is Ace Gang rules that we do sharesies about snogging."

Rosie and Mabs raised their eyebrows at me, but I *ignorez-vous*ed them.

Ellen heaved herself into her Dithermobile and said, "Well, Declan showed, well, he showed me something and—"

Inspector Bonkers of the Yard winked, sucked on her pipe and went, "Ay ay."

Ellen went even redder and more dithery.

"No, I mean, it was his Swiss Army knife."

Inspector Bonkers got out a pretend notebook. "All right. So you looked at his knife and then did you snog?"

Ellen said, "Well, when we were, like, leaving to go back to camp – he gave me a number three and then—"

"Then quickly went on to number four."

"Well, no, he..."

"He missed out number four and went straight for the nungas?"

"No, well, he – he, like, he said, he said, 'See you later.'"

Oh dear God, we were once more in the land of S'later. Will we never be free?

One minute later

But at least it stopped anyone going on about the Dave the Laugh fiasco.

One minute later

Jas turned up. She looked quite nice actually, if you like that mad fringey look. She said, "I was just talking to Tom on the phone. He's playing footie this arvie with the lads. He's got some new boots."

I said, "No!! Honestly!"

And she gave me a huffty look. I don't want to have more rambling lectures from her, so I went and gave her a hug and a piece of chuddie.

Anyway, we had just settled down and I'd got out my

postcard from Masimo to show the gang, when Jools said, "Oh God, Blunder Boys alert!"

They were shuffling about by the bushes at the far end of the swing park. Mark Big Gob was absent, probably carrying his tiny girlfriend around somewhere. Junior Blunder Boy was with them though. I noticed he had a belt round his elephant jeans. So now he didn't look like a twit any more. He looked like a twit with a belt on.

Mabs said, "Don't look at them and they'll get bored."

I said, "Can we get back to the matter I hold in my hand?"

Rosie went, "Oo-er."

I gave her my worst look and went on, "What do you think 'I am playing fun' means?"

Ellen said, "Well, erm, I don't know but you know, well – well, you know when a boy says 'See you later', well, like when Declan said 'See you later' and that was, like, three days ago now. So, er, this is, like, later, isn't it? Or something. And he hasn't, like, seen me."

Even though we were actually officially having the official Ace Gang meeting officially for me (as I had officially called it), I did feel quite sorry for Ellen. And also it has to be said it would be a bloody relief if she did get off with Declan.

Then she would leave Dave the Laugh alone.

Not that it is any of my business whether she leaves Dave the Laugh alone or not.

I mean, he has a girlfriend anyway.

Probably.

Unless he has told her about the accidental snogging and she is even now taking kickboxing lessons for when she next sees me.

Anyway, shut up, brain. He has got a girlfriend, which is good because so have I.

Well, not a girlfriend exactly, but an Italian person.

Who incidentally does not have a handbag.

Or a sports bra.

Whatever Dave the so-called Laugh might say. Why is Dave the Laugh sneaking about in my brain???

Jools said to Ellen, "Maybe he's a bit shy."

Ellen said, "Yes, but he, I mean, he showed me his Swiss Army knife."

I looked at her. What is the right response to that? I said, "Well, maybe he is a bit backward then?"

Ellen looked like she was going to cry. Oh Blimey O'Reilly's Y-fronts, if she starts blubbing, I'll never get round to talking about the Italian Stallion.

I said quickly, "I know... Jas can ask Tom to get Declan and the lads to come along to Sven's gig, and hopefully that will be a good excuse for him to get his knife out again (oo-er) and everything will be tickety-boo and so on."

Ellen looked a bit cheered up.

I said, "Now, shall we get back to the official meeting? What do you think 'I am playing fun' means?" And that is when an elastic band hit me on the cheek.

"Owww, bloody owww!!!"

Amazingly, not content with being complete losers, tossers and spoons, the Blunder Boys were flicking rubber bands at us from behind our tree. And then hiding behind it as if we wouldn't know where they were. Like the Invisible Twits. Not.

I got up and went behind the tree where they were all larding about, puffing smoke from fags and hitching their trousers up. Dear God. I said to one of the speccy genks, "What is it you want?"

And he said, "Show us your nungas."

They all started snorting and saying, "Yeah, get them out for the lads."

Rosie came up behind me and loomed over them. She is not small. She said, "OK, that's a good plan. We'll show you our nungas, but first of all we need to see your trouser snakes, to check that all is in order."

Ellen and Jools and Mabs and even Woodland Jas came and ganged up in front of them.

I said, "Come on, lads, drop the old trouser-snake holders."

They started backing off, holding on to their trousers.

Jools said, "Are you a bit shy? Shall we help you?"

They started walking really quickly backwards as we kept walking. Then they just took off and got over the fence at the back of the park.

Twelve minutes later

The Ace Gang wisdomosity is that "I am playing fun" and "Are you playing fun?" roughly translated into Billy Shakespeare language is "I am having a nice time but am missing you. Are you having a nice time but missing me?"

Which is nice.

So all should be smoothy friendly friendly, except that there is always a Jas in the manger.

After about two hours of talking about it, we were all going home and I just innocently said, "So what do you think I should wear when he phones up?"

And Jas immediately climbed into the huffmobile for no apparent reason. She was all red and flicking her fringe around like it was a fringe-ometer.

"Why is it always like this with you, Georgia? Why don't you just say and do normal stuff? For instance, if Tom wanted me to go to the nature reserve with him he would say, 'Jas, do you want to go to the nature reserve with me? There is a conservation day and we could clear some of the canalside of weeds.'

"And I would say, 'Yes, that would be fab, Tom.' Simple pimple, not stupidity and guessing what 'playing fun' means and what to wear on the phone."

What was she rambling on about now?

I said, "Jas are the painters in, because I think you are being just a tad more mentally unstable than normal."

She really had lost her cheese now, because she shouted at me, "Look, I haven't got any sun protector on and I am almost bound to get peely peely now thanks to you going on. And the short and short of it is that HE IS CALLING YOU TOMORROW AND YOU CAN ASK HIM WHAT HE MEANS!!!" And she stormed off.

Blimey. We all looked at one another.

I said, "I think it's owl trouble."

In bed

What am I going to wear for the phone call though? I wish I wasn't so pale; I think people can tell if you are a bit tanned. Even down the phone. I bet I can tell immediately if he has a nice tan.

Two minutes later

Actually, if he is tanned I think I might faint. I can't stand him being much more gorgey than he already is.

Five minutes later

Should I prepare a speech? Or at least a normal conversation. With some handy topics in case I mislay my brain or it decides to go on an expedition to Outer Loonolia.

One minute later

So let's see, what have I done lately?

Loads of stuff.

Five minutes later

I don't think I will mention Miss Wilson exposing herself to Herr Kamyer.

Two minutes later
Or breaking my bum-oley in the river.

Four minutes later
In fact, perhaps it's better to leave the whole camping fiasco to one side. I will only have Dave the Laugh popping into my brain. I will stick to lighthearted banter.

Should I tell him about the tarts for the deaf episode?

Three minutes later
Or Junior Blunder Boy's Thomas the Tank Engine undercrackers?

Two minutes later
None of it sounds that normal, to be frank. I will stick to world affairs and art.

Two minutes later
I could ask him what he thinks about the foreign exchange rate. Well, I could if I knew what it meant.

one minute later

Where is Rome anyway? Is it in the boot bit of Italy? Or is Spain the booty bit?

I'm really worried about tomorrow now. I will never sleep and then I will have big dark rings under my eyes and...

zzzzzzzzzzzzzz.

Tuesday August 2nd
9:30 a.m.

I was just having a dream about being in Rome with the Luuurve God. I had a cloak on and Masimo said, "So, *cara*, what have you come to the fancy-dress party as?" And I dropped the cloak and said, "A fried egg."

The phone rang and I practically broke my neck tripping over Angus and Gordy, who just emerged from the shadows.

I couldn't say anything because I was so nervous.

Then I heard Grandad say, "Hello, hello, speak up."

I said, "Grandad, I haven't said anything yet."

He was in full-Grandad mode. "You'll like this: what do pigs use if they hurt themselves? Ay ay??? Oinkment. Do you get it, do you see??? Oinkment!!! Oh, I make myself laugh. Are you courting yet? You should be – there's nothing like a bit of snogging to perk you up."

Oh dear God, my grandvati was talking about snogging.

Now I have finally experienced every kind of porn. This is mouldyporn.

Two minutes later

I managed to get him off the phone by saying good morning to Libby (she purred back), and promising to visit and have a game of hide-and-seek with him and the other residents. I don't mind that so much, as when it is my turn to hide I just go to the shops and then come back half an hour later and get in a cupboard. It keeps them happy for hours.

I do love my grandad though. He is one of the most cheerful people I know and now he is going to have Maisie as his new knitted wife. Aaaahhh.

Mum was wandering around in the kitchen like Madame Zozo of, erm, Zozoland. In a semi-see-through nightie. It's her day off and she looked like she might settle in for hours. I must get rid of her.

I said in an interested and lighthearted fashion, "What

time are you going out? In a minute or two? To make the best of the day?"

She sat down, actually resting her basoomas on the tabletop, presumably because she was already tired of lugging them about. Please save me from the enormous-jug gene.

She said, "I thought you and I could go out and do something groovy together."

Groovy?

I said, "Mum, are you mad because I tell you this for free a) I am not going out with you and b) the same with knobs on."

Mum said, "Hahaha, that worried you. Are you having a bit of a nervy spazmarama attack about *Masimo* ringing you?"

I was truly shocked. "Mum, it is not a nervy spazmarama, it is a spaz attack, which is number six on the losing it scale – hang on a minute. How do you know about a spaz attack anyway? Have you been snooping through my private drawers?"

She didn't bother to reply because she was too busy eating jam with a spoon out of the jar. She will get so fat that she will get trapped in Dad's clown car and have to drive endlessly up and down our driveway begging for snacks from passers-by. Good.

When she stopped chomping, she said, "Me and my mates

have loads of sayings and stuff. We have a real laugh. It's not just you and your mates, you know. I have a life."

I tried not to laugh.

"In aquaerobics the other day Fiona laughed so much at the instructor's choice of music that she weed herself in the pool. When she told me I nearly drowned. We had to all leave the class and I don't think we can go back."

She was hiccuping and giggling like a twerp. Is it any wonder that I find myself in trouble with boys when I have this sort of thing as my example?

I left the kitchen with a dignitosity-at-all-times sort of walk. I have a call from the cakeshop of luuurve to think about.

Back in my bedroom
Ten minutes later

What shall I wear, what shall I wear? I tell you this, I'm not going to wear anything yellow after the fried egg dream.

I could wear my bikini. My red one with the dots on it. They tend to wear red bikinis all the time the Italian girls, probably even if they work in banks and cafes and so on. Maybe not for nursing though; it might not be hygienic. My mum said that when she had an Italian boyfriend she was on the beach and this bloke rode up on a motorbike. And this girl who just had on the bottoms of a bikini and some really high heels came jogging up. She got on the back of the bike, lit a fag and they roared off with her nunga-nungas flying.

Back in the kitchen
9:45 a.m.
Why won't Mum go out? I have my bikini on underneath my ordinary clothes ready to rip off when the phone rings.

Five minutes later
She is just rambling on and on about herself. I already know more than I want to know about her.

9:55 a.m.
Oh nooooooo. Now she is talking about "feelings" and "relationships" and what is worse is, it's not even my feelings or relationships, it's hers!!! How horrific.

She says she feels that she doesn't share many interests with Dad.

I said, "Well, who does?"

♡ 69

She didn't even hear me, she just went on and on. "I think when I met him I was a different person and now I've changed."

10:10 a.m.
The Luuurve God is going to phone any minute and she will still be here.

Mum said, "I don't blame him, but people do change and want different things."

I said quickly, "Yeah, yeah, you're so right. I think you need a change – a change of, er, scenery. You need to go out into the sunshine and meet your mates and ask them what they feel. Maybe go for a slap-up meal. You've only had a pound or two of jam today, you'll be peckish. Go for a pizza and maybe have some *vino tinto* because you know what they say about *vino* in Latin. *In vino hairy arse*. Just give yourself space."

"Do you think so? Just enjoy myself and don't feel guilty?"

I nodded like billio.

Fifteen minutes later
Thank the Lord, Baby Jesus and all his cohorts. She's gone. All tarted up. It is so typically selfish of her to have a midlife crisis when I am expecting a phone call.

Half an hour later

Oh, I am so full of tensionosity. I haven't been able to eat anything apart from oven chips. With mayo and tommy sauce. And a choc ice.

Perhaps some popcorn would be good for me. It's practically health food really. In fact, don't hamsters eat it? And they are as healthy as anything. Running round and round in those little wheels for no reason, dashing up and down ladders. Ringing bells etc.

Shut up, brain! I am giving you a final warning.

Twenty minutes later

I tell you this, never cook popcorn. I don't know what happened, but I did what it said on the packet, chucked it into some hot oil in a pan and it just sort of exploded everywhere. How do you get popcorn out of light fittings?

And your hair?

And nose?

And bikini bottoms?

Angus has just done that cat thing. You know, the high-speed slink across the room with the belly nearly touching the ground. Why do they do that? Why?

Two minutes later

Now he is doing fridge staring.

Ring ring.

Ohmygiddygod. The phone. I bet all my lip gloss has disappeared. But if I go and reapply, he might ring off. Oh good, I was at number nine on the ditherspaz scale already.

I smiled as I said in my deepest voice, "Hello?"

"Georgia, have you come over all transsexual? Has he phoned yet?"

"No, he hasn't, Jas. Not that you really care."

"Yes, I do, otherwise why would I phone up to ask you whether he'd phoned you yet?"

"I don't know."

"Well, there you are then."

"You might have called just to be glad he hasn't called, knowing you."

"Well, I didn't."

"Oh, OK, thanks. Goodbye now."

"Don't you want to talk to me?"

"Er, well, not just now, Jas."

"Oh."

"I'm putting the phone down now."

There was a sort of a sobbing noise. Then a trembly little voice said, "Tom and I had our first row last night."

Oh for heaven's bloody sake.

I said, "What happened? Did he diss one of your owls?"

She was gulping and her voice was all trembly. "No, but he said, he said, what did I think about him going to uni in Hamburger-a-gogo land. And I said I didn't really want to go to Hamburger-a-gogo land, I would rather go to York. And he said that might be a good idea."

What is this, *EastEnders*?

Thirty minutes later

Good Lord. I think I know everything that is in Jas's head now and I tell you this for free, I wish I didn't.

Tom thinks they should go to separate unis or something so that they can be sure that they are made for each other. I did say to Jas, "Well, you can safely let him go. What other fool is he going to find to go vole hunting with him?"

But it didn't seem to cheer her up as such.

In the end I've said I'll go round to hers later after the Luuurve God has called.

God help us one and all.

one hour later

I am now officially going mad.

Phone rang

I said, "Yes! What is it?"

And then I heard his voice. "*Ciao*, er, is please Georgia there?"

It was him!!! Praise God and his enormous beard!!

I took a big breath and said, "Hello, yes, Georgia Nicolson speaking."

Blimey, why am I suddenly speaking like the queen?

Masimo laughed. "*Ciao ciao*, Georgia!! *Bellissima!!!* It is you! *Un momento per favore.*"

Then I head him speaking off the telephone and laughing, and there were other voices and then loud smacking noises like kissing.

Maybe it was kissing.

Was he actually snogging someone else while he was talking to me? That seemed very lax, even for the Pizza-a-gogo types.

Then suddenly he was back talking to me again. "Oh, *cara*, *mi scusi*, my brothers, my family, they are all going to the beach – later, when it is night we are having how you say in English – a bum-fire?"

74

A bum-fire? That seemed a bit mean. Setting people's bums on fire. But perhaps that is the old Roman ways emerging again.

Then he was laughing. "You are not saying anything. I have this wrong, no?"

I said, "*Sì*." And we both laughed. It was marvy speaking in different languages.

He said, "Have you missed me?"

And I said, "Oh, *muchos* and a half."

He laughed again. We were laughing and laughing.

"Me too. How was your camping?"

Uh-oh. The forbidden topic. I must remember my rule about not saying anything and get things back to world politics and so on as soon as possible. I said, "Oh, it was pretty crappio."

He said, "Tell me something from it."

"Well, you know, not much happened. Erm, Nauseating P. Green fell into the so-called toilets and it fell down and Miss Wilson was in the nuddy-pants having a shower with her soap on a rope. And then later Herr Kamyer sat on her knee and that was all that happened."

He said, "I have, how you would say, the mad girlfriend."

Oooooh, he had called me his mad girlfriend. How cool was that?

We talked for ages. Well, I said stuff and he asked me what it meant mostly. I wish I could speak more Pizza-a-gogo-ese; it's more difficult speaking to someone on the phone anyway because you can't see their face. And then he asked me when I am coming over to see him.

Good point, well made.

I haven't even asked my parents about the 500 squids I will need. If they would stop banging on about themselves, I might get a chance to ask. I didn't like to say that I didn't have any money, so I just said, "I think, probably in two, *due* weeks."

He said, "Ah, that is long. I wish you were here and then we could again, what do you say – snog. And I could touch you and feel your mouth on mine. And look into your lovely face. I was thinking about your beautiful eyes and I think they are so lovely, it makes my heart melt."

Crikey, he had turned into Billy Shakespeare. Or Billio Shakespeario, who wrote the famous Italian plays *MacUselessio* and *King Leario*.

Shut up, brain. Now this minutio. Stoppio, nowio. It still wouldn't stop it (io).

I was quite literally tripping around on a cloud of luuurve. Sadly, the four pints of Coke I had to keep me going before he phoned now wanted to come out and join me.

I tried pressing my bottom against the stool but sooner or later something was going to give. I needed to go to the tarts' wardrobe vair vair badly. But because my vati was too mean to get a modern phone that you could walk about with I was stuck. I didn't want to say, "Oh, 'scuse me, I have to go to the piddly-diddly department" because that would start another one of those international incidents. So I said, "Oh no, someone is at the door. Can you just hang on for a mo?"

He said, "*Sì, cara*, I wait."

And then weirdly the doorbell did ring. How freaky-deaky is that? I wonder who it was. Well, whoever it was, they weren't coming in. I nipped into the tarts' wardrobe. Then the shouting began.

"Georgia, come on, open the door! We know you are in there."

It was Grandad. And he wasn't alone. I could hear Libby and Maisie. Dear God.

I couldn't keep them out for long because they would probably start knitting a rope ladder and get through my bedroom window. Perhaps I could persuade them to go away.

There was a bit of a silence and then Grandad said, "We've

got snacks," and he posted a sandwich through the letter box. I think it was spam.

I went back to the telephone. "Masimo, I have to go now. My grandad is posting sandwiches through the letter box."

He laughed. But he laughed alone. Then he said, "Phone me when you can. The *telefono* is Roma 75556666121." He did kissing stuff down the phone and then he was gone.

I didn't even remember to say when shall we speak again or anything because I was so flustered by the elderly loons. And I wanted to write the number down before I forgot it.

Five minutes later
People will not believe this, I know, but Maisie has knitted Libby a miniskirt and matching beret for her bridesmaid's outfit.

An hour later
They have gone, thank the Lord.

Four minutes later
Hearing Masimo's voice has made everything simple for me *vis-à-vis* the General Horn, ad-hoc red-bottomosity etc.

I am putting the accidental snogging scenario with Dave

the Laugh into a snogging cupboard at the back of my brainbox. A snogging cupboard that I will never be going into again. I have locked the door and thrown away the key.

Well, I didn't throw it away actually, but I have put it somewhere that I will never be able to find again.

One minute later
The snogging cupboard is in fact next to another cupboard that has got other discarded boy stuff in it. Like the Mark Big Gob stuff. The resting his hand on my nunga-nunga episode, for instance. Which I have also completely forgotten about and will never remember.

One minute later
That cupboard has also got the snogging Whelk Boy fiasco in it. Erlack a pongoes.

One minute later
And that cupboard is next to the set of drawers that has pictures of Robbie the original Sex God in it. Funny I haven't heard anything from him since I sort of dumped him. I hope

he is not on the rack of love. Although that would be a first. Usually it is me that is on the rack of love.

Thirty seconds later
I'll just close the drawer now.

Ten seconds later
I wonder if Robbie has got the megahump with me? I daren't ask Tom. Especially as he might be Mr Ex-Hunky.

One minute later
I hope Robbie is not too sad without me. I don't like making boys cry. Although to be frank I would rather they were crying than me.

Life can be cruel.

Especially if you are vair vair sensitive like I am.

Two minutes later
I don't know what to do with myself now. I am full of excitementosity. And tensionosity. And just a hint of confusiosity.

One minute later

Maybe I should fill in time by learning some Pizza-a-gogo-ese. For when I go over. Only being able to say *cappuccino* is going to wear a bit thin after a few days.

Masimo said he was off to some party tonight in Rome.

Five minutes later

Should he be out having fun while I am hanging about like a monk in a monkhouse? That is the drawback to being the girlfriend of a rock legend, you have to hang around a lot.

I may be driven to going round to listen to Wild Woman of the Forest ramble on about Hunky.

On the way round to Jas's

If I am nice to her, she may smash open her secret piggy bank and give me spondulies to go to my beloved.

Or else I could just steal the piggy.

Round at Jas's

Both her little eyes were swollen up. I put my arm around her and said, "Jas, I have found that when you are troubled, it is often better to think of others rather than yourself. I think you would feel much better if you got me some milky coffee and Jammy Dodgers and I told you all about me."

I had only just started when we were interrupted by Jas's mum saying there was a phone call from Rosie for Jas. Did she want to take it on her phone in the bedroom?

Jas and I each listened on an extension. I was nestled up among the Owl Folk and Jas was in her mum and dad's bedroom on the other extension.

Every time I ask for an extension and so on, Dad has a complete nervy spaz saying rubbish stuff like, "Why don't you just have a phone glued to your head?" And so on.

I am not surprised that Mum says she doesn't share many interests with him. What I am surprised about is that she shares any.

Ro Ro said, "*Bonjour*, groovers. I have had *la bonne* idea. Don't you think it would be groovy and a laugh for us to work out some backing dances for Sven's gig?

I said, "*Mais oui*, that would be *beau regarde* and also *magnifique* and possibly groovy."

Jas said, "Well, as long as they are not silly."

Rosie and I laughed, then I said, "We could have a Nordic

theme. We have many Viking dances in our repertoire: the Viking disco inferno, the bison dance. We could make up another one."

Rosie said, "Yeah, grooveyard, we could have furry miniskirts and ear muffs."

Home again
9:00 p.m.

I have cheered Jas up and told her we will think of a plan *vis-à-vis* Tom.

I didn't mention the piggy bank, but I think it is on the shelf near her bed. Behind her mollusc collection.

9:19 p.m.

I don't know why I didn't realise I was born for the stage before. It is blindingly obvious even to a blind man on blind tablets that I am a backing dancer. That will be my career. I will travel with the band giving the world the benefit of my Viking disco inferno dance and so on. And it is very convenient romance-wise because with Masimo as the lead singer of the Stiff Dylans and me as backing dancer, we can travel the globe of luuurve.

The turbulent washing machine of luuurve

Friday August 5th
Early Evening

Masimo hasn't called again. Officially it's my turn to call him on the number he gave me. That is what I would do if he was a girl, which he clearly isn't, even if Dave says he is.

Shut up about Dave.

I feel a bit shy about calling Masimo. In one of my mum's mags it said, "Be a teaser, not a pleaser." And it said you should never ring a boy; they should always ring you. So essentially, I am once more thrashing about in the washing machine of luuurve.

Oooh, what shall I do? Maybe I should send him a postcard.

Five minutes later
But if I go out and buy a postcard, he might ring while I'm out. I wonder if Mum has one lurking about in her drawers. Oo-er.

In Mum's bedroom
Honestly, this house is like living in a tart's handbag. I've found a card but it is of a girl walking by with huge nunga-nungas and a bloke on a veg stand holding two melons in front of his chest. The caption is "Phwoar, what a lovely pair of melons!" What is the matter with my parents?

Two minutes later
But even if I did manage to send a card, when would I say I was coming? I still haven't managed to steer the conversation around to Mutti and Vati giving me the spondulies for my trip.

One minute later
However, I have more than romance on my mind. Masimo will have to understand that my career comes first

sometimes. There is a rehearsal round at Rosie's tonight for our planned disco inferno extravaganza, so I'd better get my dance tights out.

Sunday August 7th

Waited for the postie at the gate yesterday, but he didn't have any letters for me. I asked him if he was hiding my mail, but he didn't even bother to reply.

More damned rehearsals for Sven's dj-ing night today. I am so vair vair tired. I am a slave to my art.

9:45 p.m.

I am quite tuckered out with dancing. Even though it is still practically the afternoon, I may as well go to bed.

In bed

Sven turned up at Rosie's while we were there and snogged the pants off her (oo-er).

We all felt like a basket of goosegogs.

In fact, when we were walking home, Jas said, "I felt a bit jealous."

I tutted. But actually I felt a bit jealous as well.

9:50 p.m.

The door slammed and I heard Vati come in. Accompanied by Uncle Eddie, a.k.a. the baldy-o-gram since he took up taking his clothes off for women. They pay him to do it, that is the weird thing.

Dad yelled, "The vati and the baldy-o-gram are home, sensation seekers!"

Ten minutes later

I can hear the sound of sizzling from the kitchen and the cats are going bananas. That will be the twenty-five sausages each that Dad and his not very slim bald mate will be having.

Now I can hear the spluttering of cans of lager being opened.

Neither of them will be able to get through the kitchen door at this rate.

Five minutes later

They must have chucked a couple of sausages out into the garden for Angus and the Pussycat Gang because there is a lot of yowling and spitting going on.

And barking.

And yelling.

Oh, here we go. Mr Next Door is on the warpath.

I looked carefully through my bedroom curtains as I didn't want the finger of shame pointing my way.

Yes, there was Mr Next Door in his combat gear (slippers and towelling robe) shouting, "Clear off!!!"

He's a fool really. Angus will think he wants to play the sausage game with the Prat Poodles.

One minute later

Ah, yes. Angus has bounded over the garden wall and he is having a sausage tug-of-war with Whitey. Mr Next Door has gone for his broom.

I'm not going to look any more as I may accidentally glimpse Mr Next Door's exposed bottom in the furore.

10:15 p.m.

Dad and the baldy-o-gram are arsing about, laughing and giggling like ninnies in the front room. Dad yelled upstairs, "Georgia, my dove, your pater and his friend are engaged in a very serious business matter. Would you get another couple of cans from the wine cellar. You may know it as the 'fridge'. Thank you so much."

I just shouted down, "Not in a million years, O Portly One."

He shouted back, "I will give you a fiver."

Huh, as if bribery is going to make me his slavey girl.

Two minutes later

When I went into the front room with the cans of lager, Dad was lying on the sofa like a great bearded whale.

Uncle Eddie winked at me as I came in.

Dad said, "So, Eddie, what is your life like, now that you are a sex symbol?" Uncle Eddie belched (charming) and said, "Well, Bob, Georgia, it has its ups and downs like most celebrity lives. For instance, last night I got mobbed by women in the chippie after the gig. Which is nice. And I got free chips and a pickled egg. But, on the other hand, when I got home I found they had bloody stolen another of my feather codpieces. Which I have to have handmade."

Oh, how vair vair disgusting. Now I have been exposed to every sort of porn in this house: mouldyporn, kittyporn, earporn and now baldyporn!!!

Speaking of kittyporn, where are Angus and Naomi? And cross-eyed Gordy?

Back in my room

It's all gone suspiciously quiet. I looked out of the window over Next Door's garden. I can't see the pussycat gang, but I can see Gordy.

Four minutes later

I am concerned that Gordy is hanging around with the wrong crowd. He is actually playing with the Prat Poodles and, I can hardly believe my eyes, he is chewing on their rubber bonio. It's not right. It's probably just an adolescent phase he is going through.

11:29 p.m.

I went down to get a drink of water and a Jammy Dodger to ward off late-night starvation. Mum came in a bit red-faced from too much *vino tinto*, or just sheer embarrassment at being her. She went into the front room where Dad and Uncle Eddie were practising some sort of dance for Uncle Eddie's act. I couldn't bear to go in and have a look, but I will just say this, the music they were using was "I'm Jake the Peg, diddle diddle diddle dum, with my extra leg" by Rolf Harris.

Mum slammed off to bed without saying goodnight.

Dad came out of the front room and said to me, "Uh-oh, women's trouble!"

Midnight
I must get away from here. I must get to see the Luuurve God. Dad owes me a fiver for being his slavey girl. So that means I have only £495 to go.

I wonder if he will believe me if I say he promised to give me £50 to get his lager?

Monday August 8th
8:30 a.m.
I am still not used to having the bed to myself. I wouldn't say I am exactly missing Libby, but I feel a space in my bed where her freezing bottom used to be. Even Angus didn't come in last night. He's probably too bloated with sausage to haul himself up the stairs.

In the kitchen
Oh brilliant, Mutti and Vati are not speaking AGAIN. They are so childish.

Dad yelled from the bedroom, "Connie, have you seen

my undercrackers?" And Mum went on buttering her toast.

There was a long silence and then Dad said, "Er, hello... is there anybody there?"

I looked at Mum and she was chomping away on her toastie.

I said, "Mum, I would like to discuss dates with you, about my Italian holiday. Do you remember that we agreed I would go next week? Well, do you think I should travel to Rome on the Friday or the Saturday? It would be better on the Saturday because then Vati could drive me to the airport. It would be best all round, don't you think, that he hired a proper car. For safety and embarrassment reasons."

Dad yelled again from the bedroom, "Connie, stop playing the giddy goat. I'm going to be late. I cannot find any of my undercrackers."

Mum said to me, "You don't need to worry about the lift and so on."

I said, "Thanks, Mum."

She said, "You don't need to worry about a lift because you are not going anywhere."

What???

Then Dad came into the kitchen, with a towel wrapped around what he laughingly refers to as his waist. He said to

Mum, "Where are all my undercrackers?" Mum pointed to the kitchen bin.

Dad went ballisticisimus. And a half.

It didn't really seem the right moment to ask him about a lift to the airport. Or the £500 I would need for proper spendies, so I skipped back up to the safety of my room.

Fifteen minutes later

Well, it's good that the whole street knows about my dad's undercrackers and my mum's insanity. It makes for a tighter community spirit.

I do think that Dad should learn that, as our revered headmistress Slim says, "Obscene language is the language of those of a limited imagination."

Tuesday August 9th

10:00 p.m.

Jas has driven me insane today with all her Tom talk. I think she is hoping he will just forget about the going to different universities and having their own space fandango.

Well, let sleeping dogs lie is what I say.

Although it is not what Gordy says. He is worrying me.

I was calling him and tapping his food tin with a spoon earlier when Mr Next Door popped his head over the fence. He said that Gordon was sleeping in the Prat brothers' kennel.

I said, "Yeah, you'll never get him out, I'm afraid. They will have to sleep in the house."

And Mr Next Door said the weirdest thing.

"Oh, they are in there with him."

Blimey.

Wednesday August 10th

Ok, it's over a week now since I heard from Masimo, so I'm going to send a cool postcard. I've got one of a kitten covered in spaghetti being fished out of a pan with a ladle, and you can't get much cooler than that in my humble opinion. So here goes:

Ciao, Masimo,
   It is me here. It was vair fabby and marvy to hear your voice.

Hang on, he might not know what vair means, or fabby or marvy. Blimey, it's going to take me the rest of my life to write this postcard. I'll do it tomorrow.

Thursday August 11th

I keep looking at the number I have got for Masimo. What would I say if I called him? And anyway, if he likes my eyes so much, why hasn't he got on the phone again?

Lunchtime

Even though I am plunged once more into the turbulent washing machine of luuurve, I am quite looking forward to going to Sven's dj-ing gig on Saturday.

We are having final rehearsals round at Rosie's for our backing dance routines. Honor and Sophie, the trainee Ace Gang members, are getting their big break because they are allowed to join in the rehearsal sessions. Although they won't be doing the real thing as there is not enough room on the stage and not enough ear muffs to go around. But that is showbiz for you.

We are going to do our world-renowned (well, lots of people have seen it at Stalag 14) Viking bison disco inferno dance. Also as a world premiere in honour of Sven's gig, we have come up with a dance called the Viking disco hornpipe.

It is a new departure for us as it involves costume and props. Of course, we have used props before – the horns in the Viking and bison extravaganza. And also bubble gum up the nose for the snot dance. (Incidentally, we have left out the snot dance from our programme for the night as Jools said she thought that prospective snoggees might find it a bit offputting.) So, as I say, we have used props before but we have never toyed with both costume and props.

In the Viking disco hornpipe extravaganza we will be wearing ear muffs and mittens, for the vair vair chilly Viking winter nights. And we will also be using small paddles.

At Rosie's
Evening
Jas is being annoyingly droopy.

Especially as Rosie had traipsed all the way to the fairy dressing-up shop for kiddies in town, to get the muffs. And they had special tinsel and everything. Jas wouldn't wear the ear muffs because she said it was "silly".

I said, "Jas, if we didn't do stuff just because it was silly, where would we be?"

She was still on her hufty stool and said, "What are you talking about now?"

It is vair tiring explaining things to the vair dim, but it

seems to be more or less my job in life.

"Jas, do you think that German is a silly language?"

She started fiddling with her fringe. (Incidentally, another example of 'silliness', but I didn't say.) She was obviously thinking the German thing over.

I said, "Quickly, quickly, Jas."

"Well, it's a foreign language spoken by foreign people and that can't be silly."

"Jas, they say *SPANGLEFERKEL*. The word for snogging in German-type language is *KNUTSCHEN*. WAKE UP, SMELL THE COFFEE!!!"

In the end she got her muffs and mittens on.

One hour later

The official Viking disco hornpipe dance is perfected!!!

(Just a note, costume-wise: the ear muffs are worn over the bison horns. It is imperative that the horns are not removed, otherwise it makes a laughing stock of the whole thing.) So:

The music starts with a Viking salute. Both paddles are pointed at the horns.

Then a cry of "Thor!!!" and a jump turn to the right.

Paddle, paddle, paddle, paddle to the right,

Paddle, paddle, paddle, paddle to the left.

Cry of Thor! Jump turn to the left.

Paddle, paddle, paddle, paddle to the left,

Paddle, paddle, paddle, paddle to the right.

Jump to face the front (grim Viking expression).

Quick paddle right, quick paddle left x 4.

Turn to partner.

Cross paddles with partner x 2.

Face front and high hornpipe skipping x 8 (gay Viking smiling).

Then (and this is the complicated bit) interweaving paddling! Paddle in and out of each other up and down the line, meanwhile gazing out to the left and to the right (concerned expression – this is the looking-for-land bit).

Paddle back to original position.

On-the-spot paddling till all are in line and then close eyes (for night-time rowing effect).

Right and left paddling x2 and then open eyes wide.

Shout "Land AHOYYYYY!"

Fall to knees and throw paddles in the air (behind, not in front, in case of crowd injury).

Friday August 12th
In my bedroom

> Dear Masimo,
>   Ciao. Last night we were practising our new
> Viking hornpipe dance. At first we had trouble
> with our paddles and Rosie nearly lost an eye,
> but by the high hornpipe skipping we had an...

Hang on a minute. Maybe he doesn't know what a Viking hornpipe is. Or paddles. Or skipping. Good grief, international romance is vair tiring.

Saturday August 13th
OK, if I haven't heard from the Luuurve God by the fifteenth, I will take it as a sign from Baby Jesus that I should get on the blower.

Mind you, I don't know what I would say about when I am coming over. I found £1.50 down the back of the sofa. And that would make £6.50 towards my fare except that I accidentally bought some new lip gloss (raspberry and vanilla flavour) at Boots.

Monday August 15th

10:30 a.m.

Another postcard from the Luuurve God!!! Yes, yes and three times yes! Yesittyyesyes!!!

Oh, I am so happy. He posted it ages ago, so the post in Pizza-a-gogo land must be as bad as it is here.

Two minutes later

I bet our postie has taken postie revenge for having to lug huge sacks of letters round. I bet that is what he does. I bet he doesn't deliver people's mail, he just pretends to, and he has a hut in his back garden bursting with letters and postcards.

Anyway.

The postcard has a picture of a bowl of pasta on the front and it says:

> Ciao, cara Georgia,
>   Plees come for to see me. I am having the hunger for you.
>   Masimo xxxxxxxxxxxxxx

Wow wowzee wow!

100

That is it!! As soon as I can persuade Mum and Dad to give me spondies, I am off to see my Italian boyfriend.

Hmmm, it sounds quite groovy to say that. Not "My boyfriend that goes to Foxwood School and will probably work in a bank" but "My Italian boyfriend, who will be a world-famous pop star!"

Yessssss!

Tuesday August 16th

I tried special pleading with Mum today *vis-à-vis* money. She said, "Don't be stupid. I haven't got £500 and even if I did have, you would not be getting it to go and see some Italian bloke in Rome. Gorgey or not. You can have a tenner. Make it last."

I hate her.

Wednesday August 17th

I have gone through nearly the whole having-the-hump scale. From number one (*ignorez-vous*ing) to number six (pretendy deafnosity) and Mum hasn't even noticed.

Thursday August 18th

2:30 p.m.

Blimey, life is quite literally a boy-free zone. No sign of Dave the Laugh, no sign of Robbie. I haven't even seen the Blunder Boys around. Which is good. But weird. Even Tom has gone off to stay with some mates at uni for a few days.

Sooooo boring.

And hot.

I would do light tanning in the garden but every time I get comfy Angus comes and starts digging near me. (Not with a spade, with his paws. If he did have a spade, it wouldn't be quite so boring and annoying.)

Viking hornpipes a-gogo!!!

Saturday August 20th
Sven's Viking extravaganza gig night
6:30 p.m.

In my bedroom. I am meeting the rest of the gang at the clock tower. Jas is coming round here and we are walking up together so that she "doesn't miss Hunky". Good Lord.

We have got our ear muffs and mittens and horns in little matching vanity cases that Rosie also got from the fairy shop. She says that Sven gets a lot of his stuff from there. Blimey.

6:45 p.m.

At the back of my mind. I'm a bit worried that Robbie might turn up tonight. I know he hasn't gone off to Kiwi-a-gogo because I feel sure I would have heard it on the Radio Jas news round-up. Even if I didn't ask.

6:50 p.m.

Jas turned up at mine with her vanity case.

The vanity cases are, it has to be said, a bit on the naff side. Very pink and glittery. Jas said, "They look just like ones that fairies would use."

I gave her my "Are you mad?" look, but she didn't notice. She is too busy being a piggy-bank hogger.

However, I feel free to carry silly fairy vanity cases and to wear my horns ad hoc and willy-nilly because there is not going to be anyone at the gig that I need to impress, now that Masimo is my one and only one.

7:00 p.m.

Yippee and thrice times yippee!! I am allowed to stay at Jas's. And I don't mean my parents have allowed me to stay. Lately they don't even notice if I am in or out, they are so busy with their own 'lives'. I just said, "I am staying at Jas's tonight," and they went, "OK."

It was Jas I had to persuade to let me stay. She has been in and out of her huffmobile for the last week, but I have promised not to mess about with her owls or steal her piggy bank, so she says I can stay.

Anyway, there is no point in going home. Dad is out all the time with Uncle Eddie and his other sad portly mates, going to "gigs" or pratting around with their loonmobiles. Mum is out all the time as well because Libby is still round at Grandvati's. So, apart from the kittykats (who are also out all the time), I am practically an orphan anyway.

Buddha Lounge
8:00 p.m.
Quite cool vibe in the Buddha Lounge and rammed already. A few people I know and loads of peeps from Notre Dame School.

Jas is busy pretending that she doesn't care whether Hunky turns up or not. She thinks he might be back from his mates' tonight, but she says she has too much pridenosity to try and find out. I am not going to mention his name either, or ask about Robbie, because it will just be an excuse for her to drone on and on about the "vole years" and what larks she and Tom had by the riverside shrimping and so on. Or whatever they do. Hand snog probably, but I won't think about that now.

In the tarts' wardrobe

Ellen was in a complete ditherama and tiz wondering whether Declan would turn up. She was shaking and dithering so much that she accidentally got lipstick in her eye. That is how much she was dithering. Mabs was almost as bad about Edward.

I was tarting myself up in the mirror and said, "Oh, I am so vair vair glad that I am free to enjoy myself, unlike you lot – I shall dance, I shall let my nungas run free and wild, my nostrils can flare and obliterate my face to their heart's content. Because there is no one here tonight that I am bothered by. I am simply the girlfriend of a Luuurve God."

Mabs said, "Has he phoned since he last phoned?"

I said, "In the language of luuurve that would be called 'over-egging the pudding'."

She said, "He hasn't phoned then."

I smoothed down my internal feathers because she was slightly annoying me. Calm calm, think luuurve, think warm Italian nights and soft lips meeting in the shadow of the leaning tower of Pisa... or whatever it is they have in Rome. I said, "Actually, I am going to take the pasta by the horns and I am going to phone him and tell him that I am coming over."

Jas came out of her Tom coma. "Have your parents actually agreed that you can go? To Italy? By yourself to stay with a boy? Who is older than you?"

I tossed my hair in a tossing way like someone who has tossed their hair all over the world might do.

"*Sì*."

All of the Ace Gang looked at me.

Jas said, "That is a big fat lie, isn't it?"

"*Sì*."

Back on the dance floor

All right, I haven't actually got the parents to agree a date for me to go. Or give me the money or anything. But they will be too busy with the custody battle – about who doesn't get the children or the cats when they split up – to bother about me popping over to Italy for a few days.

 107

That is what I feel.

I will get on the old blower tomorrow to let Masimo know I am coming, and then I will start my buttering-up-the-elderly-insane plan.

8:30 p.m.

Sven walked on to take over the decks to that song "Burn, baby, burn, disco inferno." He was wearing a fur cloak and bison horns and, joy of joys, the old lighting-up flares!! And he had his own vanity case!!! Yesssss!

The lights went crazy and he stood over his decks as we all clapped and went mental.

I said to Rosie, "You should be very, very proud. You, without the shadow of a doubt, have the maddest boyfriend in town."

She said, "I know. I can't wait to get off with him again."

8:35 p.m.

It is really alarming watching Rosie and Sven. She is dancing in front of him, sticking her bottom out at him and so on, and he is winking at her and licking his lips. I can't watch this, it's Nordyporn!!!

9:00 p.m.

Funny, there not being many people we know here. No sign of Tom or Declan or Edward or Rollo or, erm, who else – erm... oh, I know, Dave the Laugh. And his girlfriend.

I, of course, don't really mind for myself but the rest of the Ace Gang are driving me mad with all their: "Oh, I wonder why Rollo isn't here yet?"

"Oooh, I wonder where Edward is. Do you think he's with Tom and the rest and they have gone somewhere else?"

And Ellen going on and on. "Erm, it's, like, I wonder if, like, do you think that, er, Declan is, like, with Tom and the rest and they have gone somewhere else?"

I am beginning to feel a bit full of tensionosity, so I have decided to take diversionary action before I start babbling wubbish like Ellen. I said, "Let's do our dance routines now, get this party started."

I went and told Rosie, and Sven said over the microphone, "In one minute we haf the dancing girls in their horns!!!"

Rosie disentangled herself from him (which took about a million years of licking – honestly) and we dashed off to the tarts' wardrobe and got dressed in our horns. I felt so vair vair free. It must be what being a Blunder Boy feels like. No matter what you do or how you are dressed, you are just not aware of being a prat.

I said, "Right, let us bond now. Group hug!!!"

We did the group hug and one quick burst of "Hoooorn!!!" And we were ready for our big moment.

Out in the club

We are gathered at the side of the little stage that Sven is on. I like to think we look attractively Nordic. With just a hint of pillaging and extreme violence about us.

For our grand finale (the Viking disco hornpipe extravaganza) we have put our paddles, ear muffs and mittens in a little pile by a speaker. All the crowd were looking at us.

Sven put on a traditional Viking song "Jingle Bells", we adjusted our horns and off we jolly well went:

Stamp, stamp to the left,

Left leg kick, kick,

Arm up,

Stab, stab to the left (that is the pillaging bit),

Stamp, stamp to the right,

Right leg kick, kick,

Arm up,

Stab, stab to the right,

Quick twirl around with both hands raised to Thor
(whatever),

Raise your (pretend) drinking horn to the left,

Drinking horn to the right,

Horn to the sky,

All over body shake,

Huddly duddly,

And fall to knees with a triumphant shout of
HORRRRNNNNN!!!!

It was a triumph, darling, a triumph. Even Ellen managed not to stab anyone in the eye. The crowd went berserkerama!!! Leaping and yelling, "More, more!!!"

Sven said over the mike, "OK, you groovster peeps, this time is your turn!! Let's go do the Viking bison disco inferno dance," and he put "Jingle Bells" back on and we started again.

Everyone joined in with us. The whole room did stab stab to the right, and even the huddly duddly and fall to the knees bit. It was marvy seeing everyone down on their knees yelling, "HORRRRNNN!" And people say that teenagers today do nothing for people.

I'm a star, I'm a star!!! I shouted to Jas above the noise, "I want Smarties in our dressing room. I want a limo for my mittens – I want EVERYTHING!!!"

And then it was time for the *pièce de* whatsit: the Viking disco hornpipe extravaganza. We put on our ear muffs and mittens, and picked up our paddles. Then we got into position with our backs to the crowd and when they had quietened down, we waited for our musical cue. As the dub version of *EastEnders* sounded out from the decks, we raised our paddles proudly. The music was going: "Na na na na naa naa naaaa, na na na-na naa na na na na naa naa, duff duff duff, na na na naa naa naaaa..."

We turned round to face our audience and as we did so, the doors flew open and Mark Big Gob and the Blunder Boys walked in. Oh, brilliant.

Still, what did we care? We would get our bodyguards to toss them aside like paper towels from the paper-towel dispenser in the loos. They could go down the piddly-diddly hole of life!!!

We did the dance with gusto and also vim, and everyone applauded and went crazeeee again at the end. They were yelling, "More horn, more horn. We want more horn!!!"

God, I was hot. I said to Rosie, "I can't do it again without some drink. Send one of our runners for drinks."

Rosie said, "Righty ho."

She came back a second later and said, "Who are our runners?"

And Jas said, "We haven't got any, she has just gone temporarily insane."

But she said it in a smiley way.

One minute later

We did the dance again and everyone went mad AGAIN!!! This was the life. Even though Ellen caught me a glancing blow with her paddle.

Then the Blunder Boys started shouting wubbish in their dim way.

We just ignored them and were coming down from the stage when Mark Big Gob yelled out, "Oy, you, the big tart in the middle, give us a flash of your nungas." He was shouting at Rosie.

Sven took off the record he was playing and stood up.

There was silence.

He took off his fur cape and adjusted his horns.

Oh dear God.

Sven slowly stepped down. His flares lit up and he walked towards the group of Blunder Boys. Everyone else was backing off. People were saying, "Calm down, calm down, leave it out, lads."

Well, apart from Rosie. She was behind Sven, saying, "Go on, big boy, tear their little heads off."

Two minutes later

Now Sven is big, but there were about eight of the Blunderers facing up to him. I was a bit frightened actually.

But then it was just like a Western because the doors opened again and in came Tom and Declan and Edward and Dom and Rollo and a load of their mates and, last but not least, Dave the Laugh.

Dave the Laugh looked at what was going on and then said to Mark Big Gob, "Mark, go and get your coats and handbags. You and your sisters are leaving."

Three minutes later

There was a bit of argie-bargie from the Blunder Boys.

One of them said to Dave, "Who's gonna make me leave?"

And Dave went and stood over him and said, "I am."

And the Blunder Boys said, "Oh, OK, well, I was just asking, mate."

And there was some shoving past people and spitting from the Blunder Boys as they went off to the door. Declan and Tom and Dave did a gentle bit of frogmarching Mark through the door. And there was a lot of shouting and kicking of cars once the Blunderers were safely out in the street.

Unfortunately the venue owners had called the police, and we heard the police sirens outside.

Sven said, "Now that is how to have the good Viking night."

Dave the Laugh found me. He was holding his hand as if he had hurt it. He smiled at me and said, "Are you OK, Miss Kittykat?"

I said, "Oh, Dave, thank goodness you came. What has happened to your hand?"

He said, "One of the hard lads bit me – I may never play the tambourine again."

It was luuurvely to see him. And I felt really odd that he was hurt. I wanted to stroke his hand; in fact, maybe I should. I may have healing hands.

I was just thinking about doing it when I heard a voice say, "Dave, Dave, are you all right??? Oh God, your hand!! You poor thing, let me help you."

It was Emma, dashing about like Florrie whatsit – Nightingale.

Dave looked at me and gave a sort of rueful smile. He said, "Too many trousers spoil the broth," and got up and did pretendy limping off with Emma.

His girlfriend.

Twenty minutes later

We were all turfed out. The police gave Sven a warning and asked us if we wanted to dob anyone in. I wouldn't have minded seeing the Blunder Boys behind bars, preferably in a zoo. However, as Sven had in a way started the proceedings, we just mumbled a bit about things getting out of hand. "Sorry, Officers" etc. And tried to shuffle off home.

I saw Jas and Tom talking together in the dark over by a bench. Oh Good Lord, I would be doing goosegog all the way home now if they made up.

I tried to think of something to say that would make Jas get in her huffmobile with Tom. Or perhaps I should just go and stand between them in a friendly way and not go away. Take my goosegog duties seriously.

Thirty seconds later

A policeman came by me and said, "Stop hanging about here. Clear off home now and don't cause any more trouble."

That's nice, isn't it? No words of comfort. No "Now don't you worry, young lady, the nasty boys won't be bothering you any more. Here's £5 for a cab home to see you safely on your way."

In fact, as he looked at me I sort of recognised him. Uh-oh, he was the one who had brought Angus home in a bag one night after he had eaten Next Door's hamster. Unfortunately, Angus didn't like the bag and had attacked the policeman's trousers.

Then he recognised me. "Oh, it's you. I might have known. How's your 'pet'? Hopefully gone to that big cat basket in the sky."

I said, with dignitosity at all times, "Thank you for your kind inquiry, Officer. I must go home now. Mind how you go and remember, it's a jungle out there. Be safe."

Do you see? Do you see what I did? I pretended I was a policeman to a policeman!!!

But I was walking quickly away from him as I said it and calling to Jas, "Jas, we have to go now. The nice officer of the law said so."

Jas came over smartish. She is terrified of policemen and is the bum-oley licking expert around them. She said, "Thank you so much, Officer. You do a wonderful job." Oh, pleeeeease.

Then she waved back at Tom. He blew her a kiss and she sighed. Good grief. Can't they stay split up for more than half a day? It's pathetico.

We walked on home. I said to Jas, "Did you see Dave the Laugh getting stuck in to save us?"

Jas said, "Yeah, Tom was keeping me behind him so that I wouldn't get hurt. And when one of the Blunder Boys said to him, 'Do you want some, mate?' he said, 'Oooh, fear factor ten,' and did a judo hold that we learned when we went on our survival course and just marched him to the door. It was fab."

Oh, shut up about Hunky.

I said, "When I said to Dave, 'Are you OK? Have you hurt your hand?' he said, 'I may never play the tambourine again'! He is quite literally Dave the Laugh."

Jas said, "Oh no, you've got your big red bottom AGAIN!!"
Have I?

In bed with the owl (and her mates)
1:00 a.m.

Jas has built a small barrier of owls between us, but has said that if I don't wriggle about I am allowed to sleep in her bed because it has been such a traumatic night of violence. Blimey, she should live round at my house if she thinks this has been a traumatic night of violence. My bedroom is littered with dismembered toys, and if I move in bed, I am attacked viciously by either Angus, Gordy or Libby. Or all three of them.

Jas said, "Tom still thinks we should go to different unis or see the world or something. He said we might never know if we have done the right thing otherwise. But it doesn't mean he doesn't love me."

I said, "Well, what do you think?"

She mused (that is, flicked her fringe and cuddled Snowy Owl). "Well, I like fun as much as the next person."

I said, "Can I just stop you there, Jas. You have to be realistic if we are going to get anywhere. You do not like fun as much as the next person. Your idea of fun and the

♥ 119

next person's idea of fun are vair vair different."

"Well, all right, what I mean is, maybe Tom is right that we are too young to decide everything now. Maybe I could do things by myself and that would be good."

I sat up. "That is the ticket, pally. I mean, there are many advantages to not having a boyfriend, you know. You wouldn't have to pretend to be interested in wombat droppings and varieties of frogspawn."

She looked puzzled. "I'm not pretending."

"Er, right, well..."

God, it was hopeless. Everything I thought of, Jas had an answer for. She doesn't want to let her red bottom run free and wild. She doesn't mind the vole-dropping stuff and looking interested. She IS interested. She doesn't want to flop around in her jimmyjams if she wants to because she already can, because Tom, Hunky the Wonderdog, likes her just the way she is, whatever she looks like.

In a nutshell, Tom is her one and only one and that is the end of the matter. I wish I were her.

Well, of course I don't wish I were her. That would be ridiculous. I'd have to chop my own head off for a start, because I'd be annoying myself so much.

Sunday August 21st

Home

11:00 a.m

I have got post-gig comedown, I think. Everything was tickety-boo when we were doing the dancing and it was a laugh. And even the fight was sort of exciting. But then seeing Dave the Laugh go off with Emma, and Jas talking about being with Hunky, it's sort of made me a bit full of glumnosity.

And I haven't spoken to the Luuurve God for ages; anything could be happening.

Boo and also poo.

It's all gloomy in the house: even though it is sunny outside it is raining inside. Well, not really, but you know what I mean. Mum has gone off with Libby, I think trying to placate Josh's mum. I'd like to think it's because she cares, but really I think it's because Grandvati has gone off for a camping trip with Maisie. She has probably knitted the tent. Who knows where Vati is; he is never in these days.

I didn't think the day would ever come when I said this, but I wish they would get back to 'normal'. I would even try not to be sick if they touched each other.

What if they split up? They would make me do that choosing thing. The judge would say that I could decide who I lived with.

It is so clearly not going to be Dad. I may warn him that he is dicing with never seeing me again by his brutal lack of care for me. He will not give me the least thing. I tried to ask him for a couple of hundred squids towards my trip to Rome yesterday, and he laughed.

Two minutes later

I wonder if he will laugh quite so much when all he has to remember me by are the press cuttings of me on world tours etc. Doing backing dancing for the Stiff Dylans in exotic locations. And when I do interviews in showbiz mags, and they ask me about my father, I will say, "I would have liked to have been close, but once the family split up and my work took me all over the world, I sort of outgrew him."

I won't add "like he outgrew his trousers" because that would put me in a bad light pop culture-wise.

Five minutes later

Hey, maybe I could say that if he will give me £500 to go to

Pizza-a-gogo, I will consider seeing him three or four times a year for an afternoon.

Excellent plan!!!

Ten minutes later

Phone rang. At last. I bet this will be my Pizza-a-gogo Luuurve God-type boyfriend on the blower from Roma *bella*. I have got an Italian book for idiots, so I must look through it. Mind you, if it is anything like our French or German textbooks it will be rubbish. They are always to do with losing your bike. They are not based on real life; there is nothing about how to snog in different languages. Absoluto stupido and uselessio.

And also too late-io.

I picked up the phone and said, "*Ciao!*"

"Oh, erm, *ciao* or something – er – I, well, it's me or something. I don't know if—"

"Hello, Ellen."

"Georgia... Could I – I mean, are you in?"

"No, I'm sorry, I'm not."

"Oh, well, will you be in later or something?"

"ELLEN, I am answering the phone. How can I not be in???"

Half an hour of ditherosity later

Miracle of miracles, Declan has actually asked her on a date. They're meeting by the clock tower tomorrow evening, so she has come to the Luuurve Goddess (*moi*) for advice.

It passes the time helping others.

I said, "Ellen, here in a nutshell are my main top tips. Don't drink or eat anything, not even a cappuccino, unless you know for sure your date is an admirer of the foam moustache. If he is – dump him. Secondly and vair vair importantly, do not say what is in your brain. And, above all, remember to dance and be jolly. Although be careful about where you do spontaneous dancing. If you do it in a supermarket, he will just think you are weird."

4:00 p.m.

Right, this is it. I can't stand waiting any more. I am going to quite literally take the Luuurve God by the horns and ring him up.

I've been going through my Italian book for the very very dim. (It's not actually called that, but it should be. It has got the crappest drawings known to humanity. I think it must be the same person who did the illustrations for our German textbook about the Koch family. Under the section "Fun and Games" it has got a drawing of some madman with sticky-up hair and big googly eyes juggling balls. That cannot be right in anyone's language.)

Anyway, I have worked out what to say from the section called "Talking on the Phone".

4:30 p.m.
I think I have got the code right and everything.

Rang the number. Ring ring. Funny ring they have in Pizza-a-gogo land.

The phone was picked up and I said, "*Ciao.*"

A man's voice said, a bit hesitantly, "*Ciao.*"

I wondered if it was Masimo's dad. What is the word for "dad" in Italian? I hadn't looked it up. It couldn't be "daddio", could it?

I thought I would try. "Er, *buon giorno,* daddio, *je suis* – erm, *non non – sono* Georgia."

"Georgia."

"*Sì.*"

Masimo's dad said, "Ah, *sì.*" Then there was a bit of a silence.

Oh, buggeration. How do I say I want to speak to Masimo? I said, "Io wantio – *un momento, per favore.*"

I scrabbled through the book. Oh here we are, a lovely big ear drawing to show me that it is the on-the-phone section. "I want to speak to..." I read it out slowly and loudly: "*POSSO PAHR-LAH-REH A MASIMO?*"

There was a silence and then a Yorkshire voice said, "Po what, love? You've lost me."

It turned out that I was actually speaking to a Yorkshire bloke on holiday in Rome.

I said, "Oh, I'm sorry, but you said *ciao* and I thought you were Italian."

The Yorkshire dad said, "No, I'm from Leeds, but I do like spaghetti."

Two minutes later

Anyway, he was having a lovely time, although you couldn't get a decent pickled egg in Roma apparently, but he wasn't letting that spoil his fun.

Blimey, it was like a Yorkshire version of Uncle Eddie. He was rambling on for ages like I knew him.

Ten minutes later

In the end I got off the phone. I must have got the number wrong. Or misdialled it. I could try again. No, I couldn't take the risk of getting hold of "Just call me Fat Bob" again.

Big furry paw of fate

Tuesday August 23rd
In the kitchen
5:30 p.m.

My darling sis is back at Chaos Headquarters (that is our house). Mum said, "I've managed to get Libby off with a warning. She can go back to nursery later this week, but I have to promise that she won't be allowed to play with sharp implements. So don't let her have any of your knives and so on."

"Mum, I haven't got any knives. It was you that let her have the scissors to cut Pantalitzer doll's hair. Has Josh got the word BUM off his forehead yet?"

Mum said, "Blimey, that was a fuss and a half, wasn't it? It was only indelible ink, not poison."

I said, "Mum, some parents actually, like, DO parenting. They act like grown-ups; they protect their young."

Mum was too busy flicking through *Teen Vogue* to listen.

6:00 p.m.

Libby is preparing a cat picnic on the lawn. Some crushed-up biscuits on a plate and three dishes of milk. I can see Angus, Naomi and Gordy skulking off to hide. They have been made to go to her cat picnics before. And once you have had your head shoved violently into a saucer of milk and a spoonful of Jammy Dodger rammed down your throat, you don't accept another invitation easily.

Time to start buttering up the mutti.

I said, "Mum, if I stayed with you and not Dad, well he would pay like maintenance and child support and so on. And I could use a bit of it, say like £500, because it would be mine really, wouldn't it? It's like me that is being supported, isn't it?"

Mum went, "Hmmm, but I would need a lot of help round the house."

I said, "Yep, yep, I could do that. It would be like sort of earning my own money and I could pay my own way to Pizza-a-gogo land and then it would be all right, wouldn't it? Because actually it wouldn't really be costing you anything because I would be being paid out of my own money really. And you want me to be happy and have a boyfriend and so on; even Ellen has got a boyfriend now. And when you leave Dad you might get one. You never know. Never say never."

Mum said, "Georgia, are you saying that you would be prepared to do the ironing and help around the house and be pleasant?"

I said, "Oh, *mais oui*, yes!!"

"OK, well, start on that big pile of Libby's stuff in the washing basket."

Lalalalala. It's the ironing life for me. Quickly followed by a snogtastic adventure in Luuurve God Heaven.

Half an hour later

How boring is housework? I tell you this for free, I will not be doing any more of it when this is over. I said to Mum, "I think I have got ironer's elbow. It won't go from side to side any more, it will only go up and down. I hope it hasn't ruined my backing dancing career."

7:15 p.m.
I am a domestic husk.

I said to Mum, "I think I will go on Saturday as I suggested."

She said, "Yeah, good idea."

I said, "I will ask Dad if he can drop me off at the airport."

"He's away that weekend, he and Uncle Eddie are going away fishing or prancing around in the clownmobile. He says it will give him time to sort his mind out."

I said, "So can you take me then?"

"Take you where?"

"To the airport."

"Why are you so interested in watching planes all of a sudden?"

"I'm not interested in watching them. I am only interested in getting on one to go to Pizza-a-gogo."

"Well, that is not going to happen, is it."

And that was that.

She never intended to let me go, she just wanted me to do

the ironing. That is the sort of criminal behaviour I have to put up with. I know you read all sorts of miserable stories about kids being holed up in cellars by their mean parents and called "Snot Boy" all the time, but I think my story is just as cruel.

As I slammed out I said to Mum, "Mum, I quite literally hate you."

At Rosie's in her bedroom
8:00 p.m.

Rosie's parents are out again. It's bliss at her house. I think she only sees them about twice a year. I told her what happened. She said, "That is crapola, little matey. When you are all stressed out and having a nervy spaz you have to look after your health – have a Jammy Dodger and some cheesy wotsits."

As we crunched through a couple of packets I said, "I am just going to sneak off anyway, creep out at night with the money I will get from my guilty dad and hitchhike to the airport. Or maybe get one of the lads to take me. Do you think Dom might do it?"

Rosie was really into it now. "Brilliant plan. Just say, devil take the hindmost and *ciao*, Roma!!!"

9:00 p.m.

I was going to call Dom about taking me to the airport, but I sort of chickened out. If I could, I would ask Dave the Laugh because he would understand. Or maybe not. Maybe asking my matey-type matey person to take me to catch a plane to see a Luuurve God is not megacool.

Anyway, he would only go on about my lesbian affair with Masimo.

Still at Rosie's
9:20 p.m.

Making a list of what to take with me clothes and make-up-wise. It will be hot, so I will have to take most of my summerwear, bikinis and flip-flops.

I said, "Do you think I should take a book to read on the beach for those quiet moments?"

Rosie looked at me. "What quiet moments?"

10:00 p.m.

Oh, I feel quite pepped up now. In fact, I think I will start packing when I get in.

As I was leaving Rosie's I said, "Thank you, tip-top pally."

She said, "*De rigueur.* Hey, and don't forget your passport, chum."

I laughed.

On the way home
Fifteen minutes later

Hmmm, where is my passport?

An hour later

I'll tell you where my passport is. At Dad's bloody office, that's where.

Why? What sort of person takes official documents to work with them?

My dad, that is what sort of person.

I said to him, "Why would anyone do that?"

He said, "They're all there. I know you, you would lose yours or put make-up on it or Angus would eat it. This way I know where it is."

I said, "Well, now I know where it is as well, so why don't you go and get me MY passport. Which is issued to me in MY name. By her Maj the Queen. Because it is MY passport. Do you see? Not yours. And while you are in the safe, you may as well get me the £500 child support you promised me."

He said no.

I said to Dad as I stormed off to bed, "Dad, I quite literally hate you."

Ten minutes later

So this is my life:

I am best friends with some Yorkshire bloke called Fat Bob.

I will have to explain to my marvy and groovy new pop idol Luuurve God boyfriend that I am not allowed my own passport.

And I have got £1.50 to get to Pizza-a-gogo land.

What could be worse?

Midnight

Libby put an egg under my pillow to "get a baby chicken".

It has gone all over my pyjamas.

Wednesday August 24th

8:00 a.m.

I am the prisoner of my utterly useless and mean parents. Just because they have a crap life they are determined to make mine crap as well. I would have said that to them if I were speaking to them. Or they were speaking to each other.

In my bedroom

Dad came knocking on my door.

I said, "The door is locked."

Dad pushed open the door and said, "You haven't got a lock on your door."

I said, "You might not see the lock but the lock is there, otherwise I wouldn't be."

But he's not interested in me. He said, "Look, I am going away for a few days and—"

I said, "What is it like to be able to walk around on the planet wherever you like?"

He said, "You're not still going on about visiting this Italian Stallion lad, are you? He'll be back in a week or two anyway."

"Dad, I might not be alive in a week or two – things happen. If I were a mayfly, I would be dead in about half an hour and that would have been my whole life."

He just looked all grumpy, like a big leatherette grumpy fool. What was he wearing? A leather jacket.

I said, "You're not thinking of going out in that jacket, are you?"

He said, "Look, don't start. I've just come to say goodbye and to say that, well... you know that Mum and I have been, you know, not hitting it off."

"She threw your undercrackers away."

"I know she bloody did. Most of them were covered in cat litter when I fished them out."

Oh really, do I have to listen to this sort of thing? I will quite literally spend most of my superstar money on psychiatric fees. He still hadn't finished though.

"Don't worry too much, we'll sort it out, and if, well, if things don't get any better, sometimes people have to..."

Oh no, I think he might be going to get emotional. If he starts crying, I may well be sick. But then he did something much, much worse; he came over and kissed the top of my head.

How annoying. And odd.

one hour later

As Mum went off to "work" she said, "You look a bit peaky."

I said, "It's probably a symptom of my crap life. Which is your fault."

She just ignored me.

I know what she is up to though. She isn't bothered about

me having rickets or something, she just fancies a trip to Dr Clooney's. That will be the next thing. She'll start peering at me and saying stuff about my knees being a bit knobbly or that I don't blink enough or something and then suggest a quick visit to the surgery. She will have to drag me there.

10:40 a.m.
The post arrived. I may as well check if there is anything for me.

One minute later
Oh joy unbounded, there is a postcard from the Luuurve God!! It has a picture of a donkey drinking a bottle of wine on the front. Is that what goes on in Rome? You never know with not-English people.

Shut up, brain, and read the postcard from the beluuurved.

Ciao, bella.
I am mis you like crazy. I am not for long to wait to see you. Todaya we go to the mountains. I have song in my heart for you.
Masimo xxxxxxx

Aaaaaahhhh. He has a song in his heart for me. I hope it is not "Shut uppa you face, whatsa matta you". Or, as it is in the beautiful language of Pizza-a-gogo land, "Shut uppa you face, whatsa matta you".

Oh, I sooo want to see him.

I wonder if I had a whip-round of the Ace Gang I could get the money. I bet Jas has got hundreds stashed in her piggy bank. But then what about my passport? Maybe I could make a forgery?

I HATE my parents.

Evening

To celebrate our last days of freedom before we get sent back to Stalag 14, we have decided to have a spontaneous girls' night in. We are all staying round at Jools's place because she has her own sort of upstairs area with her own TV and bathroom.

Now that is what I call proper parenting. Getting a house big enough so that you don't actually have to have anything to do with your parents. No growing girl should ever run the risk of seeing either her mutti or vati in undercrackers.

11:00 p.m.

I've perked up a bit.

Rosie, Jools, Mabs and me are in one huge bed and Jas, Ellen, Honor and Sophie are in the other one.

Jas amazed me by saying, "Actually, it's quite nice being single for a bit, isn't it? You can really let yourself go mad and wild. I mean, this is the first time I've worn my Snoopy T-shirt for ages."

I said, "Blimey, Jas, calm down."

Rosie said, "What we all have to remember is that yes, boys and snogging are good, but luuurve with a boy may be temporary and Miss Selfridge and Boots are yours for life."

Vair vair wise words. Then we got down to serious business.

Mabs said, "Well, I dunno really, what do you think of this? I saw Edward in the street, across the road with his mates, and he did that phone thing... you know when you pretend you have got a phone in your hand and you do a dial thing. Meaning, you know, bell me."

We all looked at her.

I said, "So have you?"

She said, "No, because I didn't know if he meant, like, I'm going to bell you or you should bell me. I'm sort of all..."

I said, "Belled up?"

And she nodded.

Blimey.

This was worse than s'laters.

Ten minutes later

We've decided that Mabs can't take the risk of an ad-hoc bell-you fandango and therefore the only thing to do is to accidentally bump into him and see what happens.

Jools said, "I know that they play five-a-side in the park on Thursday arvies, so we could accidentally on purpose be there. The last time I saw Rollo he said the same to me. He said, 'Give us a bell.' But then I did and he seemed sort of busy. He was on his way out to practice and he said, 'Give us a bell later.' But I didn't because that was like a double fandango: give us a bell and also s'later. Nightmare scenario."

Hmmmmm.

Then Ellen told us about going out with Declan.

I said, "Please don't tell me you went to a penknife shop for the evening."

Ellen said, "No, we, well – erm... he and I—"

I said, "I know you feel sort of sensitive about this and, you

 141

know, shy and a bit self-conscious, but you are among your own kind now; you are with the Ace Gang – your best pallies, your bestiest most kindiest maties. So let me put it this way – WHAT NUMBER DID YOU GET UP TO ON THE SNOGGING SCALE AND ARE YOU GOING TO SEE HIM AGAIN???"

Forty years later

So, just to save precious hours, I will sum up Ellen's evening with Declan. After a lot of chatting and Coke drinking (good choice drink-wise *vis-à-vis* foam moustache etc.), Declan had said goodnight and they had done one, two, three and a bit of four. Hurrah, thank the Lord!!!

On the down side, as she went into her house Declan had said, "We must do this again sometime." And gone off.

We decided that "sometime" is in fact s'laters in disguise.

I told them my mum's theory about boys being gazelles in trousers that must be enticed out of the woods (i.e. away from their stupid mates). We decided that the best thing was to be alert for sightings of the gazelles (playing footie etc.) and to be attractively semi-available.

Jas then got all misty-eyed about first meeting Tom. She said to me, "Do you remember when I first saw Tom and he was so hunky, working in the shop? And we had a plan to make him notice me. And I went into the shop to buy some onions and then you came in and made out like I was the most popular girl in the school sort of thing. And the rest is history."

She looked a bit sad and said, "Quite literally, the rest might be history."

To cheer her up, and also to stop her moaning on about the vole years, I suggested we get down to talking about serious world matters. Like the beret question for winter term. Could we improve on last year's lunchpack theme?

Sophie said, "My very favouritist was 'glove animal'. Couldn't he come back for a reprise this term?"

Midnight

We were comparing notes snogging-scale-wise and also saying what number we thought people had got to.

Jools said, "Do you think Miss Wilson has ever snogged anyone? If so, what number do you think she has got up to?" Erlack.

I said, "No man alive could get through all that corduroy."

Rosie said, "Oh, I don't know, she has a certain charm. I think I may be on the turn actually, because I thought she looked quite fit when I saw her in the nuddy-pants with her soap on a rope."

We all looked at her. Sometimes even I am surprised by how mad and weird she is.

I said, "Jools, swap places with me. I am not sleeping next to Lezzie Mees." And then Rosie started puckering up at me. I stood up in bed and started kicking her off and she grabbed my ankles and pulled me over.

Mabs yelled, "Girl fight, girl fight!" and we started a massive pillow fight. At which point the door opened and Jools's mum came in. Oh dear.

She looked very serious. Here we go with the "We give you girls a bit of freedom and you just take advantage, when I was a girl we didn't even have pillows, we slept in a drawer and—"

But she just said, "Georgia, your mum is on the phone for you. You can take it on the extension up here if you like, dear."

I wondered why she was looking at me so funny? Maybe Mum was drunk on *vino tinto* and having an Abba evening with her friends and had decided to start a new life with a fireman that she met at aquaerobics. Well, I tell you this for free, I am not going to live with her and Des or whatever he is called.

Mum was actually crying when I picked up the phone. Oh

brilliant, she had already been dumped by Des and I would have to listen to her rambling on about it for the rest of my life.

She said, "Oh, darling, I am so, so sorry." Then she started crying again.

I said, "Er, Mum, I will not be moving in with you and Des."

She didn't even bother to reply; she was just gulping and crying. Actually, I was a bit worried about her because she did sound very upset. Oh blimey.

She went on, "Mr Across the Road came over – and oh, it was so – when I opened the door, I thought, I thought he was carrying a baby – all wrapped up in a blanket... and then, oh love, and... and, oh, one of his paws fell out of the, out of the blanket and it just... hung there... all limp."

And she started weeping and weeping. I couldn't understand what she meant.

I said, "What do you mean? Whose paw?"

And she said, "Oh, darling, it's Angus."

I couldn't speak and my brain wouldn't work. I could hear Mum sobbing and talking but she sounded like a little toyperson on the end of the phone.

"Mr Across the Road found him at the bottom... of our street... by the side of the road – you know how much he liked cars... he, he thought they were big mice on wheels, didn't he – and he must have been – and he was just lying there."

Then tears started coming out of my eyes, all by themselves, just pouring out of my eyes and plopping on my pyjamas. My mouth was dry, and I felt like I was choking on something.

Mum was still talking. "Georgia, love, please talk to me. Please say something, please."

I don't know how long I stood there with the tears falling, but then I felt a big pain in my heart like someone had kicked it and then stuck a knife in it. And I think a noise came out of me – you know, like when people are in pain and they make like a deep groan. It didn't feel like my voice, just like someone in pain very far away.

I think it must have been real because the next thing I knew Jas had her hand on my shoulder. She said, "What's happened, Gee? What's the matter?"

I couldn't say. I could only cry and shake. Jas took the phone out of my hand.

"Hello? It's Jas. What has happened? Oh no. Oh no."

As she was speaking Jas had her arm around me. "Yes, yes, I'm here. I'll look after her. I'll come with her in a taxi. Yes, yes, I'll look after her. We are all here; we'll take care of her."

By now the Ace Gang had come out into the hall and when they saw me, they all came and hugged me. I just wanted to be unconscious, I think. I wanted to tear my head off so it wouldn't have anything in it.

I can't really remember what happened, but I know I was shaking so much that Jools's mum wrapped me in a big blanket, and then the taxi arrived. I cried and cried into Jas's shoulder and she made those noises that people do – not really words, just like "there, there – sshhhh" – like you do when little children have nightmares. She was rocking me.

When we got to our house all the lights were on in the front room. I could see Mum looking out of the window as we pulled into the driveway.

When I tried to get out of the cab I couldn't make my legs work and the cab driver got out of his seat and came and picked me up. He said, "Don't worry, love, I've got you."

He carried me into the house and when he put me down, Mum and Jas got hold of an arm each to make me safe. As he went the cab driver said, "Look after her, there's no charge. God bless."

My voice was all croaky when I tried to speak. I said, "Where... is he?"

And Mum said, "I put him on the sofa."

It was really weird going into the front room. It was like a gale-force wind was blowing; I was sure it was real. I could hear it whooshing against the door, trying to keep me out. I felt like I was walking into the wind trying to get to Angus.

He was on the sofa wrapped up in the blanket. His eyes were all closed and his mouth half open. There was a big deep red gash on his head. I went over to him and looked down and my tears splashed on to his face. How could I live without my furry pal? He wasn't supposed to leave me. In that moment I would rather it was me lying there.

I sat down beside him and put my finger on his nose and stroked it. It was the first time I had ever been able to do that. He would have attacked my hand when he – when he – and I started wailing again, just saying, "Oh, Angus, Angus, I love you, I love you more than anything."

And then a little noise came out of him. Like a little growl.

I yelled, "Mum, Mum, he's alive!!! He's moving!!! He's alive!!!"

Mum came over and put her arms around me. "I know he's still breathing, love, but when I phoned the vet I told him what had happened and what he looked like. The vet said he would have internal injuries and that really the best, the kindest thing, would be to put him to sleep. He's coming over now and going to take him to the surgery and—"

I leaped up. "He is NOT going to be put to sleep. If anyone tries to do that, I will KILL them. I mean it, Mum. It is NOT going to happen. No, you can't let him. I won't let him."

The doorbell rang.

Thirty seconds later

I must have looked like I was going to kill the vet. He looked at me and then said, "Let me have a look at the poor fellow."

He gently felt all over Angus and lifted up his legs. They just flopped back. Angus didn't make any more noises.

The vet sighed. He said, "I'm afraid there will be a lot of internal injury. I think the kindest thing all round would be—"

I just said, "No."

The vet looked at me. He shook his head.

I said, "Please try. I love him." And the tears started plopping out of my eyes again.

I stroked Angus's face and he did a bit of a growl again.

I said to the vet, "You see?"

After a minute or two the vet said, "All right, I'll try,

but I'm being honest with you, cats don't often survive this sort of thing."

He packed Angus in blankets and said he would give him X-rays and drips and anything he could at the surgery.

I said, "Thank you."

I didn't mean to but I gave him a hug.

And he's got a beard.

Vet's surgery

Angus has bandages everywhere, even on his tail. He has not made any noise since the little one when I stroked his face. He is on a drip and his tongue is lolling out.

But I am not annoyed about his tongue lolling out. I can't imagine ever being annoyed with him again about anything. If he lives, he can have anything he wants.

I said to Jas, who was still with me, "When I get home I am going to pray for Angus to Baby Jesus, and if he will let Angus live I will try to be a really good person." And I included Jas's fringe flicking in that. And my dad's leather trousers. That is how serious it all was.

Angus was going to stay in the surgery overnight and the vet said I could come the next day as soon as they opened.

He looked tired and a bit sad. And now I noticed it he also looked very beardy. No, no, I don't want the tired and sad beardy vet. I want the handsome, thrusting ER vet who says, "I've done it, he's going to pull through. Have a nice day."

Dr Beardy said, "I want you to know that I love animals very much, and I know what he means to you, but it doesn't look good. If I keep him alive, he will probably die in a few hours from something I can't fix."

I just said, "He is not going to die. That is a fact."

Jas said she'd come and stay with me at my house but I said no. I wanted to do some heavy praying. She gave me a little kiss on the cheek when she left. I know it was dark and a lezzie-free zone, but it was still nice of her.

Thursday August 25th

Dawn

I don't think I slept. I just nodded off now and again and then woke up, and for a few moments life felt normal and then I remembered. Even Gordy, not world-renowned for his caring, sympathetic nature, cuddled up next to me and didn't attack me once even when I moved my foot.

Five minutes later

Gordy came and sat on my chest and looked at me with his yellow eyes. Well, one of his yellow eyes; the other one was glancing out of the window. He was looking at me unblinking. Then he let out one of those strange croaky noises that makes him sound like he is a hundred-a-day smoking cat. And he leaped down from my bed.

I think he knows something. I think he knows about Angus and he is on my side.

Even if he is a homosexualist half-cat half-dog, it doesn't matter. Love is all you need.

Ten minutes later

Looking out of the window, Gordy is playing chase the bonio with the Prat brothers.

That is not right in anyone's book.

To think of his father lying in a vet's surgery while his son scampers around with ridiculous poodles. He has no pridenosity.

Five minutes later

I remembered my vow to Baby Jesus – about being a jolly good egg about everything. Even very annoying things.

Deep breath and – look, look at Gordy playing happily with other creatures made by God.

All right, curly, annoying yappy creatures, but God's creatures nevertheless.

I mean, not many people like maggots, do they? But that is not the point. Mr and Mrs Maggot love them. Probably. And that is what counts.

Oh shut up, brain. Just love everything and get on with it.

7:30 a.m.
Please let him be alive. Please.

I started to get myself some Coco Pops, but I couldn't eat them. Mum got up and her eyes were all swollen. I went into the bathroom and looked in the mirror. Blimey, I had no eyes. They had disappeared in the night. I was now just a nose with two eyebrows. And the places where my eyes had been ached and ached. In fact, everything ached.

Mum said, "I think I am going to ask Grandad now he's back if Bibbs can stay there for a couple of days just until this is all over – I mean, you know..."

I said, "Just until Angus comes home for convalescence you mean?"

Mum looked at me. "Georgia... you know what the vet said."

I shouted, "What does he know? His beard is so bushy, he probably can't even see what animal he's treating unless it says 'Who's a pretty boy then?' Or starts barking or neighing."

Mum said, "Calm down. He's doing his best."

I said, "He'd better be."

one minute later
Hello, God and Baby Jesus, erm, I might have given the wrong impression about Dr Beardy the vet in that I implied he was a beardy fool. But I meant it in a lighthearted and gay way.

one minute later
When I say "gay" I don't mean gay as in an "OOOOhhhh, do you like my big beard?" sort of way. I mean that I was merely being cheerful.

one minute later
Dear G and BJ, I am signing off communication-wise as

I have to go to the piddly-diddly department.

Surgery
9:00 a.m.

I had awful collywobbles tum trouble as we waited. The nurse took us down to the cat cages bit. It was so sad in there. Doped-up kittykats with drips and bandages and charts. We went over to Angus's cage and he was just lying there. He didn't look like he had moved since last night. But the little machine was going *click click*, so he was breathing.

Dr Beardy came in and said, "No change, I'm afraid. I think you had better try and prepare yourselves for him to go. All his internal organs are so swollen up from the impact, I can't tell what damage has been done, but there is sure to be some bleeding, and then—"

At home
11:00 a.m.

Mum has gone to work. She said she would call in sick and stay with me, but I know she will get into trouble. And anyway, she will get bored and start telling me stuff about her and Dad and her inner dolphin. Or how she wants to fulfil her creativity by becoming a belly dancer at firemen's balls.

So, all in all, it's better to be by myself.

Five minutes later
I am so restless, I don't know what to do.

Ten minutes later
Jas rang. The Ace Gang are going for a ramble. Just a casual ramble to the park. But actually I know it is because they hope that the lads will be playing footie and that they can accidentally bump into them to solve the s'later and "sometime" fandango.

Jas was being very nice actually, although she was chewing. I didn't say anything because of my vow of nicenosity. She said, "Come with us. It will take your mind off things. You can get a nice tan while you are miserable. That would be good for when Masimo comes back."

She is being sweet to me, and she was a big pally cuddling me and looking after me when I heard about Angus. And I know she is miz about Tom, so I said I would go.

In the park

Phew, it's bloody boiling. We are all lolling under a tree. We are doing leg tanning again by having our legs in the sun and the rest of us underneath the shade of the tree. Well, apart from Rosie, who has her own method of tanning. She makes Sven stand over her head with his jacket held out to make a nice cool shadow. He is burbling on in a Sven way.

It's quite soothing listening to him talk. As Jools said, "It takes your mind off things because it sounds like it should make sense, but it doesn't."

He was saying, "*Ja* and when I take you my bride, Rosie, to my people, they will laugh and sing and kill the herring and make the hats with the herrings."

This can't possibly be true.

I said to Rosie, "Is Sven saying that his mum and dad will make you a herring hat?"

She said, "Yes, exciting, isn't it?"

Then we heard Rollo yelling from across the park. "Oy, Sven, fancy a game of footie, mate?" And Sven went off.

I sat up and I could see Rollo, Tom, Declan, Edward and Dom having a kick about.

Ellen, Jas, Jools and Mabs immediately lost their marbles.

They were trying to hide behind the tree trunk to put more make-up on.

Jools was saying, "Oh my God, do you think Rollo saw my legs? They are so pale. They didn't look so bad in the house but now I'm practically blinded by them."

Mabs said, "Do you think this is a lurking lurker on my chin or a dimple?"

Even Jas had gone into mad fringe-flicking mode. And Ellen practically dithered her own head off.

I just looked at them. How very superficial it all seemed. I don't think I could ever really care what I looked like again. I might even stop shaving my legs.

In fact, that is what I could say to Baby Jesus if he lets Angus be all right. As a mark of solidarity with my injured furry friend, I will let my own body hair run free and wild. It can shoot happily out of the back of my knees or grow so long in my underarms that I can make it into small plaits.

I won't care.

Thirty seconds later

I don't think even a wrathful god would demand that I went as far as the one mono eyebrow though.

Jools was looking over at the lads kicking a ball about. "Do you think they will come over?"

Mabs said, "Do you think we should amble over there to be a bit nearer, or is that like breaking the rubber-band rule?"

Ellen said, "Er what, I mean, what is like, the rubber band rule, or something?"

Mabs said, "You know, what Georgia told us from that *How to Make Any Twit Fall in Love with You* book, where you have to display glaciosity and let them come pinging back like a rubber band."

We were saved from thinking about a plan by what happened next.

Robbie arrived on his scooter and on the back was Wet Lindsay.

Bloody Nora. Everyone looked at me.

What was she doing on the back of his scooter? He hadn't even had a scooter the last time I saw him. Perhaps he was trying to be like the Luuurve God. How weird.

Not as weird as having Wet Lindsay clinging round your waist though.

Then, as they took their helmets off, Dave the Laugh arrived through the trees holding hands with Emma.

The Ace Gang looked at me again.

Rosie said, "Crikey."

Five minutes later

Everyone else wants to go over and watch the lads play and find out what's going on.

If I don't go, it will look like I really care about what Robbie and Ms Slimy-no-forehead-knobbly-arse are doing together. Or it might seem that I am avoiding seeing Dave the Laugh and Emma. I am quite literally surrounded by *ordure* and poo.

After a squillion years of tarting up (not me, the others. I just put on some lippy... well, and a bit of mascara and eyeliner... and face bronzer... but I only did it to be brave, not for vanitosity like the rest), we all walked over to the lads. I was right at the back. I must remember I am the girlfriend of a Luuurve God. As we got to the sidelines the lads went on playing but they were whistling and calling out stuff to us.

Rollo said, "Back off, girls, this is a man's game."

And Declan said, "Look at this for ball skills... whey hey!!!" and he headed the ball right into the goal (two coats and a can of Fanta). Then he bent down, pretended to sniff the grass and banged his bottom with his hands. And all the other boys did the same. I will say it again, because I never tire of saying it, boys are truly, truly weird.

Dave and Robbie were getting their footie boots on. Wet Lindsay looked daggers at me when she saw me. She was sitting on the back of the scooter wearing some ridiculous short skirt. How very naff to wear that on the back of a scooter. I would never do that. Well, I had done it, but I would never do it like her.

I looked away from her. I must say something loudly about Masimo in a minute. I was saved the trouble by Dom yelling out as he passed by dribbling the ball. "I got a bell from Mas and he said you were off to Pizza-a-gogo land – *hasta la vista*, baby."

And then he was viciously tackled from behind by Sven and there was a bit of an argie-bargie.

Everyone's attention was on the rumpus and I sort of sensed someone behind me. It was Robbie. I looked round at him. He looked at me very seriously. He was about to say something when Wet Lindsay called out, "Robbie, hon, could you fetch me a Coke before you go on?"

He hesitated and then turned round and said, "Sure, babe," and went off to the sweet stall. How amazingly naff and weird.

Lindsay got off the scooter and came over to me. The rest of the gang were crowded round the arguing lads and so she got me on my own. She stood right next to me and said, "If you mess this up for me, Nicolson, your life will not be worth living at school. I am head girl this year and believe me, if there is any way I can make your life difficult, I will. He's mine this time; he's sick of losers. Ta taa." And she slimed off.

Oh marvellous! How I am looking forward to Stalag 14. Not.

Then I remembered Angus and I thought, if he doesn't live, I'm not even going to go back to school. I'll get a job, or do voluntary service in a kittykat home abroad or something. I wonder how he is?

All by himself in the vet's. Maybe he's all lonely and frightened. Or in pain. Or...

I had to see him so I decided I would go to the surgery and find out what was happening. I wouldn't bother telling the others; they would understand, and besides, they were too busy tarting around in front of the lads.

I started walking off towards the gates. I had to pass quite near Dave and Emma. Dave was just about to join in the game. I must try for a naturalosity-at-all-times sort of attitude.

As I went by I said cheerily, "Hi, Emma, Dave, you young

groovers. I would hang around, but I've seen more fights than I can eat this holiday. S'laters."

Dave stopped tying his boots. "Er, Georgia, are you all right? Normally, you like a bit of fisticuffs."

I smiled in a sophisticosity-at-all-times sort of way and was about to walk on when Emma said, "I was just talking to Dave about you. I thought your Viking hornpipe dance sounded really groovy. Will you be doing it again at a Stiff Dylans gig? Are you really going to Italy to see Masimo? How very cool. Isn't that cool, Dave? It must be luuurve. When are you off?"

And she was all smiley and nice. Why? Why was she so smiley and nice? Why was her hand on Dave's hair all the time? Did she think it would fall off if she didn't hold it on?

Dave was looking at me. What was I supposed to say?

I was going to say something smart and funny or maybe even sing "O Sole Mio" if my brain entirely dropped out, but I couldn't. There is something about Dave's eyes that makes me tell the truth, so I said, "Well, actually, my cat – well, he's not very well. He was run over and – and I think, I think I will have to cancel my trip and look after him."

Oh, nooooo. I could feel the tears welling up again, I must go. And I walked off really quickly.

 163

At the vet's
5:00 p.m.

Angus is still just lying there. The vet says there is no change and that he thought he would have "gone on" by now. He said it nicely, but I wanted to hit him.

He said, "I'll speak to your mum in the morning and see what she says. You see the thing is, Georgia, it costs an awful lot of money for him to be here and your mum and dad, well – maybe they—"

Walking home

Oh, I am so miserable. I don't know what to do. I can't give up on him, I can't. I wish I had someone to help me.

Lying in my bed
6:30 p.m.

Mum came into my room. Libby is coming home tonight. I said to Mum, "What are we going to tell her? Shall we say, oh, Libby, you know Angus that is your pussycat that you lobe, well, Mummy and Daddy can't be bothered to look after him because he is sick?"

Mum burst into tears. "Oh, Georgia, that is so mean."

She's right actually. I put my arms around her.

"I'm sorry, Mum, I don't mean it."

Bloody hell this is quite literally Heartbreak Hotel. And I am in the sobbing suite again.

9:00 p.m.

Libby is in bed with me. I have read her *Sindyfellow* and *Heidi* twice. Which has turned my brain to soup.

She snuggled down with me and Mr Potato Head (literally a potato with one of her hats on). Gordy came in and leaped on her and started tussling her knees under the covers. She was howling with laughter and hitting Gordy with the potato.

"Huggyhugghoghoghog. Funny pussycat. Get off now." And she just got hold of Gordy around his neck and flung him off the bed. He shook himself and sneezed and growled and she laughed.

"Heggo he laaaikes flying. Snuggle now, Ginger." And she got me in a headlock and started sucking my ear going, "Mmmmmmmmmmmmmm."

After a little while the sucking stopped and she started snoring quietly. I looked at her face in the moonlight; she is such a dear little thing really (when she is unconscious). I didn't want her to ever be sad or upset. I kissed her soft little head. Poo, it smelt of cheese. What does she smear herself with? She stirred in her sleep and put her pudgy arms up in the air. Then she sat up.

"Georgie, where is big pussycat?"

Oh blimey.

I said, "Erm, well, he's in the – kittykat hospital. He's hurt his – paws."

She got out of bed. "Come on, Ginger, let's get him." And she started putting her welligogs on over her pyjamas. She was still half asleep.

I started to say something and she flung Mr Potato at me and started waggling her finger. "Don't you bloody start, you baaaad boy. Get up."

In the end I told her that he would be snoozing and that we would go and get him in the morning and she eventually went to sleep.

Friday August 26th

Libby only went to nursery on condition that I went and got Angus.

I looked at Mum. Mum looked at me. But looking at each other wasn't going to help, was it?

9:00 a.m.
Phone rang. Oh God. What if it's the vet?

If I don't answer it, he can't tell me anything I don't want to know. But...

I answered the phone. It was Dave the Laugh.

"Georgia, what's going on?"

"Oh, Dave, it's Angus, and the vet says, and he's all in his tubes and tongue lolling and even his tail is broken, and Libby said go and get him and she had her welligogs over her jimjams, and I can't bear it."

And I started to cry. Again.

He said, "I'll come round. Cover your nungas up."

At the vet's
10:30 a.m.
Standing in front of the cage looking at Angus with Dave the Laugh.

Dave said, "Blimey. He's a bit bent."

I couldn't stand Angus being in a cage any more. In a

strange place. I said to Dr Beardy, "I have to take him home."

The vet tried to persuade me not to.

I was beginning to feel hysterical. I had to take him. I had to. If he was going to die, I wanted him with me, in his own little basket.

Dave the Laugh was ace. He even called the vet "sir" like he was at Eton.

He said to Dr Beardy, "We understand you have done your very best, sir, but now Georgia wants to take care of him, so we'll just take him home."

The vet said to me in a serious voice, "I'm just warning you that he might wake up violent and demented."

Dave said, "I'm usually in quite a good mood when I wake up, sir." Which very nearly, even in such poonosity, made me laugh.

Dr Beardy said, "I mean Angus."

And Dave said, "Actually, I think you would have needed to know him before, sir."

The vet laughed for once and said, "I did look through my predecessor's notes *vis-à-vis* the, erm, castration operation and there was some suggestion of quite wild behaviour. In fact, the notes did say never to let this cat in the surgery again."

Two hours later

When we had got Angus in the house and tucked up, things went a bit awkward. Dave was on the other side of Angus's basket looking at him. And then he looked up. And our heads were very close to each other. He said to me, "Don't cry any more, you'll make your eyes hurt." And he stroked my face.

I looked at him and he looked at me. Uh-oh.

Then he just suddenly stood up and said, "I'd better go, Kittyk – er, Georgia. I'm, well, I'm meeting Emma at six."

I stood up quickly and I smiled, although my mouth felt a bit stiff. I said, "Oh yes, yes, of course, yeah you would. Dave, can I just say – thanks so much, I don't know... I..."

For a second he looked like he was going to give me a bit of a kiss but he stopped and just chucked me under the chin and said, "Remember, I am not God in trousers but merely Dave the biscuit..." And he went.

11:00 p.m.

Angus is in the laundry room in his basket under a big blanket. He hasn't moved or anything for hours. On the way home in the cab he did a little *miaow*. It was just a little *miaow*, but it was something.

169

He didn't open his eyes or anything. But I think a *miaow* is a good sign.

Saturday August 27th

His eyes open now and again but they are all unfocused like he has really overdosed on catnip. Libby and me are giving him water in a little dropper thing because the vet told us to keep him hydrated.

11:00 p.m.

I have tucked in my charges and am off to beddy byes at last. I truly am a great human being. I hope Baby Jesus is noticing. I may get myself a nurse's uniform tomorrow. Libby is already wearing hers.

What if Angus really is brain-dead or can't walk any more or something? Will I have done the right thing? What if I have to push him around in a cat wheelchair for the rest of his life? I can't see any boyfriend putting up with that.

11:20 p.m.

But I would do it. If he can just come round and know who I am, that will be enough for me.

Sunday August 28th

I went downstairs to look in at Angus and he opened his eyes!!! And let out a really creaky *miaow*.

Hurrah, gadzooks and larks a mercy!!! As Billy Shakespeare and his pals would have said. Thank you, thank you, Baby Jesus!!!

I bent down to the basket and said, "Hello, big furry pally, it's me!" And I put my hand on his face and stroked it. He even purred!!! I started to cry again. Oh well, devil take the hindmost – if you can't have a blubbing fest when your cat has nearly gone to that big cat basket in the sky, when can you have a blubbing fest???

I rushed into the kitchen and opened the fridge. I had got kittykat treats just in case he wanted anything. Cream and everything.

Hey, they should make special-flavoured ice cream for cats called mice cream. Do you get it??? Do you see??? Oh good, I have gone hysterical. Hurrah!!!

I got a little dish of cream and carried it into the laundry room. He was lying there with his bandage over his head and stitches everywhere and his tail strapped up, but his eyes were open. I put my finger in the cream and put it to his mouth. At first he didn't respond, but then his tongue came out and licked off the cream. God, I had forgotten how disgusting his tongue was, it was like being licked by someone with sandpaper on their tongue. Possibly. I'll ask Rosie what it is like snogging someone with sandpaper for a tongue. She probably knows!!!

Hahahahaha. I must be cheered up, my brain is chatting rubbish to itself like normal.

I knew when Angus had had enough cream because he bit my finger quite hard. No damage in the jaw department then!

Phoned the Ace Gang to tell them the news. They are all going round to Jas's house for an all-girl barbecue.

Jas said, "Are you coming to the all-girl barbecue to celebrate?"

I said, "Which of you is going to do the barbecue?"

And Jas said, "Dad is."

"It's not exactly all-girl then, is it, Jas?" But then I thought of Jas's dad and I thought actually...

I can't go though. I'd like to because I haven't seen another human being for days. But I can't bear to leave Angus when he is so poorly.

(I said that to Mum earlier on. "Oh, I wish I had some

human company while I nurse Angus." She said, "I've been here all the time as well." I said, "As I said, I wish I had some human company." And she stropped off to have a bath. That was about two hours ago and she is still in there. I don't know what she does in there for so long; it's vair selfish.)

Jas said, "We're going to give one another manicures and try different make-up. Don't you want to have a go?"

I was tempted but I said, "No, I can't, he's still too poorly, but will you phone and let me know all the goss?"

And Jas said, "Will do, Florrie Nightingale. In fact I'll come round tomorrow in the arvie. I went for a walk with Tom yesterday, it was soooo fab. I'll tell you all about it. We actually saw a red admiral, and they are very rare. I thought it was a sign of hope and—"

I said, "Jas, I think my mum might be coming out of the bathroom and I might be able to get in there for the first time in about a year, so hold that thought about the mothy type thing and—"

"A red admiral is a butterfly actually; moths are—"

"Byeeeeeeeeeeee."

Good grief, I had nearly stumbled into Voleland by mistake.

Monday August 29th

Woke up and went to check on Angus. Found Gordy sleeping in the cat basket with him. Soooo sweet. Gordy was all curled up beside his dad.

His dad might not be so keen if he knew about Gordy's homosexualist tendencies.

Jas came round and kept me company for the afternoon. We mostly tried different sorts of sexy walking. I practised my beach walk.

Jas said, "Your feet are turning in like a duck."

"Jas, I am doing that on purpose; that is how supermodels walk."

"Is it? Why?"

"Jas, I don't know why, they just do. That is *le* rule. Why do they put their tongue behind their bottom teeth when they smile? I don't know, it is a simple rule. Let us just get on with it."

But Jas had gone off into Jasland. "Anyway, why are you practising your beach walk? You aren't going to go to Pizza-a-gogo land now. Which reminds me, Tom was talking to Dom and Dom said that Masimo had phoned him up and was really glad that you were coming. He wouldn't be if he could see you poncing around like a duck. And also if he knew that you aren't coming anyway."

I stopped for a moment to hit Jas over the head with a pillow.

She did have a point though.

I said, "Jas, will you try that number I have got? I tried it again last night and it was the same Yorkshire bloke. I slammed the phone down, but I bet he knew it was me."

She said, "No."

Which is nice.

9:00 p.m.

I wonder why I haven't heard from Masimo. He must be back from the hills by now. Do they have hills in Rome or do they have hillios?

He is expecting me to arrive any day, so how will he know when to meet me if he doesn't get in touch? Perhaps he has got the humpio because I haven't phoned him.

Phoned Jas. "Please help me find out if I've got the right number for Masimo. Pleasey, please, please."

"I've got a face pack on."

"Well, when you take it off then."

"Then I am doing my cuticles."

I slammed the phone down, she is sooo annoying. Ooooh, what shall I do??? Who might know the number?

Angus started yowling. He's getting a bit bored in his basket of pain now and I have to go and dangle stuff in front of him that he can biff with his nose.

Thirty minutes later

I had a quick mini-break from cat care.

Phoned Rosie. "Rosie, will you get Sven to pop down the snooker hall and see if any of the lads are there and if they have got Masimo's number?"

"Okey-dokey. I'll call you back, *amigo*."

Forty minutes later

None of the Dylans are in town. Now what shall I do?

Looked in at Angus before I went to bed. Gordy is in the basket, and Naomi and Libby.

She said, "Night night, me sleepin' with big Uggy."

Tuesday August 30th

10:00 a.m.

The Portly One has landed. He leaped out of his robin mobile like he had been to Antarctica instead of pretending to go fishing with Uncle Eddie. I notice he had no fish.

He kissed Mum on the cheek and she seemed a bit shy and not saying much. But at least she said hello and didn't hit him.

Dad went and looked at Angus and was quite shocked, I think. He bent down to the basket and stroked his head and I heard him say, "Poor little chap, you've been in the wars, haven't you?" Quite touching really.

I went into the kitchen and said to Mum, "Hmm, well it seems like—"

At which point we heard from the laundry room, "Bloody hell, you big furry bastard, you nearly had my bloody finger off!!!"

I went on, "It seems like dear Pater is back."

In bed
All quiet on the parent front. They are talking really quietly so that I can't hear them. But Mum did laugh once and I thought I heard some kind of slurping noise. Er, yuck. I hope they were eating jelly.

Midnight

I am eschewing Jas with a firm hand because she is obsessed with her stupid cuticles and wouldn't even help me phone Masimo.

He must phone soon, surely?

Wednesday August 31st

The phone rang. I leaped to get it. It was Dave the Laugh.

"Hi, Gee, how is the Furry One?"

I should have been disappointed that it wasn't Masimo, but to be honest, I had a really warm feeling when I heard Dave's voice.

I said, "He pretended to be asleep and ill, but when Dad put his hand on his nose, I mean Angus's nose not his own nose, because that would be a bit odd even for my dad. Well, when he did, Angus bit it."

Dave laughed, "Brilliant. So you are a bit cheered up?"

I gabbled on. "Yeah, actually it was funny, you would have laughed, but I tried to phone Masimo and I got some bloke called Fat Bob from Yorkshire and he said he couldn't get any decent pickled eggs in Rome!"

Dave said, "Right, so you're off to Rome then?"

I said, "Er, well, I don't want to leave Angus and, well, I—"

Dave said, "Actually, Georgia, I have to run, so I'll see you around. Bye."

Wow, that was a bit brutal. I wonder why he had to run? Maybe Emma had turned up or something. You would think that she could wait for just a minute, wouldn't you? Why did he ring if he didn't really want to speak to me?

How weird.

Why can't everyone just speak English?

Thursday September 1st

8:00 a.m.

Joy unbounded. Angus tried to stand up today!!! And he ate some kittykat food. Libby fed it to him with a "poon" and most of it went in his ear, but hurrah hurrah!!!

To perk him up I put on his favourite tune, "Who let the dogs out?" and did an impromptu disco inferno dance. I did the Viking bison dance and, as a special tribute to his kittykatness, I substituted paw movements for the bison horn bit. I think I am a genius dance-wise!!! And even though Angus just let his tongue loll out and closed his eyes, I can tell that deep down he is secretly thrilled at my tribute dance.

That is what I think.

I have quite literally single-handedly nursed Angus out of danger.

Well, I have had a bit of help.

It was nice of Dave the Laugh to go and get Angus with me.

Vair nice.

Two minutes later

So how come he is Mr Big Pal one minute and the next minute he is too busy to speak to me on the phone?

I hope he doesn't turn into a puppydog boyfriend that just does everything his so-called girlfriend says.

Perhaps he really, really likes Emma. Because maybe she is a top snogger.

Actually, I don't think she is. Her lips are quite thin and I bet that means that there is a bit of toothy exposure during number five on the snogging scale.

Urghh no, I don't want Dave snogging Emma in my brain. I'll hum something to block the picture out.

10:30 a.m.

Phone rang. I said, "Casualty department, Nurse Nicolson speaking."

And a voice said, "*Mi dispiace*, I lookin for Georgia, she for not here?"

Masimo!

I said, "Masimo, it's me, it's me. Georgia. I tried to phone... er phonio you-io and couldn't – I spoke to some people from Yorkshire. I don't know who they were but they were on holiday in Italy and having a lovely time, but – I – oh, it is soooo nice to hear from you."

Masimo was laughing. "Ah, Miss Georgia, you are funny. I am back from ze hills, and I am thinking when you are for to come a Roma. *Mi dispiace*... I am sorry for my English. Now I am with my *famiglia*, it is like I *stupido*... how you say, even more crappio."

I said, "Masimo, well, the thing is, about me coming to Rome, well, my pussycat – you know my..."

Damn, what was the word for cat? Surely it couldn't be cattio?

I said, "My cattio is not well."

He sounded puzzled. "You are not well? Why, what is wrong with you?"

Oh merd-io.

"Not me, my cat. You know, Angus is..."

And I started doing pathetic *miaowing* down the phone. Oh good, I was talking to my Italian Stallion sophisticated boyfriend and pretending to be a cat. Excellent.

In the end I managed to get Masimo to understand. He said, "So you are not for to come for me?"

I felt quite upset, he sounded really sad. And I wanted to see Rome, although I would probably starve to death there, and never get to the lavatory or anything. It had taken me almost all of my life to tell Masimo that Angus was ill. Why can't everyone speak English? Are they just too lazy? I didn't say that though.

Twenty minutes later

We talked and talked. Well, we tried to talk, but people kept coming in to where Masimo was talking to me on the phone and he would shout at them in Pizza-a-gogo-ese. It was all sorts of people – boys, girls, his mum, his dad, aunties, uncles, dogs, and I can't be sure but I think a parrot came in as well.

They certainly seem vair sociable, the Italianos. And quite good-natured. If my family had been in the house when I was talking to Masimo, it would have been mostly shouting and swearing – and that would have just been Libby.

Then his brother came into the room and Masimo said, "*Cara*, Roberto and I will sing for you a song from the heart."

I started to say, "Well, it's all right, I – you needn't..." But they had already started.

When they finished Masimo said, "It is an old song called 'Volare' and it mean that my love has given me the wings."

Blimey. A bit odd, but that is the romantic Latins for you.

When we said *arrivederci*, Masimo kissed me down the phone. He asked me to do the same. I must say I felt a bit of a prat kissing the phone. But that is transcontinental romance for you.

Five minutes later

I've never had anyone say they love me before. Libby lobes me, that is true, but there is something a bit menacing about the way she says it.

One minute later

And Dave the Laugh kind of said he did. What was it he said when he fished me out of the water in the woods? Oh, yeah. "And that is why I love you."

But he doesn't seem to love me now. In fact, to be frank, he seems to be doing a Jas. Also known as having the humpty with me.

Anyway, shut up, brain. Concentrate on the Luurve God in the hand, not the Dave the Laugh in the bushes.

Ten minutes later

Masimo is going to fly back to Billy Shakespeare land on the 14th. Which is ages away.

Unlike the 12th, the day we go back for more torture and ordure at Stalag 14.

I've said this once and I will say it again. What is the point of school? It is really only to keep the elderly insane off the streets, in my opinion, and to provide shelter for girl-haters.

Ten minutes later

I am quite literally on Cloud 9, luuurve-wise.

One minute later

Tip top of the Love-ometer. I couldn't be happier even if I was a hamster on happy pills scampering up my ladder.

One minute later

The only thing is, though, that I get the hurdy-gurdy knee trembling and wubbish brain whenever I speak to Masimo. He makes me feel shy. And I don't really know what he's like. I mean, when you look at the nub and the gist of the situation, I have in effect only snogged him three times.

Three minutes later

I wonder who I have snogged the most times?

I may have to compose my snogging history until one of my so-called friends can be bothered to phone me up. I am always doing the calling up, so let them make an effort for a change.

Two minutes later

Tragically, my first sexual experience involved incest. My cousin touched me on the leg when we were sharing a room. And then he suggested we play "tickly bears".

I am probably scarred for life mentally, but I don't complain. At least I don't get made to hang out with him now because he has joined the navy. So with a bit of luck he will turn gay.

One minute later

Then there was Peter Dyer, also known as Whelk Boy. Dave the Laugh still can't believe that all us girls actually went round to Whelk Boy's house to learn how to snog. We used to queue up politely outside his door. And he had a timer.

One minute later

In fact Dave the Laugh said, "Now that is a top job. Teaching girls to snog. It is quite literally the Horn come true."

Back to my list.

Next came Mark Big Gob.

One minute later

To tell you the truth, my list is not perking me up much so far. In fact, it is depressing the arse off me. What was I thinking of, snogging Mark Big Gob?

I can't even bear to look at him now. How could I snog him??? I think he must have sort of hypnotised me into doing it. I think I was so mesmerised by the sheer size of his mouth that I was paralysed.

Anyway, it is giving me the droop to think about it, so I will move swiftly on.

Then was it the Sex God? Or did I accidentally snog Dave the Laugh first?

No, I think it was the Sex God because then he said I was too young for him and I used Dave the Laugh as a red herring to make him jealous.

And it was a bit of a surprise because Dave was quite good at snogging.

In fact, very good. He did the lip-nibbling thing, which was quite groovy. But, anyway...

Then it was the Sex God deffo.

Aaah, Robbie. My first love. Funny that you can care so much about someone and then they are just another bloke. Not that I don't care about him. I do. It's just that – oh, I don't know. I hope he is not still so upset. He looked like he was going to say something to me at the footie, until Miss Octopussy Head started asking him to get her a Coke and so on. And then threatening me with torture at Stalag 14.

I can't think about it. I'll get on with my list.

Blimey, then I'm afraid it was the Hornmeister again, encouraging me towards the General Horn. Bad, bad Dave the Laugh...

Then the Sex God again.

Then Dave the Laugh.

Then the Luuurve God.

Then Dave the Laugh again.

I am beginning to see a pattern emerging here. Hmmmm.

One minute later

Of course, I have not included animal snogging, like when Angus accidentally stuck his tongue in my mouth.

Or weird toddler behaviour. Libby snogging my ear. Ditto knees.

Five minutes later

Jas phoned at last. And I was full of coolnosity with her. But she didn't notice because she only wanted to talk about making Tom so fascinated by her that he will forget about going away to college.

I said grumpily, "Well, you can start doing glaciosity right now. You must start eschewing Tom with a firm hand forthwith and lackaday."

She said, "Rightio."

Hmm. Good, that will serve her right. See how she likes not having a boyfriend around.

Ten minutes later

I am on cat patrol because Angus is trying to escape from his basket. I have tucked the blankets around him really tightly so that he can't leap about and spoil all his stitches and so on. In the end I had to clip his lead on and fasten it to the basket.

He's livid.

But he is still a bit weak and after he had yowled a bit he went off to Snoozeland.

When I went to Boboland, tired from my day of constant caring, I said to Mum, "You should try caring, Mum. It's vair vair tiring."

Friday September 2nd
Up at the crack of 10:30 a.m.

Angus is getting stronger and more mad every day. He hates being in his basket. And he has chewed through his lead. I'm going to have to get him a metal one. He is the Arnold Schwarzenegger of cat land.

Twenty minutes later

I can't stand the sound of moaning and miaowing and yowling any more. Maybe if I take him outdoors, he will calm down a bit. Besides which, he has eaten so much of his basket, it is practically just a pile of old sticks.

11:00 a.m.

Jas came round to report on her boy entrancing skills *vis-à-vis* Hunky.

I am preparing myself to forgive her, just to pass the time actually.

I said, "Right, what did you say when you last saw him?"

She did a bit of fringe fiddling and then said, "Hmmm, I said, see you later."

I said, "Right, that's good, very good, nice and vague, give him time to wonder what you have been up to and so on. When did you last see him?"

She did more fringe-fiddling and thinking then she said, "Erm, let me see – erm, it was about half an hour ago."

"Half an hour ago! Jas, you are not as such getting this, are you? You are officially giving him space so he can come pinging back like an elastic band. Seeing him half an hour ago is not having space; that is seeing him all the time."

"I like to see him."

"That is as maybe, but it is not the key to entrancement."

"What is then?"

"You must be more mysterious and unavailable. You must gird your loins and display glaciosity and so on. You must make him jealous."

"Why?"

"Because jealous is good *vis-à-vis* entrancementosity."

"How do I make him jealous? Shall I say I found some unusual molluscs and not show them to him?"

"No. I am not talking about nature, I am talking about the game of luuurve. You have to flirt with other blokey fandangos."

"How do you mean?"

"I mean, you flirt with other blokey fandangos."

"That is all very well for you, Georgia. You are inclined to thrust your red bottom about, but it is against my nature."

Oh, she is soooo annoying.

In the end I got her to agree that she will practise flirting with other boys. And she will play Tom at his own gamey and win. She said, "Right, I'm going to start now. I am practising glaciosity. This is me being unavailable." And she tilted her nose up and flicked her fringe.

"No, Jas, that is just you looking stupid in my house

where Tom can't even see you. You have to do something that he will notice."

She had a bit of a think and then said, "Right, I'm going to phone him and say that I think he's right that we should have more space and that I need more space actually, because he has been my only one and only. And that I will see him when I have a spare moment."

"Good, that is good, Jas."

She went off to phone him and I started rooting around in the garage for a cat transporter. I hope I don't get attacked by bluebottles. Usually when dad has been fishing he leaves his maggots in their little maggot home thing, forgets about them and they turn into huge bluebottles. I peered in. No menacing humming going on – so – now then, what can I put Angus in as a sort of cat wheelchair? Aha!!! Libby's old pushchair!!! Perfect.

Four minutes later

Jas came back looking a bit flushed. I was trying to work the straps out on the pushchair and she was flicking her fringe around like a madwoman.

She said, "Well, that's done. I've told him. I said I was

193

having a bit of space and that he should have a bit of space. And he said OK. Which is a bit weird. What do you think he meant by OK?"

I said, "I think he meant OK. Now, where is the bit that clicks into the buckle?"

"Anyway, whatever he means, I'm quite looking forward to a bit of freedom. You know, trying out my entrancing skills and so on. What is the special entrancing walk thingy?"

I showed her the hip hip wiggle wiggle hip hip thing. And also did a bit of flicky hair.

Two minutes later

She managed the hip hip wiggle wiggle thing, but when she tried to incorporate flicky hair at the same time, she banged into a wall.

Ten minutes later

We carried Angus out to the driveway in the washing-up bowl. We tried to lift the cat basket up, but the bottom just fell out and Angus was yowling like a cat who has just crashed to the floor out of its basket.

Both of us were wearing gardening gloves. I'd like to say

that Angus was really looking forward to his little outing and in his catty way appreciated what we were doing for him, but the spitting and pooing would suggest otherwise.

I said to Jas as we shoved him down the drive in the pushchair, "You have to be cruel to be kind. Some things in life are not pleasant, but they have to be done. For instance, German and maths. And, well, school. I can't believe the holidays have gone so quickly and we are being forced back into the torture chamber of life."

Jas said, "I'm quite looking forward to it now. We're doing *Romeo and Juliet* in English. I wonder if I will get a part like I did in last year's production. You know, I really felt that I got into the Lady M part. It took quite a lot out of me."

I said, "It took quite a lot out of me."

But she had gone off into Jasland. Is it likely that she will be cast as Juliet? Because that is what she is thinking. Whoever heard of a Juliet with a stupid flicky fringe and an obsession with owls? Billy Shakespeare didn't write, "Hark what owl through yonder window breaks?"

Five minutes later
Angus is nicely strapped into the pushchair. I have put a

little blankin over him and tucked a couple of sausages under his armpit so he can reach them for a nibble.

As we wheeled Angus out of our gate Mr and Mrs Next Door were coming back from walkies with the Prat brothers. They were looking unusually unusual today in matching pink collars. And the poodles looked ridiculous too!!! Hahahaha, did you see what I did there? Oh, nevermind.

Mr Next Door looked at us wheeling Angus along and said, "He's not dead then?" And he didn't say it in a pleased way.

Naomi followed us for a while doing that mad high-pitched thing that nutcase Burmese cats do. But then, when she reached the end of the road, the big black manky cat was lurking around by the dustbins and she caught his eye. Angus went ballisticisimus when he saw Manky and tried to bite through his straps. I started pushing the pushchair really quickly. Naomi is an appalling tart; she just lay down in the road and started squiggling around on her back, letting her womanly parts run wild and free.

How disgusting. I said to Jas, "Put your hand over Angus's eyes."

Jas said, "Er, no, because I'm not mad and I don't want it bitten off."

It's awful really. Poor crippled Angus seeing his woman offering herself to other (manky) men.

I started jogging along with the pushchair, but I hadn't got my specially reinforced sports nunga-nunga holder on, so I had to stop as there was a bit of a danger of uncontrollable bounce basooma-wise.

Four minutes later

We ambled along towards the park. It was quite a nice day. I put a sun bonnet on Angus because there are some baldy patches on his head where the stitches are and he might have got sunburn. I thought he looked quite cute but he didn't agree and was trying to biff me with his big paw.

When he was under his blankin and with his hat over his face, you couldn't really tell he was a cat. I said to Jas, "It would be quite funny if people actually thought he was a baby. Then they might bend down to say 'Aaaahhh' and see his mad furry face staring out at them. And that would be a hoot and a half."

Jas said, "Yeah, groovy." But she didn't mean it because I could tell she was concentrating on practising doing wiggle wiggle, hip hip, flicky hair, flicky hair, fall off pavement etc.

In the end, Angus made such a racket and the bonnet fell down over his eyes, so I took it off. I told Jas she could wear it to keep her fringe in check but she didn't want to. She is quite literally a fun-free zone.

I said to Jas, "I bet you that the teachers are actually looking forward to going back to Stalag 14 because they have no lives. I bet Slim already has her knickers laid out ready to go. Hawkeye will be practising shouting."

Jas said, "Oh, I meant to tell you something. Tom told me goss about Robbie and Wet Lindsay."

"Jas, I told you not to do any earwigging *vis-à-vis* Droopy Knickers."

"I didn't do earwigging. Tom just brought it up. Apparently Wet Lindsay goes round to Tom's mum and dad's all the time. Even when neither of the boys are there. She just goes and hangs out with the parents. How sad is that? And they get on really well. So Tom asked Robbie what was going on, was she like the official girlfriend etc. and Robbie said, and I quote, 'Well, it's nice to have someone who is sort of ordinary around and who really likes me.' Oh, and he also said that she bakes him cakes."

I just looked at Jas. "What sort of person bakes cakes for boys?"

Jas said, "Well, I made a lemon drizzle cake for Tom when we went camping and—"

"OK, let me put this another way, what sort of twit besides your good self makes cakes for boys? It is tremendously sad and odd. It doesn't say one word about cake baking in my *How to Make Any Twit Fall in Love with You* book and it says some pretty bloody strange things, I can tell you."

Of course, for no apparent reason, Jas hit number seven on the having-the-hump scale. (Number seven is, of course, walking on ahead, one of Jas's specialities).

I said, "Jazzy, don't be silly. I bet Tom luuurved your drizzly cake. It's just odd for Wet Lindsay to do it, isn't it? She's not exactly a domestic, is she? It's not like her to do anything for anyone else, is it? Is it, little pally? I bet even Tommy wommy said that it was a bit odd, didn't he?"

Jas didn't want to say, but she couldn't help it. She said, "Well, actually, he did say he thought that she was, like, a bit insincere and that she was trapping Robbie by being nice."

Hmmm. That has made me feel a bit guilty about Robbie. If he was on the rebound because I had eschewed him with a firm hand, I had sort of made him go back out with the octopussy prat of the century. It was bad enough having him cry in front of me, but for him to then be driven into her no-forehead world was awful. I didn't want him to be with Lindsay because of me. Maybe I would have to save him from her somehow.

Twelve minutes later

We were wheeling Angus along in the park singing "Always Look on the Bright Side of Life" quite loudly to cheer him up (he was yowling along to the chorus, I like to think) when round the corner of the loos came Dave the Laugh and Emma, and Tom and a friend of Emma's called Nancy. They were laughing together.

Dave saw us first and he came over and bent down to look at Angus. "Wow, you dancer! Attaboy. You're de man!!!"

He said it in a sort of admiring way and I felt really proud of Angus. He had come back from the edge of the heavenly cat basket in the sky like supercat. And it was nice to see Dave. He looked very cool in a class shirt and he looked up and winked at me – then spoiled the moment by saying, "Emma, come and have a look at Angus; he is the kiddie."

Emma came trolling across all girlie. "Ooooh, isn't he cute?"

I should have warned her not to put her face too near Angus but, well, that is the law of nature. It's only cat spit, after all. You would have thought that it was viper juice, the way she carried on. She went scampering off into the ladies' loos and Nancy went with her.

Jas had not said a word since she saw Tom. She had gone very, very red, even for her, that is how red she was.

Tom said, "I just bumped into Dave and the girls at the snooker hall..."

Jas said, "Tom, what you do is really your business. Come on, Gee, we don't want to keep the gang waiting." And she actually said to Tom, "S'laters. Maybe bell you sometime." Has she finally snapped?

I followed after her with the pushchair, leaving Tom and Dave looking at us.

When we got round the corner, Jas burst into tears.

"How can he just go and get off with some other girl, just like that? It's only half an hour since I said he could be free."

I said, "Well, it says in my *How to Make Any Twit Fall in Love with You* book that boys don't like feeling bad, so they get another girl really quickly."

Jas said, "That's awful. What's the point of seeing anyone then or caring about boys at all?"

I said, "Well, there is some good news."

"What?"

"Well, it says that they get another girl really quickly and it is usually a disaster. And they remain frozen emotionally for the rest of their lives, so that's good, isn't it?"

But she didn't cheer up as such.

Saturday September 3rd
9:00 a.m.

Jas phoned. She said, "Tom came round and said that there was nothing going on with Nancy. He just bumped into them and they had a bit of a kick around with the other lads in the park and the girls watched. And, anyway, Nancy has got a boyfriend. She is just, like, Emma's best mate."

I said, "What did you say?"

"Well, I remembered, you know, about the glaciosity and so on. And I said, 'I suppose that when you are having space you can't always ask what someone is doing and so on but we can be friendly to each other.'"

I was amazed. I said, "Jas, my little matey, that is almost quite good tactics. You are not only displaying glaciosity, you are also incidentally displaying maturiosity as well. *Muchos buenos,* as our Pizza-a-gogo friends might say."

Then she spoiled it. "I miss him though."

I said, "Go cuddle your owls and be brave."

She said, "Am I allowed to snog him if he comes round?"

I said, "No, he has to go off and then ping back. You can't do the pinging first. It is not in the book."

Tuesday September 6th

Six days to Stalag 14. God help us one and all. But on the bright side the Luuurve God comes back in eight days!!! I am keeping up my grooming and plucking so that I do not have to do it all in one go. I am ruthless with any stray hairs. Also I am a lurker-free zone. I just wish I could find some tan stuff that makes my legs not so paley, but not orange like last time. Anyway, it doesn't really matter because we will be back in tights for school.

4:00 p.m.

Angus went for his first walk today. I put him on top of the dividing wall so that he could see the Prat Poodles. They usually give him *joie de vivre* and so on. His tail is still all bandaged up but his stitches come out next week and he is eating A LOT.

I popped him up there but he still seemed a bit wobbly on his old cat pins. He wobbled up and down once or twice and then crashed off over the wall into Mr and Mrs Next Door's garden. I clambered up and looked down, and he was lying in the cabbage patch. He did that silent *miaowing* thing and then got to his paws again. He started walking and then careered off into a bush. Then he got up again, walked for a few paces and crashed into the lawnmower. Oh noooo, perhaps he really did have brain damage.

I leaped down into Next Door's garden to rescue my little pally. The Next Doors were out, so the coast was clear apart from the heavily permed guardey dogs, Snowy and Whitey. They were chained to their kennel, probably to stop them larking about and getting their stupid fur all muddy. And they were yapping like billio.

I said in a Liverpool accent, "Calm down, calm down," and picked up Angus. He didn't like being picked up and struggled around. As a treat I took him quite near the Prat brothers and he gave them both a big swipe with his paw around the snout.

I took him out through the gate because I didn't think I could manage the wall and Angus the mad cat.

Ooooooh, please don't let him be a backward cat. I didn't

want to have to push him around in his pussycat wheelchair for the rest of my life.

I told Mum what had happened and she said why didn't I ring the vet, Dr Beardy.

What if he said that Angus was like a turnip cat? Would I look after him even if he was dim and didn't know how to fight any more? And started liking the Prat brothers?

Five minutes later

Yes, I would. I love him and I will look after him no matter what happens. He is my furry soul pal.

Wednesday September 7th

Amazingly, Dad was quite sympathetic *vis-à-vis* Angus being an idiot cat and said he would drive me to the vet's when he got back from work.

At the vet's
5:30 p.m.

The vet looked all beardy and serious when I told him about Angus crashing about and maybe being backward. He looked in Angus's ears and eyes and so on. Then he put him up on his table and let him walk about. Angus took two steps and then immediately fell off the table. He tried to leap up on to it again and missed and crash-landed into my lap. Which he then fell off.

It was so sad. He had been the king of leaping and balancing. His days of riding the Prat brothers around like little horsies were over. I could feel my eyes filling up.

Dr Beardy said, "It's his tail. He can't balance properly while it's all bandaged up. He'll be OK when the bandage comes off."

Oh, Allah be praised!!!

(Er, sorry about that, Baby Jesus. I don't know why I came over a bit Muslim then, but we are all in the same cosmic gang after all. Clearly I have my favourite, which is Baby Jesus, but generally I am a fan of the whole caboodle. In case any of them are also omnipotent like Big G.)

Back home

Angus has just crashed into the cat flap which he was trying to get through. Oh, I am so happy. I told Jas on the phone.

She went, "Ahuhu-ahuh." But not in a caring and listening way.

Then she said, "I don't know how you manage without a boyfriend. Who do you tell stuff to?"

I said, "Jas, I tell stuff to my little pallies, like you. Anyway, can I stop you before you go off on a Moaning for Britain campaign? I am going to ring the Ace Gang and we can have a joint celebration day for the recovery of Angus and also the reinvention of – glove animal!!!"

"Oh no."

"Oh yes."

"Oh no."

"Oh yes."

"Oh no."

"Jas, this is lots of fun chatting with you and so on – but we are meeting at mine in half an hour, so you had better dash. Pip pip."

Round at mine

I have made all of the gang coffee and Jammy Dodgers as we need nourishment to prepare us for the beginning of another term at Stalag 14.

Two hours later

My ribs are hurting from laughing. I had forgotten how much fun you can get out of a beret and a pair of gloves. It

207

was Rosie's impression of Inspector Glove Animal of the Yard that made me laugh the most. She put on the beret and pinned the gloves underneath it as ears, and then popped her beard on and started puffing on her pipe.

It was vair vair *amusant*. I said, "I think Hawkeye will appreciate the creativitinosity that we have brought to what is in fact a boring old beret."

Jas said, "She won't appreciate it; she will just give us immediate detention."

I looked at her with my eyebrows raised. "Jas, I hope you are not being the bucket-of-cold-water girl."

Jas was going on in rambling mode. "Well, it's so silly."

Rosie went over to her and took out her pipe. "Jas, are you suggesting that I look silly?"

Oh, I laughed.

To release our girlish high spirits we danced around to loud music in my bedroom and then we lay down panting on the bed.

Ellen is going on a proper second date with Declan, and Rollo bought Jools her very own rattle for supporting him at his footie matches. She is secretly thrilled, I think, although she said she would rather have had chocolates and lip gloss.

Sunday September 11th
In bed
11:30 p.m.

My bedroom is a Libby-free zone. I've got Stalag 14 tomorrow and I want to be in tip-top condition to face the Hitler Youth (prefects). And General Fascists (staff). And the Lesbians (Miss Stamp). And other assorted loons (Herr Kamyer, Elvis, Miss Wilson, Slim our beloved huge headmistress and – well, everyone else there really).

Hark! What owl through yonder window breaks?

Monday September 12th
7:00 a.m.

Oh, I can't believe the hols are over and it is back to long dark hours of boredom and – er... that's it. Still, it's now only two days until Masimo gets back. Yarooooo!!!!

In the bathroom
7:25 a.m.

I was just about to wash my face with the special face-washing soap when I realised it wasn't there. How am I supposed to cleanse and tone etc. if people keep moving my soap? I went into the kitchen and said to Mum, "Have you been using my special soap, which is specially mine especially for me?"

She didn't even look round. "No."

I looked in at Angus. He and Gordy were in the same basket and they were both frothing at the mouth.

7:40 a.m.

Why would a cat eat soap? Why?

8:30 a.m.

Walking really, really slowly up the hill towards Hell.

Jas hasn't phoned Tom and he has phoned her twice and she has pretended that she isn't in.

I said, just to check, "Er, Jas, you know how you pretended that you weren't in? Well, you didn't answer the phone and say 'I'm not in', did you?"

She hit me over the head with her rucky, which was a bit violent, I think. It is as well I luuurve her.

We are not doing glove animal today, we are keeping the element of surprise. Hawkeye and the Hitler Youth will be on high alert at the moment. All full of energy after the summer break. All pepped up for mass brutality and girl hating so we are going to lull them into a false sense of security by being good this week. And then going all out headgear-wise next week.

8:38 a.m.
The fascist regime has already started. As we came through the school gates Hawkeye was there like a guard dog and she had a tape measure!! Honestly! She was making sure that our skirts were an inch below the knee. Anyone who had turned over their skirt at the waist was given an immediate reprimand for their trouble. I may write to my MP or the European King or whatever.

Fortunately, I knew Hawkeye would be picking on me (as she has a specially developed hating muscle all for me), so I had pulled my skirt down over my knees once we were in sight of Stalag 14's perimeter fence.

Melanie Griffiths, world renowned for her enormous out of control nungas, was just ahead of me and Hawkeye pounced. Fair enough because Melanie's skirt was practically up her bum-oley.

Hawkeye had a nervy spaz attack: "Melanie, I would have expected better from you and, frankly, with your shape, you would do well to go for the longer look anyway."

I said to Jas, "Actually, I don't think that Melanie has rolled her skirt up. I think that her arse has grown and that has lifted the hemline."

As we shuffled off to hang our coats up I grumbled to the rest of the gang, "I bet they don't have people measuring bloody skirts in schools in Pizza-a-gogo land. I bet they don't even wear skirts at schools there, they are so liberal. I bet they wear fur thongs or leatherette hotpants."

Actually, I hope they don't. Masimo might quite like that. Oooohhhh, I can't wait for him to come back.

Assembly

Oh, hello to the wonderful world of mass boredom and *merde*. Wet Lindsay and her sidefool, Astonishingly Dull Monica, were lurking around on prefect duty. They love frightening the first formers, telling them their shoes are wrongly laced up and so on.

Wet Lindsay looked at me and said something to ADM and they both laughed. I didn't care though; I have an

Italian Luuurve God as a boyfriend. And, more importantly, I have got a forehead.

We were just queuing up to go through the doors into the main hall and listen to Slim, our revered headmistress, bore for England when the two Little Titches came bounding up. I haven't seen the Titches, also known as Dave the Laugh's fan club, since the last Stiff Dylans gig. They were all flushed and excited and the (slightly) less titchy one said to me, "Hello... hello, miss. We've got new trainers. We'll show you them later. And we saw Dave the Laugh yesterday at the shopping centre. He went into Boots and we followed him and he was getting some moisturiser and then we asked him for his autograph and he signed my maths book. He put three kisses and a drawing of a monkey."

Wet Lindsay shouted out, "You two lower-school girls get back in line and stop talking. Georgia Nicolson, take a reprimand for encouraging the younger girls to break school rules."

What, what? I had got a reprimand for standing in line while some tiny nutcases told me about their new shoes. Where was the justice in that?

God, I hate her. In fact, she has made me deffo decide to split her and Robbie up somehow. It is my civic duty. Also, if I can accidentally on purpose bend her stupid bendy stick-insecty legs round her neck, I will most certainly take the opportunity.

As we shuffled to our places I whispered to Jas out of the corner of my mouth, "I hate her. She is definitely as dead as a dead thing on dead tablets. Also, forgive me if I am right, but Dave the Laugh seems to have acquired his own personal stalkers."

Fifteen minutes later

Ro Ro really made me laugh during prayers because she dug me in the ribs and when I looked at her she had on those comedy glasses that have no lenses but do have a false nose with big black eyebrows on. I couldn't stop laughing and then she did it to the rest of the gang, so we had group shoulder heaving. I managed to pull myself together for the final amen.

I could see Wet Lindsay looking over our way, but she could only see Rosie from the side so she didn't get the full bushy eyebrow effect, otherwise it would have been detention all round. What larks!

Also the hymn was a top opportunity for "pants" work. The words were, "I long for you Lord as the deer PANTS for the rain."

The volume went up about a million when we sang "pants".

Four minutes later

Oh, go on a bit, why don't you, Slim. "Blah blah blah, visitors saying girls looked like prostitutes wearing short skirts, make-up etc etc... all girls going to be hung, drawn and quartered if they don't keep to school dress codes, blah blah. A lady does not show her knickers underneath her skirt."

Oh, I am so bored. Slim had worked herself up into such a state that I thought her chins were going to drop off. Also, vis-à-vis fashion etc. I am not sure that I would wear an orange dress if I were eighty-four stone. She must get them specially made. By a sadist.

Then she said, "Well girls, now let us pass on to more pleasant matters. As you know, before the summer holidays Year Eleven were lucky enough to be taken on a camping trip by Herr Kamyer and Miss Wilson. I gather that they had a marvellous time. Is that true, Year Eleven?"

Me and Rosie and the gang were murmuring, "Yes, oh yes. Are you mad? Yes, yes, cheese and onion," and rubbish, but so that you couldn't really hear it. Only Jas and her sad mates were shouting stuff like, "It was great."

Bloody swotty voley knicker types.

Then Slim asked Herr Kamyer and Miss Wilson to come up to the stage. Miss Wilson looked like she was wearing her pre-Christmas cardigan. I swear, it had reindeers on it. And Herr Kamyer had on a tweed suit and an unusual tie (knitted) and his trousers hovered proudly at ankle level, revealing attractive matching socks.

Good grief. I whispered to Jools, "It's lovely young love, isn't it?" She just looked at me.

Herr Kamyer went first. He said, "Vell, ve had ze very gut time viz the fun and larfs. Didn't ve, girls?"

We all went, "Whatever, mumble mumble."

Miss Wilson took over the dithering baton then. "It was most enjoyable. During the day we drew interesting sketches of the varied wildlife and explored our environs."

Rosie went, "Oo-er," which nearly made me wet myself but no one else heard.

Miss Wilson was back in the exciting world of tents and voles, rambling on. "But the evenings were in many ways the best times, we made our own entertainment."

Slim interrupted, "Always the most enjoyable."

Miss Wilson said, "Indeed."

God, it was like a hideous teacher love-in.

Then Herr Kamyer got the giddygoat and started being enthusiastic. "Yah, ve played some of the games I haf played when I was camping in ze Black Forest. We did the shadow animals game and Miss Vilson sang mit der girls and made ze vair *gut spangleferkel.*"

Oh dear God, I knew it wouldn't be long before we were back on the sausage trail.

Actually, I didn't mind idling time away with sausages and mad Germans because we had French first lesson, and I wanted to avoid Madame Slack for as long as I could because she hates me.

As Herr Kamyer and Miss Wilson both dithered and fell down the stairs from the stage, Slim said something scary.

"Well, I am sure there will be many more expeditions and excitements in the coming terms. Also I think it would be very nice for the whole school to share in the memories of the trip, and so I have suggested that Miss Wilson run an art project with Year Eleven. It will be lovely for them to bring their paintings and sculptures and so on of their feelings and experiences of the camping trip and put them on display here in the main hall."

Rosie whispered to me, "Will you be bringing the sculpture of your snogging session with Dave the Laugh into the main hall?"

I looked at her cross-eyed and said, "I wonder if Miss Wilson will be re-enacting, through the magic of dance, her marvellous standing in a field in the nuddy-pants scenario?"

French

I have *dit* this many times and I will *dite* it again, *qu'est ce que c'est le point de français?*

I've been to *le* gay Paree, I have experienced *le* mime, I have danced *sur le pont* d'Avignon and even (as Jools reminded me) done my world-famous impression of the Hunchback of Notre Dame outside Notre Dame. But I will not be going again.

This is *moi* point. I go out with an Italian Luuurve God and there is no point in going to France except for cheese. And I do not *aime* cheese, so there you are.

Madame Slack was just waiting to give me a good verbal thrashing, and when I innocently said in our conversation section that *"Je préfère l'Italie pour mes vacances and pour l'amour. Je n'aime pas le fromage. Merci. Au revoir."* Madame Slack said, "Ah well, *je préfère les étudiants qui ne sommes pas des idiots – mais c'est la vie. Prenez vous le reprimand."*

Bloody hell, two reprimands and I haven't even had my break-time cheesy wotsits.

Lunchtime

I wonder why Dave the Laugh was buying moisturiser from Boots? Perhaps he is on the turn. I may say that to him when I see him. I may say, "Dave, your skin is sooo soft and smooth. Are you on the turn?"

Not that I will be seeing him.

Probably.

German

Rosie has been looking in her new slang book, *German for Fools.* She said to Herr Kamyer, "In my new dictionary it says that a kiss lasting over three minutes is *abscheidskuss.*"

Herr Kamyer quite literally went red all over. And I could clearly see his ankles, so I am sure about this.

He started, "Well, yes, but this language is for slang, and of course one would not say... erm—"

Rosie said helpfully, "*Abscheidskuss?*"

German is quite literally comedy magic.

Five minutes later

Wee is *pipi*.

One minute later

And to poo is *krappe*. Hahahaha.

Still incarcerated in Stalag 14
Afternoon break

Going to school is like going through life backwards in time.

I said to the Ace Gang, "Did you see Miss Wilson choking on her fizzy orange when Herr Kamyer walked past her and asked her if she was wearing a new blouse? She luuurves him. She wants him baaaad. He is quite literally a babe magnet."

Rosie looked up "babe magnet" in the *German for Fools* book. She said, "Oh *ja*, he is a *Traum*boy."

Jools said, "When does Masimo get back?"

I said, "He said the fourteenth."

Ellen said, "What time, I mean, did he say s'later or 'give you a bell' or will he like give you a bell or will you give him a bell?"

We looked at her.

It is true though. He didn't say when exactly he would be back. I don't know what time he will be arriving, morning, afternoon or night. Which means essentially I will be on high alert and heavily made up for twenty-four hours a day. And even then he might not call me until the next day. He might have jet lag.

One minute later

I will have to go to bed fully made up and dressed in case he pops round unexpectedly.

One minute later

I have just had a spontaneous pucker up.

Bell went

As we were scampering back for English (double bubble), I had one of my many ideas of geniosity. I said, "I know what we can do to stop Herr Kamyer from making us do stuff. Let us get him to correct our German translation of the snogging scale. That I will be doing during blodge."

English

Miss Wilson announced that we are indeedy going to be doing a school production of *Rom and Jule* this term. And that because of the massive success of *MacUseless*, we are going to join forces with the boys' school again. They are going to be our "technical support". Which in Dave the Laugh's case means he switches all the lights off and people fall off the stage. Yarroooo!!!

We started yelling out, "Oh joy unbounded!" "Three cheers for Merrie England and all who sail in her!" "Poop poop!" "For she's a jolly good fellow!" until I thought Miss Wilson's bob would explode.

She was slightly losing her rag and said, "Now, girls, settle down. I know that it is very thrilling but – Rosie, get off your desk and please put your beard away."

Rosie looked surprised. "But I am getting in character, Miss Wilson. This is an Elizabethan beard, specially knitted by some old bloke in tights many moons ago."

Eventually Miss Wilson was able to say that auditions were to take place on Wednesday in the main hall and that we were to read the text and think about what parts we might like to play.

Nauseating P. Green asked if there was a dog in it. She has never quite got over playing the dog in *Peter Pan*. Miss Wilson said, "No, there is no dog in *Romeo and Juliet*. It is a tragedy."

I said, "You can say that again, Miss Wilson, because Pamela is top at fetching sticks and begging."

We laughed and started muttering "Prithee, prithee, prithee!" and doing pretendy beard stroking every time Miss Wilson started describing the plot of *Rom and Jule*.

After about ten minutes the classroom door banged open. Slim came jelloiding in, shouting and wobbling at the same time, telling us that we were making too much noise and being silly. If we didn't all want to stay behind for detention on our first day back, we should shut up. Ramble ramble, wobble wobble etc.

Charming.

I said to the Ace Gang quietly, "You show a bit of enthusiasm for the Bird of Avon, our greatest old bloke in tights, and this is what you get for your trouble."

And they wonder why the youth of today doesn't learn nuffink.

4:00 p.m.

Ambling out of the science block after the last bell. God, how many years have I been in blodge learning how to bamboozle my epiglottis?

As we rounded the corner towards the main building I saw Wet Lindsay dashing across to the sixth-form common room. She wasn't wearing her uniform; she had on a short dress that showed off her knobbly knees to perfection. She glared at me as she went past, and she was undoing her stupid hair from its stupid ponytail.

I said, "That's a nice dress, Lindsay. Who went to the fitting for it?"

She just gave me two fingers.

I said to Rosie, "She's a lovely example to us all, isn't she?"

4:15 p.m.

Walking across the playground I noticed Robbie sitting on his new (quite cool) scooter on the road by the gates. Most of the girls were getting all girlish and swishing their hair about as they passed him by. He saw me. (Damn, I wish I had put some make-up on!!! I must suck my nose in and smile in an ad hoc and cool way.) He has got really nice eyes and I could still picture him the day that I told him about me and Masimo and he had let a little tear out of his eye. Actually, considering that he and I only saw each other for a short time, we had packed in an awful lot of blubbing one way and another. We had quite literally spent most of our possible snogging time at Heartbreak Hotel.

Ah, well.

He smiled sort of sadly at me as I got near him. I smiled back. He is very good looking.

He said, "All right, Georgia?"

I said, "Yeah, fine, alrighty as two alrighty things. And you?"

He said, "Yeah, cool, things are you know, er, cool. I'm guesting at the next Stiff Dylans gig... Are... will you be coming? You know with your... er... your—"

At that moment I got a sharp prod in my bum. Owwwww buggery oww. I had been stabbed in my bum-oley. I looked round into the smiling face of Wet Lindsay. Wet Lindsay and her umbrella.

Wet Lindsay said, "Hi, Robbie, ready to go, hon?"

She got on the back of his scooter and while he couldn't see her she was mouthing at me, "You are so dead meat."

Robbie fired up his scooter and said, "See you around,

Georgia." And they roared off.

I watched them and Lindsay turned round and put her finger across her throat, meaning that I was indeedy dead meat.

I rubbed my bum. I would probably have a bruise there and I had only just recovered from my last bum-oley injury.

I grumbled to the others, "She is such a bitch. I can't believe he is falling for it AGAIN. It makes me think he is a bit half-witted."

Jas said, "Remember what you told me about boys getting someone else really quickly when they are upset? Well, maybe you have driven him into the arms of the Stick Insect Octopussy girl. S'laters."

Yep, it looks like I am going to have to make him dump her somehow. I wonder if she still wears those false nunga-nunga increasers?

Five minutes later

Jas has gone a different way home in case Tom is around. Then he will wonder where she is and she will have become entrancing to him.

As I have already been caught without make-up by an ex, I am taking no chances. We nipped into the tarts' wardrobe

227

in the park and we applied mascara, lippy and so on. And I did a bit of hair-bounceability work. (I put my head upside down under the hot-air hand-dryer.) Rolled my skirt over and took off my tie, and *voilà*!!! Georgia the callous sophisticate rides again with her Ace Gang (minus Wise Woman of the Forest)!!

Funnily enough, it was just as well we had done preparation because as we started walking down the hill, Dave the Laugh caught us up. He was with Declan, Edward and Rollo. Ellen, Mabs and Jools went into giggling-gertie mode and sort of lagged back with their "boyfriends", so it was just me and Dave and Rosie.

He linked up with us and said, "Be gentle with me, girls."

Awwww.

I told Dave about the *Rom and Jule* fiasco and he said, "Excellent, excellent. Many comedy opportunities in the tights department there then." He also said he had some kittykat treats for Angus.

Awwww.

As we got to the edge of the park we heard a lot of shouting. The Blunder Boys. Yippee. They saw Dave and gave him the finger. Then Oscar came looming along with his tragic jeans and no belt and one of the spoons yelled, "Wedgie!!!" And two of them got hold of Oscar and pulled down his jeans so that his Thomas the Tank Engine kecks were exposed to the world. Mark Big Gob grabbed the top of Oscar's underpants and lifted him off his feet. He was just dangling there, literally held up by his undercrackers.

Quite, quite mind-bogglingly weird.

Dave was nodding and said, "Excellent work."

We walked on and I said, "Erm, Dave, as you are world expert on the weirdness that is boydom, can you just explain what that was about?"

Dave said, "A wedgie is when the underpants are pulled sharply upward from behind, so that they go tightly up the victim's bum-oley."

We just looked at him.

He went on. "The ultimate is, of course, the atomic wedgie, when you attempt to get the victim's pants over their head."

I said goodbye to Rosie and Dave the Laugh at my turn-off and he and Rosie went off together. Dave looked back at me while he walked backwards. He said, "S'later, you cheeky minx!"

I watched them as they went off. They were laughing and

then did a bit of spontaneous "Let's go down the disco" dancing.

I sort of wished we could have hung round together some more. I really laugh when I am with Dave.

Ah, well.

In my bedroom

If my brain keeps adding up the minutes till Masimo might be back, I'll go mad. I am going to keep my mind (well, what there is left of it) occupied by doing (and I never thought the day would come when I would say this) my homework.

Two minutes later

Now, here we go – *Rom and Jule.*

Two hours later

Bloody hell, Billy Shakespeare can be depressing. *Rom and Jule* is not what you would call a megalarf. Mostly it is just fighting, a bit of underage snogging, more fighting, and then some mad bint who calls herself a nurse and makes useless jokes about sex.

For the hilarious side-splitting finale, Rom and Jule pretend to commit suicide and then they actually do commit suicide.

Two minutes later

I know how they feel – it's double physics tomorrow.

Midnight

If Masimo gets back at nine p.m. that makes it 7020 minutes to wait. Or maybe if he comes back at two p.m. that makes it 6600 minutes. Is there a time difference between here and Italy? Ooooooh I can't sleep. What can I do? It's too early to start my make-up routine. Angus might lick it off in the night.

Two minutes later

I know, I will use the *German for Fools* book that I have borrowed from Ro Ro and finish translating the snogging scale for Herr Kamyer and Miss Wilson. I do it only to help them with their luuurve.

I amaze myself with my caringnosity.

Twenty-five minutes later

Ach, so here is the full-frontal *knutschen* scale.

1. *Händchen halten*
2. *Arm umlegen*

3. *Abscheidskuss* (hahahahahah, once again the lederhosen types come up trumps on the mirth-ometer)

4. *Kuss, der über drei minuten*

5. *Kuss mit geöffneten Lippen* (I don't know how Geoff got in here, but that is boys for you)

6. *Zungenkuss*

7. *Oberkörperknutschen – im Freien* (outside)

8. *Oberkörperknutschen – drinnen* (inside)

9. *Rummachen unterhalb der Taille* (*ja*, oh *ja*!!!)

10. *AUF GANZE GEHEN!!!*

Wednesday September 14th
Up at the crack of 7:00 a.m.

This is my plan. I set off to Stalag 14 with my uniform "customised". (My skirt turned over at the waist to shorten it, no tie and no beret.) I do my make-up and hair for max glamorosity. Do the walky walky hip hip flicky hair thing all the way to school until just by the loos in the park. By this time I am only about one hundred yards from the school gate. Then I nip into the park loos while my very besty pally Jas stands guardey dog outside. In the loos I take my make-up off, undo customised uniform, put on stupid beret etc.

Resume looking like a complete prat, then quickly walk in the middle of the Ace Gang and pass through the Gates of Hell into Stalag 14.

8:15 a.m.

Jas was sitting on her wall, chewing her fringe. If she isn't careful, she will develop furballs like cats do. Gordy was doing that choking and coughing thing last night and then he sicked up a fur ball. Disgusting really. Especially as it wasn't even the colour of his fur. I am hoping against hope it has nothing to do with licking the Prat brothers, but facts have to be faced, and he does spend an awful lot of time in their kennel with them.

They are entering a dog show soon and if I see Gordy coming to heel to Mr Next Door and wearing a little pink collar, my worst suspicions will be fulfilled. So far, Angus has not been fit enough to ride the Prat brothers around like little horsies like he did before. But when he does start again, imagine what he will do if he drops down on to Gordy's back.

When she saw me, Jas said, "Erm, you are a dead person. Hawkeye will keep you in detention for ever and you will have to write a zillion times, 'Although I look like a prozzie I

♥ 233

am merely a tart.'" And she started honking with laughter.

She calmed down a bit when I got her in a headlock. From upside down she said, "Nurk, I am just saying that—"

I let her go because I couldn't make out what she was babbling on about and her face had gone very red. She straightened her skirt.

"I am just saying, Georgia, that when Hawkeye sees you all dolled up like a tart she will not take it kindly."

"She won't see me all dolled up. I am only all dolled up in case Masimo is anywhere in the vicinity. Before we get to the school gates I am going to make myself look like the rest of you – boring and sad."

Jas said, "Well, Tom says he likes me looking natural."

I just looked at her. "Jas, you don't look natural."

She was going to get on to the having-the-hump scale, so I quickly said, "You look bloody gorgey, that's what you look, you bloody gorgey – thing. Anyway, this is my plan. I look all glam till we get to the loos near school, then if I see Masimo all is tickety-boo luuurve-wise. However, if I don't see him, I scoot into the loos and take my make-up off and turn my skirt down etc. Ditto at home time. I nip into the loos, reapply glamorosity, turning up skirt etc., etc. You and Ace Gang

234

huddly duddly me out of the school gates just in case there are any Hitler Youth on girl-baiting duty. Then if Masimo is there waiting for me, I am a vision of whatsit. Do you see?"

She is, of course, being all grumpy about it but she will do it.

Ten minutes later

She was saying, "I read *Rom and Jule* last night – it's so beautiful, isn't it?"

I said, "No, it's weird. It's even weirder than *MacUseless*, and that was staggeringly weird."

Jas was off in Jasland though. "It was so romantic, and you know, when everyone, the nurse and all the Capulets were saying bad things about Rom, well, Jules just stuck with him. And I think there is a lesson there for us all."

I said, "Oh yes, what is it? Don't get married at thirteen to some twit in tights?"

Jas was looking all misty-eyed. "No, it means stick to what you feel, no matter what anyone else says. And that is why I have decided not to play the elastic-band game with Tom. I just love him and he can do whatever he wants. I will just love him."

Good grief. Should I start singing and banging a tambourine? Jas has turned into Baby Jesus in a beret.

Which reminds me, I have decided to audition for Mercutio. I have many literary reasons for this: mainly, he ponces around in tights for only two scenes and then is stabbed to death. Which, as a result, leaves many, many happy hours of lolling around backstage having a hoot and a laugh with my mates. And the lads.

Rom and Jule read-through and audition in the main hall 2:00 p.m.

Miss Wilson is already hysterical.

I said to Rosie, "Certain people are not cut out to be teachers of the young."

Rosie said, "Do you mean people with out-of-control bobs?"

And I said, "Yes."

She has brought it on herself. You would have thought that after the fiasco of the orange-juggling in *MacUseless* she would have learned not to be innovative. But you just can't tell some people.

This time she has suggested we might try puppetry and mime in our production. That immediately caused an outbreak of us all pretending to be Thunderbirds puppets. Oh, we laughed.

Then, when we had almost stopped and got ourselves under control, she said that in Ye Olde Days the audience was not very quiet and would shout rude jokes and stuff out at the actors.

Rosie said, "Like Romeo, Romeo, wherefore art thy PANTS, Romeo?"

And that once more introduced the old pants theme into everything that we did. Miss Wilson only has herself to blame.

Ten minutes later

Jas was being annoyingly Jasish. She has learned all Juliet's lines for the first two acts. How incomprehensibly botty-kissing is that? She has done it because she genuinely thinks that she is Juliet.

And that Tom is Romeo.

As I said to her, "We'd better say ta taa then, Jas, because you die at thirteen. Which was two years ago."

She just stropped off to be with the others who are taking the whole thing seriously.

Ten minutes later

I was being the prologue person and I was giving it my all at the front (oo-er). I said:

"Two households both alike in dignity,

In fair Verona, where we lay our scene,

From ancient grudge break to (and I couldn't resist the comedy opportunity) new nudity,

Where civil PANTS makes civil PANTS unclean."

Oh, we laughed. I thought that Rosie was going to have a spaz attack.

Miss Wilson was yelling, "Girls, girls stop this silliness. Saying pants all the time is not funny."

It is, though.

Twenty-five minutes later

Anyway, the horrific outcome is that Miss Bum-oley Kisser Jas is in fact Juliet. This is going to be unbearable for the next few weeks. She is soooo full of herself. Discussing stuff with Miss Wilson. I actually overheard her say, "Yes, perhaps a puppet dog would add to the whole Elizabethan feel of the production. It is very likely that Juliet would have had a little dog as a companion."

Perhaps a swift rotten tomato in the gob might add to the whole Elizabethan feel.

Rosie has been cast as the nurse, which I think is an act of theatrical suicide. Ellen is Tybalt and I am Mercutio – hooray!!!

Miss Wilson had to spoil things by saying, "I am casting you, Georgia, because although you have been silly this afternoon, I know you are not going to let me or the team down."

Jas went, "Humph."

She is at number three on the having-the-hump scale (head-tossing and fringe-fiddling) and we haven't even done the first read-through yet.

Although I don't know why we are bothering rehearsing the final scenes, because with Ellen dithering around with a sword as Tybalt, it is quite likely that none of us will survive longer than Act Two.

In the loos
4:00 p.m.
I've sent Jools on a little scouting mission to see if there are any signs of an Italian Luuurve God anywhere outside the school gates. My hands are trembling a LOT and I've nearly blinded myself twice with my mascara brush. Fortunately, we haven't had to prance around like ninnies doing sport today, so my hair has retained its bounceability factor.

239

Ten minutes later

Jools came into the loos.

"Oh my giddygod, Gee, he's here. He's on his scooter at the gates. And he's sort of brown, and well, I mean, I like Rollo but I mean, phwoooaaar is all I can say!!! Times ten."

My bottom nearly fell out of my panties. I sat on the edge of the sink. Blimey. My heart was racing.

Thank God the prefects were having a late meeting about discipline, because I know Wet Lindsay is just waiting to get me for something. She has a plan for me and I will not be liking it. But at least she is out of the way for now.

All of the Ace Gang came into the loos. I said to them, "Right, I am ready. I want you all to metaphorically hold my hand across the playground so that I do not fall over."

Jools said, "I haven't done metaphorical hand-holding. How does that go?"

I said, "You all walk across the playground and we chat and laugh like it is normal to be meeting a Luuurve God, but while you are chatting and so on, you are also mentally holding my pandie so that I do not fall over."

Jas, who has not come down to earth since she became Jule, was still going on like Mrs Owl the Dim. "When you say mentally holding your hand, do you mean we hold your hand and go mental?"

"Jas, Jas, please do not make me mess up my hair by beating you to a pulp. You know very well what I mean. Just do it."

We laughed and chatted all the way, step by step. I have absolutely no idea what anyone said, least of all me. I had never felt so nervous in my life. I took a quick look up from my casual laughing and saw him sitting on the seat of his scooter, with his long legs crossed. My heart skipped a beat; he was quite literally gorgey porgey. How could he like me? It was like being in a film.

When he saw me he got up and took off his gloves. He was wearing a pale blue leather coat and his hair had grown. And he looked so – so – Pizza-a-gogoish!

Then he did a wave and shouted, "Ay, Georgia, *ciao, cara, ciao!*" and started walking towards me and the gang.

He said to them, "*Ciao, signorinas*, and here is the, how you say, the very lovely, *molto bellissima* Miss Georgia."

And he came right up close to me and lifted me off my feet and kissed me properly and quite hard on the mouth. No warmsy upsies. Just a proper snog. And he didn't even make it a short one. I was still off my feet and I hadn't closed my eyes because I was so surprised, so I had gone slightly cross-eyed. His mouth felt lovely but not very familiar to me. Then he put me down and he kissed me quickly and said, "Oh, I have waited long for this. Come on, miss." And he took my hand and led me off to the scooter.

I turned back to the Ace Gang and they all went, "Oooohhhhhhhhhhhh get you!" in a high-pitched camp tone.

one hour later

We drove off through the streets on his scooter. It felt soooo full of glamorosity. He accelerated up the High Street quite fast. We stopped at the lights and he put down the bike stand and got off his seat, leaving the engine running. We were surrounded by cars and there were people passing by. I wondered what he was doing. Should I get off? Were we parking at the lights and going for a cup of coffee? Or did he think I should have a go at driving? Even though I can't even ride a bicycle properly.

Then he took off his helmet and he said, "I must snog you more." Blimey. And he did. He bent down and pushed up my goggles and then kissed me on the mouth. How erm... interesting. It was nice but I couldn't really concentrate because everyone was looking at us. I could see some kid in the back of a car picking his nose. People were honking their horns and some lads were going, "Get in there, my son!!!"

Masimo didn't seem to notice. He even put the tip of his tongue in my mouth, which made me go a bit jelloid. Then he said loudly, "Ah, that is better. Now I can continue. Thank you," and he bowed to the people in cars and to passers-by.

He leaped back into his seat, shoved his helmet on (without fastening the strap... I could imagine what Jas would have said about that), kicked away the bike support and revved off.

We went to the woods and it was a lovely soft warm just beginning to be autumn evening. As we went into the trees we found a little babbling brook. It was quite literally making a babbling noise as it went over pebbles and rocks. If I had to talk to Masimo any time soon that is what I would be doing – babbling.

I felt incredibly nervous. And I couldn't think of anything to say.

That was because we snogged. It was groovy gravy and I felt all melty like I didn't know the difference between his mouth and mine.

Fifteen minutes later

I am still feeling incredibly nervous and I can't think of anything to say. But that is all right because we are in snog heaven. Having a snogtastic time.

Rosie was right – foreign boys do that varying pressure. Soft and then hard and then soft again.

I wonder what would happen if we both did the same thing at once? For instance, if we both did hard together and I didn't do yielding, well, would we end up with really stiff necks? Or if I yielded when he yielded, would we both fall over? Or if he went to the right and I went to the right as well and we clashed teeth, would we – oh shut up, brain.

Funny, when I snogged normally, my brain went on a mini-break to Loonland. It didn't usually enter the debating society competition on snogging techniques.

Then Masimo stopped mid-snog and just looked me straight in the eyes. He didn't say anything, just looked me in the eyes. I didn't like to blink because it seemed a bit rude, but in the end I had to look down because my eyes were beginning to water. When I looked up he was still looking me in the eyes. He is, it has to be said, gorgey porgey times twelve.

He has really long eyelashes and a proper nose. I couldn't

even see up his nostrils. And a lovely mouth, with just the suggestion of hairiness around the chinny chin area, like a sort of designer stubble. Not like a little vole lurking around like Dad has on the end of his face. And it wasn't bum fluff like Oscar has. And it wasn't prickly like when Grandad gave me "chin pie" but it was deffo hairy stuff.

And also, I think, although I didn't like to stare like a staring thing on stare tablets, there was also a bit of chest-type hair coming out of the top of his shirt.

Blimey.

It must be brilliant to be a boy and not have to worry about suppressing the orang-utan gene. To be able to just let it grow wild and free. Of course, you can take anything too far, and some of the lads who play footie in the park are quite literally chimpanzee from the shorts downwards. I don't know about the top bit, and I don't want to know about the top bit.

Thirty seconds later

Dave the Laugh is a bit hairy as well. Anyway, shut up about Dave the Laugh; he is not in this scenario.

Ten seconds later

And Dave the Laugh is not right about Masimo being a lezzie and that is *le* fact.

Then Masimo said, "*Cara*, it is how you say nippy nungas."

I looked down at my nungas. Please God I hadn't had a sudden outbreak of sticky-out nip nips. No sign of them – phew, I was OK. I looked up again and he said, "Brrrr." And put his coat round my shoulders.

I said, "Oh, you mean nippy noodles!" And I laughed, but not in a good way, in a sort of heggy heggy hog hog way. Oh good, I am starting to laugh like my mad little sister.

One minute later

As we walked back towards his scooter, the Luuurve God said, "My – erm – other girlfriend, in Italy, I would like for you to meet her."

What what?! Am I in a *ménage à trois* (or *uno menagio d trois* –io)?

Two minutes later

It turns out that Masimo is talking about his ex-girlfriend, the one I saw at the Stiff Dylans gig and the one he went out with before me. Gina. Anyway, she has met an English boy and they are going to get married! And he would like me to meet her when she comes over in a couple of weeks.

Blimey.

I hadn't done ex-girlfriend work before.

And she was getting married.

Wow.

And not like Rosie. Not a Viking marriage in twenty-five years time. But a real one. One without horns and probably not wearing a hat made out of herring.

My *How to Make Any Twit Fall in Love with You* book had better have a section on conversational hints with ex-girlfriends. You know, how to avoid past snogging chat.

I must never say, "So, what number on the snogging scale did you get up to, Gina? With my present boyfriend?" Get out of my head, past snogging scale!!!

We walked along a bit in silence holding hands. I couldn't think of anything normal to say. Then the Luuurve God said, "I am going to the Stiff Dylans' rehearsal tonight. Do you want for to come?"

Inwardly I was thinking, *Er, nothing would make me go and sit through two hours of nodding along and then going home in the equipment van and sitting on Dom's drum and falling through it.* Like I did the last time I went to a Stiff Dylans' rehearsal. Dom still stands in front of his drum kit any time I go near.

There are, it has to be said, about a million reasons why nothing will make me go to a Stiff Dylans' rehearsal. In fact, I would rather be covered in frogspawn. And slightly roasted.

But I didn't say that. I said, "Erm, no, I've got homework to do."

Masimo smiled and chucked me under the chin and said, "Aaaaah, the little girl has her homework to do."

He said it in a nice way. But I still felt a bit stupid. So no change there.

I was saved from being more of *la grande idiote* because we got on his scooter and raced through town.

It is vair vair groovy being with him; all the girls look as we go by. I did a casualosity-at-all-times just lightly holding on to one of his shoulders thing. Until we went round a corner a bit fast and I had to grab hold of his helmet.

When we got to my place Masimo got off and started giving me a big snog goodbye. I could see Mum hiding behind the curtains in the front room. How vair vair embarrassing. I went a bit red and said to Masimo, "Oh God, my mum is watching us."

He looked up and smiled towards the window and then he blew a kiss and said, "Perhaps she wants to join in."

Ohmygiddygod, how horrific is that as an idea? Now I am involved in Europorn!!!

When I went into the house I heard Mum scampering into the kitchen and as I closed the door she called out, "Georgia, is that you?"

I said, "Mum, I saw your head bobbing around like a budgie."

She came out of the kitchen and said, "He is quite categorically gorgey."

I didn't say anything. I just went up to my bedroom in a dignitosity-at-all-times way.

Midnight

Ah well, Angus is on the road to recovery – he is sleeping comfortably on my head. And as a precaution against him tumbling off and waking himself up, he has his claws lightly stuck into my scalp.

Thursday September 15th

It is vair vair hard work being the girlfriend of a Luuurve God. Constant grooming is required; the public expects it. However, as I do not wish to be flogged to within an inch of my life by the fascists (Hawkeye etc.), I have not applied any make-up. Just put on a touch of foundation, lip gloss and mascara. And a teeny white eyeliner line round the inside of my eyes to make them look gorgey and marvy and uuumph.

Stalag 14

When I got to the school gates this morning Masimo was there waiting for me with a present! Honestly! How romantico is that? *Molto molto* romantico. It was a bottle of perfume from Italy called Sorrento.

I've never been bought perfume before. Libby made me some perfume from rose petals and milk but that is not the same. Especially as Gordy drank it.

All the girls were going mental, flicking their hair and doing mad pouting around him. It felt quite groovy. I was doing my shy smiling and looking up and looking down business, with just a touch of flicky hair, nothing like the other fools around me. I thought maybe he would kiss my hand and zoom off but then he snogged me! Full-frontal snogging in front of everyone. And by everyone I mean Hawkeye.

As Masimo took off she appeared like the Bride of Dracula shouting, "Georgia Nicolson!! You are an absolute disgrace and a shame to your uniform. What kind of an example are you to the younger girls, behaving like a prostitute in front of them. What on earth will they think?"

Actually, I could have told her what they thought because as I slunk off to see Slim for part two of the ranting and raving, the Little Titches passed by and went, "Coooorrrr, miss," and winked.

As Wet Lindsay escorted me to Slim's office she said, "You appalling tart. Personally I think Masimo should get some charity award for even touching you."

Oh, I hate her. I hate her so much you could bottle it.

Slim rambled and jelloided on for three million and a half centuries. "Blah blah, terrible example... blah blah... shouldn't be canoodling with boys... plenty of time for that... in my day... no canoodling until we were eighty-five etc., etc..."

RE
9:45 a.m.
When I finally escaped with double detention I went and sat down next to Rosie and she sent me a jelly baby and a note: Did the nasty jelly lady scare you with her chins?

I wrote back: No, but she did say "canoodle".

I feel a bit sick.

Art room
OK, on the dark side I have double detention, but on the bright side I am a bit perked up because I am wearing my new Italian perfume given to me by my groovy gravy boyfriend. And I am among my besties, the Ace Gang, doing an art project on the camping fiasco. Instead of proper lessons. What larks!!!

Miss Wilson is beside herself with excitement again. This has been a big week for her creativitosity-wise. First her puppet version of *Rom and Jule* and now the camping-fiasco project. Her bob is practically dancing the tango.

Jas is also vair vair excited. And she is walking funny. Sort of floating along and shaking her hair about. Why?

Thirty seconds later

Oh, I know what she is doing, she is walking in what she fondly imagines is an Elizabethan way. But actually looks like someone with the terminal droop.

She has brought in her collection of newt drawings and some jamjars of frogspawn.

I said to her, "Jas, that is not frogspawn, it is clearly a bit of snot in a jamjar." She didn't even bother to reply.

I am making a hat out of leaves.

Rosie said, "What is that?"

I said, "It is a hat made of leaves and so on. It is a triumphant celebration of the great outdoors."

Rosie said, "No, it is not. It is some old leaves and it is WUBBISH."

Yes, well, that is as maybe, but it is better than her "natural orchestra" which is essentially a bit of rice in some tins and a couple of spoons.

Herr Kamyer popped by and Miss Wilson went into a spectacular ditherama at the sight of her "*traum*boy."

I must tell her about the snogging scale in German so that she is ready, should Herr Kamyer leap on her for a spot of number three – *abscheidskuss*.

Five minutes later

Jas was actually humming "The hills are alive with the sound of pants" as she arranged her jamjars.

I said to her, "Jas, do you know what 'snot' is in German? It is '*schnodder*'. Comedy gold, isn't it, the German language?"

She said, "Shhh."

I said, "Do you know what shhhh is in lederhosen talk?"

But she started humming even louder.

Two minutes later

In a spontaneous outburst of madnosity Rosie has joined in with Jas's humming and started singing, "The hills are alive with the sound of pants", accompanying herself on rice tin and spoons. She was singing, "The hills are alive with the sound of pants, with pants I have worn for a thousand years!!!"

It was very infectious. I started improvising a woodland wonderland dance which involved a lot of high kicking and leaf work.

We were yelling, "I go to the PANTS when my heart is lonely—" when Herr Kamyer put his foot down with a firm hand.

He shouted, "Girls, girls, ve will not continue ze project if this kafuffle goes on!! Vat is the big funniness *mit* pants?"

We stopped eventually but I said under my breath, "*Kackmist.*" Which means buggeration. Oh, what a hoot and a half.

4:20 p.m.
Oh goddygodgod, how boring is detention. Miss Stamp was my guard. I am sure she was grooming her moustache as I wrote out, "A predilection for superficiality leads remorselessly towards an altercation with authority."

A million times (ish).

But I have my German book on my knee. Tee hee.

Canoodling is *rummachen.* Absolute top comedy magic.

5:30 p.m.
Freedom, freedom!!!

I skipped out of the school gates, and carried on doing a bit of ad hoc skipping down the hill past the park.

Which is when Dave the Laugh emerged from the park loos!! *Caramba!* I stopped skipping but it was too late. He said, "Excellent independent nunga-nunga work, Georgia."

He had just been playing footie and was a bit sweaty. His hair was all damp. I quite liked it. He's got a nice smell.

He walked along with me and said, "What have you been up to?"

I didn't mention exactly why I had been kept behind. Well, actually, I lied. I said that I had been given detention because I had done an improvised dance to "The hills are alive with the sound of pants".

He said, "Top work."

I felt a bit bad about lying, but on the other hand I didn't want to say that I had been punished for snogging Masimo at the school gates.

Four minutes later

Dave does make me laugh. I told him about the German snogging scale and he was nodding and going, "*Oh ja, oh ja!!! Ich liebe der* full-frontal *knutschen. Ich bin der vati!*"

Then he said, "You don't fancy a spot of *rummachen unterhalb der taille*, do you? Just for old times' sake?"

I said, "Dave, how dare you speak to me like that."

And he said, "You know you love it, you cheeky *fräulein*."

I just walked quickly off. I have my pridenosity.

He caught me up and said, "Stop trying to get off with me."

I was amazed. "Er, Dave, I think you will find that it was you who asked to *rummachen*."

"No, it wasn't."

"Er, yes, it was, Dave."

"No, you thrust yourself at me. Because you cannot resist me. It is sad."

I stopped and looked at him. "Dave, I can resist you. I have an Italian Luuurve God as a boyfriend."

Dave said, "Oh, he is so clearly gay."

"Dave, he is not gay."

"He has a light blue leather coat."

"That does not make him gay; it makes him Italian."

Dave said, "I rest my case."

I looked at him. And then he just bent down and looked at me. He has lovely lips and I sort of forgot where I was for a minute. I felt my lips puckering up and... then he pushed me away from him so that I nearly fell over.

He said, "Look, Georgia, stop it, try and control yourself, you are making a fool of yourself."

I was speechless. What, what??? I didn't know what to do I was so amazed, so I shoved him quite hard. He looked at me. And then he shoved me quite hard back, and I fell over. I got up and went and shoved him again.

He said, "Look, leave me alone. Your girlfriend will be really cross and get his matching leather handbag out."

He is sooo annoying. I was just marching over to shove him again when Masimo whizzed up on his scooter.

Dave waved at him and as he went off he said, "Oooh, she doesn't look very pleased."

And in fact he was right. Masimo did look a bit cross. He smiled when I came over though and said, "*Ciao*... you are fighting with Dave?"

I said, "Erm... no, it was just that, er, he was showing me how he, er, scored a goal. And he was saying that he and his girlfriend, Emma, are coming to the Stiff Dylans gig."

Masimo looked a bit confused but then he said, "Come, I will take you for a coffee."

Coffee bar

I feel like a prat and a fool. I have just dashed to the loos to put make-up on. Funny I didn't remember I hadn't got any on when I was with Dave. So I've done the lippy mascara thing, but there is not much I can do about my uniform. I hope I don't see anyone I know.

one hour later
I tried to explain the German snogging-scale thing to Masimo and he laughed, but I don't think he really gets it.

At home in bed
Oh God, it was like twenty questions when I got home. Where have you been? Blah blah blah, school finishes at four p.m., it's now eight p.m. That's four hours gap.

I made the mistake of saying to Dad, "Dad, I am not a child.'

Then he rambled on saying stuff like, "No, you can say that again, you are not a child, you are a spawn of the Devil." etc., etc.

In my bedroom
10:30 p.m.
I tell you this: I'm not the only spawn of the Devil in my family. Some complete fool (my dad) has bought my sister (also known as the littlest spawn of the devil) a "hilarious" fishing souvenir.

It is a stuffed fish on a stand and when you press a button it starts squiggling around doing a trout dance and singing, "Maybe it's beCOD I'm a Londoner" over and over again.

10:50 p.m.
Libby lobes it. It is her new besty. And new besties always sleep in my bed.

10:52 p.m.
Bibbs is fast asleep but I'm not because I have fins sticking up my nostrils.

11:00 p.m.
Also, why has she still got her wellies on?

11:05 p.m.
Oh god, now Angus has come into my room and is trying to get on to the bed.

11:12 p.m.
I'm going to have to get out of bed and haul him in. He's already crashed into the dressing table twice and is now in the

wastepaper basket. I'll be glad when his tail is back to normal.

11:20 p.m.
So, here we all are then, tucked up together: Libby, Mr Fish, Angus, a jar of potted fish (Libby's snacks for Mr Fish) and me, hanging on to half an inch of bed.

11:28 p.m.
But I'm happy. I have a Luuurve God as a boyfriend!!! Yes, yes and thrice yes! Or *sì, sì* and thrice-io *sì*, as I must learn to say.

11:30 p.m.
Wait till I tell the Luuurve God about the Mr Fish episode tomorrow when he picks me up at Stalag 14. I bet he will laugh like the proverbial drain-io.

11:35 p.m.
Perhaps I will save the Mr Fish story because he didn't exactly fall about when I told him about the German snogging scale.

11:40 p.m.

Dave the Laugh did though. He thought it was a hoot and a half.

11:45 p.m.

How dare he insinuate I am a cheeky *fräulein*? If anyone's a cheeky *fräulein*, he is. And he said that I was thrusting myself after him, but it was him who asked to *rummachen*. Anyway, shut up, brain. I'm not thinking about Dave the so-called Laugh.

Midnight

I think Masimo is a bit jealous of Dave. Tee hee. I'm a boy-entrancing vixen.

12:30 a.m.

Oh, dear God, I've accidentally set Mr Fish off. How disgusting to have it writhing around in bed and singing. I will never sleep at this rate. It's like Piccadilly Cir...

zzzzzzzzzzzz.

Friday September 16th

I woke up laughing about Dave the Laugh asking if he could *rummachen unterhalb* my *taille*. Tee hee.

Not that I want him to.

The puckering up thing was just a knee-jerk reaction. Like if you think of lemons, your mouth waters. So if someone looks like they are going to kiss you, you pucker up.

It is just biological.

Nothing to worry about.

4:10 p.m.

I cannot believe this!

Wet Lindsay came up to me as I was coming out of the loos. The Ace Gang had gone on ahead because I am meeting Masimo at the school gates. She said, "Go and get your hockey kit; you have volunteered for extra practice. Miss Stamp's thrilled with you."

I said, "I think you will find that actually I haven't volunteered and that I am going off to meet my boyfriend. Do you know him? He is a Luuurve God."

She stood in front of me. "If you know what's good for you, you will get changed and get out there on that pitch."

Merde. I would just do a runner but she would only report me and then I would have to go to the elephant house (Slim's office) and be beaten to death by chins again.

I slumped off behind her.

She hasn't even got a bottom.

We passed Miss Stamp in the corridor and she said, "I am really very impressed with you, Georgia, and it is very kind of you, Lindsay, to encourage the younger girls. I will be mentioning it to the headmistress. It is a nice change to see you out of the detention room, Georgia. Keep it up."

Buggeration.

She went off into her office.

Lindsay looked at me and gave me a very scary "smile". How can Robbie snog her? It must be like snogging a cross between an octopus and a praying mantis. Erlack.

Ten minutes later

Lindsay is making me run round the hockey pitch.

She said, "Let this just be a little lesson to you, Nicolson, about how bad life can be if you cross me. Run round the pitch four times and then you can go. I'll be watching you."

I said, "Masimo will be waiting for me."

She said, "Well, you had better run like the wind, hadn't you?" And she went off into the changing rooms. I could see her looking at me through the window.

Twenty minutes later

Dear *gott in Himmel* I am shattered. I haven't got my special sports nunga-nunga holder and it is very tiring having them bouncing about. I finished the four laps and then I limped across to the changing rooms. I was so hot. I'd have a very quick shower, apply lippy etc. and then dash out to my boyfriend.

Thirty seconds later

The door was locked!

Five minutes later

I can't believe this. It's Mr Attwood's night off and no one else has a key.

I bet it's not his night off. I bet he is doing this on purpose. He is probably lurking around somewhere laughing.

Also, where is Wet Lindsay?

In the end I had to give up on getting my clothes. I will have to go home in my trackies with a massive red head. I wonder what Masimo is thinking. I wonder if he is still there? In a way I hope he isn't because I know what he will be thinking if he sees my head. He'll be thinking: *If I wanted a tomato for a girlfriend, I would have asked for one.*

 265

As I came out of the school building I saw Wet Lindsay getting on the back of Masimo's scooter and taking off!!

What a spectacular cow and a half she is. She'd done this on purpose. She said she would get me and she has.

There is only one reasonable solution to this.

I will have to kill her and eat the evidence.

Walking home redly

My knickers are sticking to my botty. This is quite literally a PANTS situation.

Two minutes later

As soon as I get in I am going to plunge my head into a bucket of cold water.

One minute later

Although with my luck I will get my head stuck in the bucket at which point Masimo will turn up on his scooter and dump me.

Home

When I walked into the kitchen Dave the Laugh was there, balancing something on Libby's nose. What? What fresh hell?

266

He looked up as I came in and said, "Blimey, you're red."

I tried to walk across the kitchen doing that hip hip flicky flick thing to distract attention from my head, but unfortunately my botty hurt so much from running I couldn't keep it up.

I turned my back to him and got a drink of water. I said, "What are you doing here?"

He said, "I just brought round the kitty treats for Angus, but Libby has eaten most of them. Still, it's the thought that counts."

I turned back to him and he looked at me. "You are quite sensationally red."

I went off into the bathroom.

He was not wrong. I looked like my head had turned into a lurking lurker.

Five minutes later

I quickly plunged my head into icy water and towel dried my hair into what I hoped was a tousled yet somehow strangely attractive style (that is what I hoped). Quick bit of lippy and mascara. I didn't want to be in the tarts' wardrobe too long in case Dave the Laugh decided to go. I expected he had come round to apologise for his awful behaviour *vis à vis* the *rummachen* incident.

Back in the kitchen
Two minutes later

I said to Dave, who was now having his hair plaited by Libby, "I suppose you have come to apologise for the *rummachen* fiasco."

And he said, "*Nein.*" Which made me laugh. He started to say, "Look, Georgia, I wanted to say that—"

At which point Mum came mumming in, talking rubbish.

She was adjusting her basoomas and flicking her hair. Surely she didn't think that Dave fancies the "more mature" lady??

She said, "Dave do you want to stay for tea? It's cool if you want to hang out for a bit."

It's cool if you want to hang out for a bit? What is she talking like a complete fool for? Oh, hang on, I think I know the answer to that one.

Dave said, "No, I'm afraid I'm away laughing on a fast camel. People to see, old people to rob, that sort of thing." And he got up to go.

Libby clung to his neck as he got up, like a toddler limpet –

just hanging round his neck. He started walking off as if he hadn't noticed he had a toddler necklace and Libby was laughing and laughing. She said, "I lobe my Daveeeeeeeeeeeeeeeee."

Blimey, she's joined the Dave the Laugh fan club as well.

I walked Dave to the gate, trying to get Libby to let go.

As I was pulling her off Masimo turned up on his scooter. He took his helmet off and sat on the seat, looking at us. Maybe he was mesmerised by my head. It still felt vair hot. I tried to do a bit of flicky hair but it was mostly sticking to my scalp.

Dave said, "*Ciao*, Masimo."

And Masimo said, "*Ciao,* mate."

But I am not entirely sure he meant the "mate" bit.

Dave scarpered off quite quickly and Libby started burrowing through Mr Next Door's hedge. She likes to go and sit in the kennel with the Prat Poodles and Gordy. But I can't worry about that sort of thing now.

Masimo looked a bit upset and he said, "Why did you not for me wait?"

I babbled on, "Well, Wet Lindsay said I had to do extra hockey, so I had to run like a loon on loon tablets round and round, like a hamster with trackie bums on, and then I was locked out, and I saw you driving off with her on the back."

Masimo said, "Aaaah. She said you had gone home and could I give her a lift."

Unbelievable!!! What a prize tart she is!!

Masimo was smiling a bit now. He really was gorgey porgey. He said, "And Dave, he came here, for you to have another fight?"

I laughed. "No, he came to bring some kitty treats for Angus but Libby ate them."

Masimo held out his arms. "Come here, miss."

I went over to him and he said, "You are very, erm, slippery."

Actually, he was right. If he squeezed me too hard I might shoot out of his hands like a wet bar of soap.

Then he kissed me. Which was fab and marvy and also number four, with a touch of virtual number five.

And that is when Dad came roaring up in his loonmobile.

I stopped kissing Masimo and leaped away from him like he had the Black Death. I said to the Luurve God; "Quickly, save yourself, my father is here. You must go now while you can, otherwise he may show you his leather trousers."

But it was too late. Vati had got out of his "car" and was bearding towards us. Oh how embarrassing. He was going to say something. I knew he was. Even though I have told him he must never address me in front of people.

He said, "Evening all. It's Masimo, isn't it? Are you coming in?"

Oh nooooooo.

I said, "No, Masimo has to go. He is rehearsing."

Masimo looked at me and I opened my eyes really wide and said, "Aren't you?"

He got it and said, "Ah, yes, *ciao*, Mr Nicolson. *Grazie*, but I must now to go. The Stiff Dylans are playing this weekend."

Dad said, "Oh well, maybe I will pop by to hear some tunes, come along and show you a few of my moves on the dance floor."

Has he snapped?

Masimo revved up his scooter. He leaned over and kissed me and said, "I will see you Saturday. I am, how you say, missing you already."

I tried to walk off in a dignity-at-all-times sort of way, but as we got to the house Dad yelled to Mum, "Georgia has been snogging an Italian stallion."

How disgusting!

I feel dirty and besmirched.

And also *kackmist*.

In bed

I wonder what Dave the Laugh was going to say to me? He does make me laugh. It was vair amusing, him sitting there having his hair plaited by Libby.

Anyway, I will ask him what he was going to say when I see him at the gig.

One minute later

If I get the chance. I expect he will be with his girlfriend.

Which is good.

And fine.

Two minutes later

I know that Emma is nice and everything but she did have a ludicrous spaz attack when Angus accidentally spat at her. Which is a bit weedy.

Anyway, I have vair many other important things to worry about. If Dave the Laugh wants to go out with a weed, that is his right. But the burning question is this: what in the name of Richard the Lionheart's codpiece am I going to wear for the gig?

Five minutes later

All the girls will be looking at me because a) I am officially going out with a Luuurve God and b) I am a multi-talented backing dancer and jolly good egg.

Fisticuffs at dawn

Saturday September 17th

8:30 a.m.

Preparations begin to become the girlfriend of a Luuurve God.

And possibly backing dancer.

So first on my list is cleanse and tone.

Done.

Face mask.

Done.

Cucumber eye patches.

Done.

Plucking.

Yessiree Bob.

Puckering exercises.

Done.

Lunch

Two jam sandwiches for max energy and nutrition.

Ellen was eating fruit gums in maths on Friday and Hawkeye asked her why, and Ellen said, "It is my breakfast." Hawkeye nearly had a complete ditherspaz and f.t. combined.

She said, "Where is the nutrition in that?"

And Ellen said, "Well, because of the, you know, erm... fruit or something."

3:00 p.m.

Charming conversation practice.

Done.

(Note to loon brain headquarters: do not mention hilarious pants jokes, full-frontal *knutschen*, glove animal or horns.)

6:00 p.m.

I think I look quite fab and groovy. That is what I think. Hair bouncing around, nungas more or less under control. And

I've got new special lash enhancing mascara on so my lashes are about two foot long. Of course I will never ever be able to get it off again but in the meantime I have max boy entranceability.

6:30 p.m.

If I can't get the mascara off by Monday it will give Wet Lindsay an excuse to attack me with a blow torch or put me on gardening duty with Elvis for the rest of my life.

She's bound to be there tonight. Poncing around like a ninny.

If I get a chance to warn Robbie about her I will. I must be cunning and full of subtlenosity.

Clearly, I would rather just rip her stupid octopussy head off to save time. But there is bound to be some busybody goodie-goodie who would complain to the RSPCA about it.

Leaving Home
7:15p.m.

Dad and Uncle Eddie were tinkering with the Robinmobile as I went off. They are both wearing T-shirts with a picture of Uncle Eddie in his baldy-o-gram costume on the front of them. And underneath the picture it says, "He dares to baldly go where no other man has baldly gone before."

Good grief.

At the Honey Club
8:30 p.m.

Quick check in the tarts' wardrobe.

Looking in the mirror. Hmmmm. Helloooooo, Sex Kitty. Grrrrrr.

A quick splosh of my perfume from Italy that my Italian boyfriend brought me from Italy, which is to the right on the map from Merrie Olde England. Possibly. And then my public is ready for me.

Out in the club by the bar

Sven and Rosie have excelled themselves. Their theme tonight is fur, fur with just a hint of fur. Did you know you could get matching fake-fur jumpsuits? In purple? Well, you do now.

I am a bit nervy actually. This is like my first official outing as the official girlfriend of a Luuurve God. Still, I have my Ace Gang to keep me company.

Ten minutes later

Blimey, I am goosegog girl because all the rest of the gang are with their "boyfriends". Even Ellen. Although she might be the last to know – or something.

Rom and Jule (otherwise known as Jas'n'Tom) are all over each other like a rash. It is quite sweet really. If you like that sort of thing.

No sign of Dave the Laugh and his girlfriend. Which is cool. They have probably gone out somewhere different. How should I know?

They might be round at Emma's.

You know. Messing about and so on.

I seem to want to go to the piddly-diddly department again.

In the tarts' wardrobe

Oh marvellous, Wet Lindsay and Astonishingly Dim Monica are in front of the mirrors. I don't know why they are bothering. Lindsay would need a head transplant to make her look less like Octopussy Girl.

One thing for sure, I am not going into a cubicle and doing a piddly diddly while they are looking at me.

Back in the club

I said to Rosie, when she was on a snog break, "I wonder where Masimo is?"

She said, "Why don't you go backstage in your capacity as girlfriend and say to him, 'I just came to say break a leg,' or whatever you say to rock stars? Maybe it's 'break a string' or 'break your trousers'. I don't know, but just go say it."

And then I saw the Stiff Dylans come in with their guitars. They must be due on soon. As soon as they appeared they were surrounded by girls. Or "tarts" as some people might call them.

Two minutes later

The Stiff Dylans are signing autographs. Honestly! Actually signing autographs. I can see the Luuurve God. He is there signing as well. And smiling and chatting to the girls. I wonder if I should go out and get my coat and then come back in again like I have just arrived? I could sneak out and—Then he looked up and saw me. He waved and started coming over. Hurrah!

Blimey. He has an amazingly cool suit on. I bet it is from Pizza-a-gogo land. When he reached me he put his arms around me and kissed me. Everyone was looking. I felt a bit red actually. I haven't done much public snogging. He didn't even seem to notice the crowd around us. He was just looking in my eyes and he said, "*Ciao, cara*, I will see you at the break, and then after the gig we go maybe to somewhere we can be together?"

Blimey O'Reilly's trousers, it's a bit early to get swoony knickers but I have got them on.

one hour later

The whole place is rocking. The Stiff Dylans have played a cracking set and Robbie has just gone on stage to join them. He is doing sharesies vocals with Masimo on "Don't wake me up before you go. Just go." I wonder if Robbie wrote that for Octopussy Girl?

I would.

She is standing looking at him right at the front of the stage. I said to Jas, "How uncool is that?"

She was too busy smooching with Hunky to bother to reply.

Lindsay has given me the evils since I got here but I am not at school now, and also I am with my mates. And also I am the girlfriend of a Luuurve God.

Which is a bit weird actually. Loads of girls that I don't even know have been coming up to me and saying, "Oooh, isn't he gorgey, what is it like going out with him? What kind of music does he like? What is his birth sign?" etc.

What am I? His press secretary?

I didn't mention to them that I am in fact a backing dancer.

Half an hour later

This is more like it. The Ace Gang rides again!! We are doing a shortened version of the Viking disco hornpipe to "Ultraviolet" by the Dylans. We haven't got any props so we are having to improvise the paddles and so on. It is a hoot and a half.

I waved my (pretend) paddle at Masimo, but he didn't wave back. I suppose it's a bit difficult when you are playing a guitar. He looked at me though. I like to think in an admiring way.

Two minutes later

Another fast one by the Dylans. Everyone is going mental.

And Dave the Laugh is here!!! I only saw him when he came up to me and said, "Let's twist!!" And he started doing this mad fast twisting thing, going down to the floor

281

and then up again. Quite sensationally insane, but funny. He was yelling at me, "Come on, Kittykat. Get down!!!"

I said, "Not in a million years. Get your girlfriend to make *le idiot* of herself."

He shouted, "She's not here. You can be substitute idiot!! Come on, you know you want to!!!"

Sven and Rosie and the whole gang joined in. So in the end so did I. It was the best fun!

Ten minutes later

I am hotter than a hot person on hot tablets. And that is hot, believe me. The Dylans are just going off for a break and Dave the Laugh has gone to get us some drinks.

Two minutes later

I was so full of exhaustiosity that I sat on Ro Ro's knee. She was sitting on Sven's knee so it was like a knee sandwich.

I said to her, "You have a vair comfy knee, little matey."

And she said, "Are you on the turn?"

I was just about to hit her when Masimo came up to me and said, "Georgia, come outside with me."

Rosie said, "Oo-er."

And just at that moment Dave came back with the drinks. He handed me a glass and went, "Yeah, groove on! Nice set, mate."

Masimo smiled, but not a lot, and then he said. "You are enjoying dancing with my girlfriend... mate?"

Dave said, "Oh blimey, this is not fisticuffs at dawn, is it?"

Masimo looked a bit puzzled. He said, "What is this fisticuffs?"

Dave put his drink down on the table and started prancing around doing his impression of Mohammed Ali crossed with a fool. He was yelling, "I am sooo pretty, I float like a butterfly. Duff duff. Put em up, put em up."

He is, it has to be said, bonkers.

I was laughing. We were all laughing. Except Masimo. He said to Dave, "Oh, I see. OK. We can do it this way. I will see you outside. Mate."

Dave said, "I'm afraid I am not a homosexualist."

But Masimo handed his jacket to me and started walking towards the door.

Surely he was joking.

Dave looked at me and shrugged. And then he went outside as well. Blimey.

 283

Jas said to me, "I told you that your big red bottom would get you in trouble and now... you see."

What what???

I'd just been doing the twist, Masimo didn't even know about the accidental nearly number five in the woods scenario. I followed them both as they went out of the doors.

In fact most of the people in the club followed us outside.

Outside

Masimo said to Dave, "OK, now we sort this out, man to man."

Were they actually going to fight over me?

I should have liked it. But...

Rosie said to me, "This is just like Rom and Jule, isn't it? If they were wearing tights. Should we lend them some?"

I said, "Look, look, lads, this is silly. Why don't you just..."

Masimo was still looking at Dave and he put up both hands like they do in movies and started circling Dave, saying, "Come on."

Jas said, "Georgia, say something! Do something normal and sensible for once."

Yes, yes, that is what I must do – display maturiosity.

I stepped into the middle of them both and yelled, "STOP!!! STOP... IN THE NAME... OF PANTS!!!"

Masimo just looked at me. But Dave the Laugh started falling about laughing. And Rosie started singing, "The hills are alive with the sound of PANTS! With PANTS I have worn for a thousand years!" And then the Ace Gang joined in.

Two minutes later

Everyone was drifting off now that there was no chance of a fisticuffs extravaganza.

Dave was still laughing. He turned to Masimo and held out his hand and said, "It's just a little joke, mate, nothing to get your handbag out for." Then he said, "Night night, Gee," and went off.

I smiled at Masimo, but he didn't smile back. He looked at me and he looked really sad.

Donner *und* Blitzen.

And also *pipi*.

And *krappe*.

I started to go over to him and he turned away from me and walked off into the night.

Two minutes later

My Luuurve God has got the hump.

In fact he has just quite literally had the full Humpty Dumpty.

But maybe it will just be an overnight hump and in the morning all will be well again.

I wouldn't mind, but I've only been the girlfriend of a Luuurve God for about a month.

And I haven't seen him for most of that time.

Has he really dumped me?

One minute later

Just because I did the twist with Dave the Laugh.

And had a German fight with him.

And accidentally snogged him in the Forest of Red-bottomosity.

Which the Luuurve God doesn't know about anyway.

Two minutes later

Oh marvellous, I am once more on the rack of love with no cakes.

All aloney on my owney.

Again.

PANTS.

Georgia's Backing Dancer Portfolio

In case you haven't noticed, me and the Ace Gang (and when I say me and the Ace Gang, I really mean me) have created some of the grooviest dance moves ever invented. I have always found that a quick burst of disco inferno dancing is a fab way to get rid of tensionosity and frustrated snoggosity. So, because I love you all so much – and also because, like me, you may be considering a career as a backing dancer – I have made a portfolio of my favourite moves. Starting with dances from the early days.

The Simple Years
"Let's go down the disco"
This was really an ad hoc dance fandango. The main thrust and nub was that when a so-called teacher turned their back to illustrate something on the board, we all leaped up and did a brief burst of disco dancing, then sat down before we got multiple detention.

The Middle Years

1. The Viking bison disco inferno

We're still practising this for Rosie's forthcoming (i.e. in eighteen years time) Viking wedding. It is danced to the tune of *Jingle Bells* because even Rosie, world authority on Sven land doesn't know any Viking songs. Apart from *Rudolph the Red-nosed Reindeer*. Which isn't one.

For this dance you need some bison horns. If you can't find any bison shops nearby, make your own horns from an old hairband and a couple of twigs or something. Oh, I don't know, stop hassling me, I'm tired. It goes...

Stamp, stamp to the left,
Left leg kick, kick,
Arm up,
Stab, stab to the left (that's the pillaging bit),
Stamp, stamp to the right,
Right leg kick, kick,
Arm up,
Stab, stab to the right,
Quick twirl round with both hands raised to Thor (whatever),

Raise your (pretend) drinking horn to the left,
Drinking horn to the right,
Horn to the sky,
All over body shake,
Huddly duddly,
And fall to knees with a triumphant shout of
"HORRRRNNNNN!!!!"

p.s. In a rare moment of comic genius, Jas, who is clearly in touch with her inner bison, added this bit too. It's a sort of sniffing-the-air type move. Like a Viking bison might do. If it was trying to find its prey. And if there was such a thing as a Viking bison.

Stab, stab to the left,
And then sniff sniff.

Hahahahahaha!

2. The snot disco inferno

For this dance you will need a big blob of bubble gum hanging off your nose like a huge bogey. It needs to dangle about so you can swing it round and round in time to the music. Dance this to your favourite TV show theme tune. It goes...

Swing your snot to the left,
Swing to the right,
Full turn,
Shoulder shrug,
Nod to the front,
Dangle dangle,
Hands on shoulders,
Kick, kick to the right,
Dangle dangle,
Kick, kick to the left,
Dangle dangle,
Full snot around,
And shimmy to the ground.

Yes, yes and thrice yes!

The Maturiosity Years
The Viking disco hornpipe
And finally, the piece of resistance and cream of the cream –

the Viking disco hornpipe extravaganza!!! For this you need bison horns, mittens, ear muffs and paddles. Do remember muffs are worn *over* horns, not horns over muffs. You will feel like a fool and a twerp if you muff it up. Danced to the tune of *EastEnders*, it goes...

The music starts with a Viking salute. Both paddles are pointed at the horns.
Then a cry of "Thor!!!" and a jump turn to the right.
Paddle, paddle, paddle, paddle to the right,
Paddle, paddle, paddle, paddle to the left.
Cry of "Thor!!!" Jump turn to the left.
Paddle, paddle, paddle, paddle to the left,
Paddle, paddle, paddle, paddle to the right.
Jump to face the front (grim Viking expression).
Quick paddle right, quick paddle left x 4.
Turn to partner.
Cross paddles with partner x 2.
Face front and high hornpipe skipping x 8 (gay Viking smiling).
Then (and this is the complicated bit) interweaving paddling!
Paddle in and out of each other up and down the line, meanwhile gazing out to the left and to the right

(concerned expression - this is the looking-for-land bit).
Paddle back to original position.
On-the-spot paddling till all are in line and then close eyes (for night-time rowing effect).
Right and left paddling x2 and then open eyes wide.
Shout "Land Ahoyyyyy!"
Fall to knees and throw paddles in the air (behind, not in front, in case of crowd injury).

Excellent in every way!

For more marvy extra stuff from moi, visit

www.georgianicolson.com

- 🐱 join the Ace Gang
- ♡ download gorgey stuff
- 🐱 win fabbity-fab prizes
- ♡ sign up for monthly G-mails from Georgia
- 🐱 post photos of your bestest pallies on the gallery
- ♡ chat to chums on message boards
- 🐱 and much, much more!

The Having-the-Hump Scale

1. ignorez-vousing

2. sniffing *(in an I-told-you-so way)*

3. head-tossing and fringe-fiddling

4. cold-shoulderosity work

5. Midget Gems all round, but not for you

6. pretendy deafnosity

7. walking on ahead

8. the quarter humpty *(evils)*

9. the half humpty *(evils and withdrawal of all snacks)*

10. the full Humpty Dumpty *(walking away, leaving behind that slight feeling that you have been dumped)*

The New and Improved Snogging Scale

$1/2$. **sticky eyes** (*Be careful using this. I've still got some complete twit following me around like a seeing-eye dog.*)

1. **holding hands**

2. **arm around**

3. **goodnight kiss**

4. **kiss lasting over three minutes without a break** (*What you need for this is a sad mate who's got a watch but no boyfriend.*)

$4 1/2$. **hand snogging** (*I really don't want to go into this. Ask Jas.*)

5. **open mouth kissing**

6. **tongues**

$6 1/2$. **ear snogging**

$6 3/4$. **neck nuzzling**

7. **upper body fondling - outdoors**

8. **upper body fondling - indoors**

Virtual number 8. (*When your upper body is not actually being fondled in reality, but you know that it is in your snoggees head.*)

9. **below waist activity** (*or bwa. Apparently this can include flashing your pants. Don't blame me. Ask Jools.*)

10. **the full monty** (*Jas and I were in the room when Dad was watching the news and the newscaster said, "Tonight the Prime Minister has reached Number 10." And Jas and I had a laughing spaz to end all laughing spazzes.*)

Georgia's Glossary

arvie · Afternoon. From the Latin "arvo". Possibly. As in the famous Latin invitation: "Lettus meetus this arvo."

billio · From the Australian outback. A billycan was something Aborigines boiled their goolies up in, or whatever it is they eat. Anyway, billio means boiling things up. Therefore, "my cheeks ached like billio" means – er – very achy. I don't know why we say it. It's a mystery, like many things. But that's the beauty of life.

Black Death · Ah well... this is historiosity at its best. In Merrie England, everyone was having a fab time, dancing about with bells on (also known as Maurice dancing), then some ships arrived in London, full of new stuff – tobacco, sugar, chocolate, etc., yum yum. However, as in all tales in history, it ended badly, because also lurking about on the ships were rats from Europe – not human ones. And they had fleas on them that carried the plague. The fleas bit the people of Merrie England, and they got covered in pustulating boils and died. A LOT. As I have said many many times, history is crap.

Blimey O'Reilly · (as in "Blimey O'Reilly's trousers") This is an Irish expression of disbelief and shock. Maybe Blimey O'Reilly was a famous Irish bloke who had extravagantly big trousers. We may never know the truth. The fact is, whoever he is, what you need to know is that a) it's Irish and b) it is Irish. I rest my case.

blodge · Biology. Like geoggers – geography, or Froggie – French.

Boboland · As I have explained many, many times English is a lovely and exciting language full of sophisticosity. To go to sleep is "to go to bobos", so if you go to bed you are going to Boboland. It is an Elizabethan expression... Oh, OK then, Libby made it up and she can be unreasonably violent if you don't join in with her.

brillopads · A brillopad is a sort of wire pad that you clean pans and stuff with (If you do housework, which I sincerely suggest you don't. I got ironer's elbow from being made to iron my vati's huge undercrackers.) Where was I? Oh yes. When you say "It was brillopads" you don't mean "It was a sort of wire pad that you clean with", you mean "It was fab and groovy." Do you see? Goodnight.

bum-oley · Quite literally "bottom hole". I'm sorry but you did ask. Say it proudly (with a cheery smile and a Spanish accent).

chuddie · Chewing gum. This is an "i" word thing. We have a lot of them in English due to our very busy lives, explaining stuff to other people not so fortunate as ourselves.

clown car · Officially called a Reliant Robin three-wheeler, but clearly a car built for clowns by some absolute loser called Robin. The Reliant bit comes from being able to rely on Robin being a prat. I wouldn't be surprised if Robin also invented nostril-hair cutters.

clud · This is short for cloud. Lots of really long boring poems and so on can be made much snappier by abbreviating words. So Wordworth's poem called "Daffodils" (or "Daffs") has the immortal line "I wandered lonely as a clud". Ditto *Rom and Jule*. Or *Ham*. Or *Merc of Ven*.

double cool with knobs · "Double" and "with knobs" are instead of saying very or very, very, very, very. You'd feel silly saying, "He was very, very, very, very, very cool." Also everyone would have fallen asleep before you had finished your sentence. So "double cool with knobs" is altogether snappier.

Eccles cake · A culinary delight from the north of England. Essentially they look like little packets of dead flies, yum yum. Lots of yummy things come from the north of England: cow heel and tripe (a cow's stomach lining with vinegar). And most delicious of all, cow's nip nip (yes I am serious). What you have to remember is that the northern folk are descended from Vikings and, frankly, when you have been rowing a boat for about three months, you will eat anything.

fandango · A fandango is a complicated Spanish dance. So a fandango is a complicated thing. Yes, I know there is no dancing involved. Or Spanish.

full-frontal snogging · Kissing with all the trimmings – lip to lip, open mouth, tongues... everything (apart from dribble, which is never acceptable).

f.t. · I refer you to the famous "losing it" scale:
      1. minor tizz

2. complete tizz and to-do
3. strop
4. a visit to Stop Central
5. f.t. (funny turn)
6. spaz attack
7. complete ditherspaz
8. nervy b. (nervous breakdown)
9. complete nervy b.
10. ballisiticisimus

gadzooks · An expression of surprise. Like for instance, "Cor, love a duck!" Which doesn't mean you love ducks or want to marry one. For the swotty knickers among you, "gad" probably meant "God" in olde English and "zooks" of course means... Oh, look, just leave me alone, OK? I'm so vair tired.

goosegog · Gooseberry. I know you are looking all quizzical now. OK. If there are two people and they want to snog and you keep hanging about saying, "Do you fancy some chewing gum?" or "Have you seen my interesting new socks?" you are a gooseberry. Or for short, a goosegog, i.e. someone who nobody wants around.

gorgey · Gorgeous. Like fabby (fabulous) and marvy (marvellous).

Hoooorn · When you "have the Horn" it's the same as "having the big red bottom".

in vino hairy arse · This is a Latin joke and therefore vair vair funny. The Latin term is "*in vino veritas*" which means "truth in wine". That is, when you are drunk you tell the truth. So do you see what I've done??? Do you? Instead of "veritas" I say "hairy arse". Sometimes I exhaust myself with my amusingnosity.

Jammy Dodger · Biscuit with jam in it. Very nutritious(ish).

jimjams · Pyjamas. Also pygmies or jammies.

Midget Gem · Little sweets made out of hard jelly stuff in different flavours. Jas loves them A LOT. She secretes them about her person, I suspect, often in her panties, so I never like to accept one from her on hygiene and lesbian grounds.

Mystic Meg · A mad woman in a headscarf and massive earrings who can predict the future. And probably lives in a treehouse. A bit like Jas really. Except that Jas hasn't got a headscarf or earrings. And can't tell the future. Apart from that (and the fact that Mystic Meg is a hundred) they are quite literally like identical twins.

nippy noodles · Instead of saying "Good heavens, it's quite cold this morning," you say "Cor, nippy noodles!!" English is an exciting and growing language. It is. Believe me. Just leave it at that. Accept it.

nuddy-pants · Quite literally nude-coloured pants, and you know what nude-coloured pants are? They are no pants. So if you are in your nuddy-pants you are in your no pants, i.e. you are naked.

nunga-nungas · Basoomas. Girls breasty business. Ellen's brother calls them nunga-nungas because he says that if you get hold a girl's breast and pull it out and then let it go, it goes nunga-nunga-nunga. As I have said many, many times with great wisdomosity, there is something really wrong with boys.

Pantalitzer doll · A terrifying Czech-made doll that sadistic parents (my vati) buy for their children, presumably to teach them early on about the horror of life.

Pizza-a-gogo land · Masimoland. Land of wine, sun, olives and vair vair groovy Luuurve Gods. Italy. The only bad point about Pizza-a-gogo land is their football players are so vain that if it rains, they all run off the pitch so that their hair doesn't get ruined.

red-bottomosity · Having the big red bottom. This is vair vair interesting *via-à-vis* nature. When a lady baboon is "in the mood" for luuurve, she displays her big red bottom to the male baboon. (Apparently he wouldn't have a clue otherwise, but that is boys for you!!) Anyway, if you hear the call of the Horn, you are said to be displaying red-bottomosity.

Rolf Harris · An Australian "entertainer" (not). Rolf has a huge beard and glasses. He plays a didgeridoo, which says everything in my book. He sadly has had a number of hit records, which means he is never off TV and will not go back to Australia. (His "records" are called "Tie Me Kangaroo Down, Sport," etc.)

spangleferkel · A kind of German sausage. I know. You couldn't make it up, could you? The German language is full of this kind thing, like *lederhosen and* so on. And *goosegot*.

spoon · A spoon is a person who is so dim and sad that they cannot be allowed to use anything sharp. That means they can only use a spoon. The Blunder Boys are without exception all spoons.

Spotty Dick · This is an olde English pudding named after an Elizabethan bloke called Dick. Which is nice. However, Dick was not blessed in the complexion department and was covered in boils and spots. Anyway, in honour of Dick's spots a pudding was made up that had currants all over it to represent the spots. Think how pleased Dick must have been with ye olde Elizabethan folke leaning out of their windows as he passed and shouting, "Oy, Spotty Dick, we've just eaten your head... with some custard."

squid · Squid is the plural of quid and I do know why that is. A bloke owed another bloke six pounds or six quid, and he goes up to him with an octopus with one of its tentacles bandaged up, and he says, "Hello mate, here is the sick squid I owe you." Do you see? Do you see?? Sick squid, six quid??? The marvellous juxtaposition of... look, we just call pounds squids. Leave it at that. Try and get on with it, people.

tuckered out · As anyone who has bothered to read historiosity will know, this comes from Friar Tuck, Robin Hood's big fat baldy mate. He was so fat and baldy that if he moved or danced and so on, he would have to lie down for a little zizz. Hence the expression "tuckered out".

vino tinto · Now this is your actual Pizza-a-gogo talk. It quite literally means "tinted wine". In this case the wine is tinted red.

welligogs · Wellington boots. Because it more or less rains all the time in England, we have special rubber boots that we wear to keep us above the mud. This is true.

LEO VARADKAR – A VERY MODERN TAOISEACH

PHILIP RYAN AND
NIALL O'CONNOR

Biteback Publishing

First published in Great Britain in 2018 by
Biteback Publishing Ltd
Westminster Tower
3 Albert Embankment
London SE1 7SP
Copyright © Philip Ryan and Niall O'Connor 2018

ISBN 978-1-78590-370-0

10 9 8 7 6 5 4 3 2 1

A CIP catalogue record for this book is available from the British Library.

Set in Adobe Caslon Pro and Futura

Printed and bound in Great Britain by
CPI Group (UK) Ltd, Croydon CR0 4YY

For our parents, Liz and Brendan Ryan, Carmel O'Connor, and especially the late Brendan O'Connor, who was proof that all things are possible to those who believe.

CONTENTS

PROLOGUE

'What have we done, what have we fucking done?' Leo Varadkar disbelievingly asked one of his closest advisers.

'You've done it, you've fucking done it, you're going to be Taoiseach,' a beaming Philip O'Callaghan responded.

'Fucking hell,' Varadkar added in a state of shock.

It was 2 June 2017 and Varadkar was sitting in the drawing room of the Mansion House on Dawson Street in Dublin city centre. Outside the door of the room, hundreds of Fine Gael supporters were anxiously waiting for their new leader to take to the stage. The Fine Gael leadership contest was a competition he had been expected to win comfortably. But that didn't make the victory any less surreal.

As he prepared to address his party, Varadkar considered how far he had come. Indeed, how far Ireland had come. After ten years serving as a national politician, he was now to become the leader of the country – the same country his Indian-born father had decided to make his home more than four decades earlier. A country steeped in Catholic tradition that had welcomed Leo Varadkar with open arms when he became the first Cabinet minister to publicly declare he was gay. Within months of coming out, Varadkar had been emboldened further by an emphatic referendum victory for LGBT rights, which had paved the way for same-sex marriage in Ireland. This small island country had come on a long journey, and Varadkar was more than just a passenger on the trip.

Thirty minutes earlier, Varadkar and his team had marched triumphantly through the television cameras and photographers into the Mansion House, where he was greeted by rapturous applause from supporters. Without a second's thought, he embraced Minister for Housing Simon Coveney, whom he had convincingly defeated to become leader of Fine Gael. Coveney could not have had any complaints about coming second. He had been outmanoeuvred at virtually every turn by an opponent who was obsessed with becoming Taoiseach.

Varadkar personally thanked his closest supporters before he was hoisted above their shoulders among a sea of placards bearing his name. Once returned to the ground, he sought out his father Ashok, mother Miriam and sister Sophie. Then he turned to his partner Matthew Barrett and they embraced as the camera flashes lit up the auditorium. Varadkar wanted to share his victory with those who meant most to him.

Soon after making his grand entrance, he was whisked away into the drawing room, where he took calls from international dignitaries who wished him well in his new job. He took a few moments to gather himself, a few deep breaths. He would have to wait a couple of weeks before he was formally appointed Taoiseach. For now, he had to address his party.

Standing on the podium in the Mansion House's Round Room, Varadkar said, 'If my election shows anything, it's that prejudice has no hold in this Republic.' He continued:

Around the world people look to Ireland to be reminded

that this is a country where it doesn't matter where you come from, but rather where you want to go. I know when my father travelled 5,000 miles to build a new home in Ireland, I doubt he ever dreamed that his son would one day grow up to be its leader. And that despite his difference his son would be treated the same and judged by his actions and character, not his origins or identity. And so every proud parent in Ireland today can dream big dreams for their children. Every boy and girl can know that there is no limit to their ambition, to their possibilities, if they're given the opportunity.

Let that be our mission in Fine Gael, to build in Ireland a republic of opportunity, one in which every individual has the opportunity to realise their potential and every part of the country is given its opportunity to share in our prosperity.

Varadkar's path to this point of his career was no accident. His accession to the highest office in the state was executed carefully and methodically. He shook off the taunts of schoolyard bullies and overcame the nagging feeling of being an outsider to become a poll-topping politician. He also fought hard to win over colleagues who considered him too erratic and aloof to lead the country's largest political party.

However, he also made enemies along the way. Internal party rows over policy and strategy did not endear him to everyone. Politicians and backroom advisers he had clashed with would be looking on with keen interest as Varadkar was handed the reins of government. The minister who 'knew best' would now have to prove that, in fact, he did. There would be no more hiding behind others. The buck stopped with him.

Varadkar's appointment as leader of Fine Gael and, ultimately, Taoiseach was met with nervous caution across Irish society. For years, he had been painted as representing the right-wing heart of Fine Gael; a politician desperate to force his conservative views on an increasingly liberal country. He had carved out a niche in his early years by tapping into Fine Gael's traditional voter base. He was anti-abortion, had reservations about same-sex marriage and pushed a low-tax agenda. Opposition politicians branded him a 'Tory boy' in reference to the UK's Conservative Party. They also drew comparisons between Varadkar and America's ultra-conservative Tea Party.

All this was before he was given the keys to the exchequer. The outspoken minister who had regularly criticised his own government was now in charge. And the young boy who had always felt like an outsider in his youth was now very much on the inside.

CHAPTER 1

ASHOK MEETS MIRIAM

Standing out among eight other siblings was never going to be easy for Ashok Varadkar. He was the baby of the family and desperate for his parents to be as proud of him as they were of his brothers and sisters.

Upon completing secondary school, Ashok enrolled in Bombay's Grant Medical College, where he studied day and night to become the first doctor in the Varadkar family. After years of toil and graft, he passed his exams and took up employment at one of the local hospitals. But Ashok had itchy feet. He wanted a different life – the chance to explore the world before settling down to raise a family in Bombay.

In the 1960s, India was still adjusting to sovereignty, having freed itself from British colonial rule little more than a decade earlier. Even with the British gone, India was still an extremely divided society. Large swathes of the country were ravished by famine and poverty, while the ruling government was distracted by border wars with Pakistan and China.

Luckily for Ashok, his medical degree was a passport and a visa all rolled into one. It didn't take him long to save up enough money to pay for his escape route out of India and he set his sights on the far side of the world. In the local travel agent's, he booked a one-way ticket to Britain. Ashok returned to his parents' home to pack his bags for a journey that, unbeknown to him, would shape the political landscape of a small island country on the edge of Europe half a century later.

Ireland was not in Ashok's thoughts as he boarded the plane. In fact, neither was Britain, really. The young doctor's dream was to become a paediatrician in one of America's top hospitals. England was supposed to be just a stepping stone. The Indian government had introduced laws preventing doctors from emigrating to the US for better-paid jobs. The country was experiencing a significant brain drain at the time, due to the exodus of well-educated medics. Before the state intervened, doctors could sit US medical exams in India before moving on to take up lucrative roles in American hospitals. The new laws put an end to this, but Ashok was determined to reach the United States, regardless of what it would take. The gateway was Europe, where Indian doctors could still sit the exams and get around their government's clampdown.

Unlike the vast majority of emigrants in the twentieth century, money was not the driving force behind Ashok's decision to leave India. Similarly, he did not believe he was saying goodbye to his country for good. As is the case in most countries, doctors need to build up a wealth of international knowledge if they are to be considered for top consultancy jobs in their home states. Ashok therefore hoped that with a few years' experience in the US health system under his belt, he would one day settle back in India.

As he relaxed into that long-haul flight to Britain, Ashok must have thought back to the journey his family had made from their ancestral home in the small rural village of Varad, some 300 kilometres north of Bombay, on India's west coast.

Ashok's parents, Vithal and Rukmunia, had moved to Borivali in Bombay, which later became known as Mumbai, before he was born. But their roots were in the small rural village of Varad. Ashok's father earned a good living working for the Indian postal service, which ensured his family of four boys and five girls could all go to university if they so wished. The boys were Madhu, Manohar, Avi and Ashok, and their five sisters were Vinal, Kalyani, Prabha, Shanau and Meena.

The family considered themselves middle class by Indian standards. They had a comfortable living and could afford to hire servants and cleaners. It was a far cry from the conditions experienced by millions of their fellow Indians in the shanty towns spread across the country. However, Vithal and Rukmunia never forgot their humble roots in rural India and retired to the village before their youngest son had finished his education.

When Ashok's parents left for Varad, it fell to the family's eldest sibling Madhu to become the head of the household in Mumbai. Madhu, or Bhai (big brother), as he was known to his siblings, was a father figure to Ashok for most of his formative years. Madhu trained as a barrister and, as is normal with large Indian families, contributed financially towards the household budget once he was practising law. During his university years, he also became involved in the Indian independence movement. He was drawn by the energy of the civil unrest and protests aimed at ridding India of British rule.

Manohar, who is the second eldest of the Varadkar siblings, studied science in university and landed a plum job on India's atomic energy board. He too became enthralled by the spirit and courage of the freedom movement and joined his eldest brother on marches. Both men were very active during the uprising and neither was afraid to lead street demonstrations against the British. But, as a result of their involvement, the two brothers were arrested, and each spent a year in prison. They were considered political prisoners, and family members say they had few complaints about the conditions of their confinement or treatment at the hands of prison guards.

Vithal Varadkar was extremely proud of his two eldest sons, as were all the family. Risking life and freedom in pursuit of independence was looked upon with a great sense of pride by most Indian families. When India eventually broke free from the British Empire, both Madhu and Manohar were decorated for their efforts during the uprising. Their sister Prabha also played a role in the independence movement and marched in demonstrations against Portuguese colonialism in Goa.

Madhu is described by his family as a 'social reformer' who once served as the mayor of Varad. Another noteworthy relation is Manohar's daughter, Shubhada, Leo's first cousin, who is a renowned traditional dancer and television newsreader in India. Shubhada has travelled the world performing Odissi dancing and has inspired people with her story of overcoming a serious cancer scare to continue dancing.

But in the 1960s, Ashok was the only Varadkar sibling who had ambitions beyond Mumbai. The rest of the family were happy to settle and raise their families in India while they waited for him to return. It would be more than eight years before Ashok walked on Indian soil again. And when he did, he was not alone.

* * *

Almost 8,000 kilometres from Mumbai, in a rural market town in the south-east of Ireland, Miriam Howell was born in the late 1940s. Miriam was the daughter of Thomas and Monica (née Whelan), who made Dungarvan in County Waterford their home. She had two siblings, older brother John and younger sister Cora.

Thomas Howell was your typical grafter who tried his hand at several trades before dedicating himself to the land. He started off as a publican and also operated a small haulage business which would see him transport crops to and from the marts for local farmers. Eventually, he saved up enough money to purchase a few acres of land and began planting crops. Once the land started producing a decent living, Thomas closed down the other businesses and focused solely on the farm.

While he was working the land and providing for his family, Monica was in charge of the home, like most women in Ireland at the time. She cooked, cleaned and looked after the farm's accounts. She was front of house while Thomas handled the manual labour. The dynamic between the couple was one that would be shared by Miriam and her husband many years later.

The Howell family enjoyed life in their coastal home town overlooking the Celtic Sea. During the good weather, they spent time on the beach and mingled among the locals and tourists in the seafront shops along Dungarvan Harbour. A modest family, they enjoyed the simple things. Monica is now in her ninety-second year and lives in a nursing home. Thomas passed away in 2005. His death has had a lasting impact on both the Howell and Varadkar families.

As Minister for Transport, Leo Varadkar sometimes spoke about a tragic accident that influenced his views on road safety. When speaking about motoring legislation, Leo would make reference to the loss of a relative in a road accident. He never went into detail or discussed personal aspects of the tragic incident involving his grandfather. That incident, which provokes painful memories for the family, took place when Thomas was returning from a medical visit in nearby County Carlow. In early June 2005, the 82-year-old was given the all-clear by doctors after a short hospital stay. It was dark outside as the car reached Bagenalstown in the south of the county just before 10.45 p.m. Thomas was in the front passenger seat and Monica sat in the back while their son John drove his parents home. What happened next is something nobody can prepare for when they get behind the wheel of a car.

Leo's sister Sonia vividly remembers being told about the freak road traffic accident. 'He was on his way home after getting a full bill of health from the hospital and a horse jumped out on top of his car,' she says. 'My grandad was in the passenger's seat; my nanna was in the back and my uncle [John] was in the front driving and both of them walked away perfect,' she adds. The horse had been loose on the road for some time before it came into contact with the Howell family's car. When the car approached, the animal panicked and jumped on the bonnet of the vehicle. The resulting crash saw the rear-view mirror come loose and hit Thomas in the head. Leo's grandfather was among six people who died over what the media dubbed 'a weekend of road carnage'. The untimely and tragic nature of Thomas's death was very difficult for his family. Leo used the painful experience to better his understanding of the trauma felt by relatives of those killed on the road.

Several decades earlier, Thomas's daughter Miriam, then just eighteen, decided to leave Dungarvan to pursue a physiotherapy career in Dublin. She packed some belongings into a suitcase and said goodbye to her parents and siblings before getting the train to the capital. Miriam enrolled in a course at Trinity College, where she made good friends. But she did not take to the training. She stuck it out for a year before deciding to change direction and applied for a nursing course in the UK.

In February 1967, Miriam once again said goodbye to her family and boarded a ferry bound for England. Emigrating was a way of life in 1960s Ireland – a place where job opportunities for people like Miriam were hard to come by. Young men and women regularly made the short journey across the Irish Sea in search of a better life. There was plenty of construction work for men, and British hospitals were crying out for nurses. By the 1970s, almost 12 per cent of all nurses in British hospitals were Irish women.

Miriam took up a position in Wexham Park Hospital in Slough, just 35 kilometres from the centre of London. Not long after she started working, she met a handsome doctor from India who was eight years her senior. Miriam's daughter Sonia says her mother regularly recounts how she first met her future husband in a busy accident and emergency ward as they both tended to a severely ill child. 'Mum talks about this all the time. She would have seen him in the distance but met him properly in casualty. There was a very sick kid because Dad was a paediatrician and they had to transfer the little child from casualty up to the wards and that's how they met,' Sonia says.

Ashok and Miriam soon started dating and romance blossomed in between shifts at the busy town centre hospital. Three years later, the couple were married in a Catholic ceremony in St Peter's Church in Maidenhead, just outside London. Coincidently, the church is in Prime Minister Theresa May's constituency and is well-known to the Conservative Party leader. Little did the Varadkars know that one day in the distant future their only son would be working closely with the head of the British government. At the time, Ashok considered himself a supporter of the UK Labour Party, which was then led by Harold Wilson.

Not long after the wedding, the young couple moved to

London, where Ashok continued to work as a paediatrician. In 1971, Ashok and Miriam welcomed their first child, Sophie, into the world. Miriam didn't have a family network in England, so she stayed at home and looked after her daughter while Ashok pursued his career in medicine.

Ashok and Miriam were deeply in love. They had settled well in London, where their daughter Sophie was growing up. But something just wasn't right for the newlyweds. They were homesick and both longed to return to their families. But would Miriam, a young girl from a rural Irish town, be prepared to drop everything and make the 9,000-kilometre trip to India?

CHAPTER 2

BEING AN OUTSIDER

ife had been good in England for the Varadkar family. But the desire to return to India proved too strong for Ashok. He pined for his home country. He missed his family and friends. But, above all, he wanted to show off his new Irish bride and daughter. In 1973, following some long discussions, Ashok convinced Miriam to leave Europe behind and travel with him to India, with a view to starting a new life.

Work was easy to come by for a doctor of Ashok's experience and he soon landed a position with one of the big hospital groups in Mumbai. But Miriam was still in her early twenties. For a young Irish woman, trying to settle in India was a difficult task. She was thousands of miles away from her family and living in a country with a culture that was alien compared to what she was used to growing up. As the Varadkar family tell it, everything was done to help Miriam become accustomed to her new life in India. 'They were very well looked after by all their Indian friends, but Mum was very young so found it difficult,' her daughter Sonia says.

The sense of homesickness coupled with the struggle to get used to the Indian culture soon prompted Ashok and

Miriam to make a judgement call. Miriam's mother Monica managed to source a job for Ashok in Ireland and convinced him to bring her daughter and granddaughter home. Ashok wanted the best for his family so, for the second time, he said goodbye to his brothers and sisters and boarded a jet bound for the west. Following their arrival in Ireland, the Varadkars rented a house in Templeogue in South Dublin before moving to Blanchardstown in the north-west of the capital. Ashok was never short of employment. He worked as a paediatrician in a number of hospitals including Our Lady of Lourdes in Louth, the National Children's Hospital and the Rotunda Maternity Hospital in Dublin.

In 1975, Miriam gave birth to their second daughter, Sonia. Four years later, on 18 January 1979, Leo was born in the Rotunda Hospital. Sonia describes her little brother as a 'perfect baby' who was obsessed over by his mother and sisters. 'Leo was such a gorgeous kid. He never cried. He didn't have to because we doted on him totally and utterly,' she says. However, the future Taoiseach did have one method for getting the attention of his sisters. 'In his cot was a little yellow chicken and whenever he wanted something, instead of crying, he used to shake it and we would all come running,' Sonia remembers.

In an interview with the *Sunday Independent*, Ashok said he was 'very excited' when his only son was born. Miriam noted in the same interview that 'when he cried, his two sisters would cry'. Ashok added, 'They used to make him cry sometimes by singing "Where's your mama gone?" [from a song made popular by Scottish band Middle of the Road in the 1970s].'

As small children, Leo and Sonia shared a bedroom. Sonia, despite being the elder of the pair, would insist on her younger brother reading Enid Blyton and Roald Dahl stories to her before they went to sleep each night. Leo, who was a keen reader from an early age, would duly oblige. 'Leo always used to read to me. It was wonderful. I'm so lazy, so Leo used to read books to me every night,' she says.

Growing up just four years apart, Leo and Sonia share many similar traits. Both are direct and inquisitive by nature but awkward in new company. However, they could also be very different. As a child, Sonia was adventurous and mischievous, while Leo was serious and studious, even a bit of a smart alec at times. 'My memories growing up would have been of the Eurovision Song Contest – me dancing and singing while Leo sat there drawing his flags and writing his countries and their politics, the whole lot,' Sonia recalls.

Once they bought their first house in Blanchardstown, the Varadkar family home doubled up as a GP surgery. Ashok struggled to gain a consultant position in the Irish hospital system and decided to try his hand at general practice. With Miriam working as the practice manager and nurse, they converted the garage of their first home into a surgery. In an interview for this book, Leo remembers how his mother handled the business side of the operation while his father tended to the patients. 'Mum really kind of ran the show. A nurse by training so she was the practice nurse, accountant and receptionist,' he says. The entire house was taken over by the practice: the garage was the surgery, the sitting room was the waiting area and the kitchen was the office where Miriam would look after the books and accounts. 'You'd have patients coming to the front door and they would sit in our sitting room. The sitting room was the waiting room, which wasn't great in a lot of ways because we couldn't really watch TV,' Leo says.

Every now and then, the children would be asked to help out in the office or with cleaning the waiting room. Sophie, Leo's eldest sister, whom he called his 'little mother' as a child, often accompanied Ashok on house calls and was rewarded with £5 for her efforts. As she grew older, Sonia would help out with the kitchen duties when her mother was busy with the practice. 'We'd all come home and Mum would be working so I'd make the dinner and if she was in with Dad I'd answer the door. Leo would be doing his homework on the kitchen table while all this was going on. It was just part of opening a business,' Sonia remembers.

Mealtime was important in the Varadkar household and Miriam insisted the family dine together. When dinner time arrived, she would stick her head out the front door and call in her children, who were playing with friends in the housing estate. Leo and his sisters would instantly stop what they were doing, say their goodbyes and trundle home. It was an important family tradition that ensured problems were shared and allowed otherwise busy parents to find out what was going on in their children's lives. Sonia says:

> You'd know if everyone was OK, if everyone is in a happy place, or if something is annoying somebody you'd spot it across the table and you'd chat about that. We talked about everything that was going on in school and everything that was going on on the road and everything else.

Leo wasn't always as forthcoming as his sisters when it came to opening up. One evening, when he was at secondary school, he shocked his family when he told them he had almost drowned two weeks earlier in a canoeing accident. The school had organised for students to be given canoeing lessons in the school's swimming pool. Leo's canoe capsized during the lesson and he had to be rescued by a lifeguard. It was a minor incident and there was no need for the emergency services to be called. But he didn't tell his family about the potentially serious mishap until weeks after the event. While the family were slightly panicked by the idea of Leo struggling underwater, they were more concerned that he had only thought to tell them a fortnight later.

When Leo was ten years old, the family moved to a bigger house in Blanchardstown. Ashok's patient list was growing all the time and he decided to build a GP surgery as an extension to the house. Things got busier in the Varadkar household, but the children now had a room where they could watch TV and play with friends.

Leo was enrolled in St Francis Xavier primary school in Blanchardstown, where former classmates remember him showing a keen interest in politics. 'Leo was always a bit different. He was always a bit more developed in his intellect than your standard kid would have been,' recalls schoolfriend Andy Garvey, adding:

> He was often top of the class, spelling-wise and all that type of stuff, and his interests would have been different to other kids. Very few kids in primary school would say they want to be Minister for Health when asked what they would want to do when they grow up.

Leo's mother also remembers her son telling a local shop owner that he hoped to serve in one of the most difficult roles in politics. 'He said he wanted to be Minister for Health and it was very embarrassing as I think he was only about seven or eight. I was actually shocked,' she told RTÉ.

In primary school and on the cul-de-sac where the family lived, Leo and his sisters stood out. As children of an Indian father and Irish mother, they looked different from the other kids. They also had an unusual surname. Leo's complexion was darker than that of his sisters, who took after their mother. He was also quite tall for his age and slightly overweight.

In the 1980s, Ireland was still considered a developing country by international standards and was never the destination of choice for migrants coming from Africa, Asia or even Eastern Europe. The country was also ravaged by an economic recession. Unemployment soared and young Irish people emigrated in their thousands. People didn't want to come to Ireland. Even the tourism sector struggled due to the violent unrest in Northern Ireland. It was only when the economy bounced back in the mid- to late '90s that Ireland started to become a multicultural society. For much of Leo's childhood, it was unusual to see people from other countries in Ireland, let alone from India. However, racism and discrimination were never problems for the Varadkar family. They felt at home in West Dublin and struck up strong friendships with their neighbours. The children mixed well with their peers, and life was very ordinary and simple. From an early age, though, Leo did realise he was different from the other children and, at times, felt like an outsider. 'Through primary school or secondary school, I always knew I was different. No matter what, you're the guy with the funny surname and you look different,' he says. I was always aware I was different and as a kid you just want to fit in. So I wasn't particularly interested in my Indian background or being half Indian or anything like that because I just wanted to fit in and be like the other kids.'

The Varadkars were popular in the community and patients would have met the children when they attended appointments in the surgery. Most of Leo's friends and neighbours were his father's patients. 'It would be wrong to say I was subjected to any horrible racism or anything because I really wasn't and when you are the local GP's kid it probably is a different experience than suddenly arriving from Syria or something,' Leo says.

But definitely it was different. Even though I was brought up Catholic, I was aware that my dad wasn't and that there would be other religions. I did my confirmation, communion. I didn't particularly go to mass. Occasionally, but not regularly. But at that time, everybody went to mass. And you'd be in the primary school and the teacher would be talking about what the priest said at mass and I wouldn't have a clue because I wasn't there.

To a certain extent, Leo neglected his Indian heritage as an attempt to fit in. He took Hindi lessons as a teenager but for the most part he did not relate to his father's culture.

In politics, his background has never been used against him in the heat of political debate. If anything, his unusual name along with his tall, dark and handsome looks have helped him stand out among the crowd when he was campaigning for office. But that is not to say he never suffered abuse or bullying over his Indian ancestral roots. In most primary and secondary schools in Ireland during the '80s, a mixed-race child would have been the subject of schoolyard taunts and insults. Leo can recall three specific episodes of being targeted by bullies because of his background. While it was not commonplace, the incidents have left a lasting impression on him to this day. 'It happened so rarely that I can only remember the two or three occasions. But the fact I can remember them speaks for itself,' he says, adding that one of those incidents involved a teacher and the others involved schoolmates. Leo is reluctant to discuss the racist slur thrown at him by a person who was supposed to be shaping his educational outlook. He even goes as far as to blame himself for the teacher's comments. 'I'd prefer not to go into the language because he was not a bad guy at all actually. I think I was misbehaving, acting the pup in class,' he says. The incident clearly left a lasting impact on the future Taoiseach and is one of very few topics he is unwilling to discuss further.

Most of Leo's friends and family say he was noticeably more advanced than most of his peers throughout primary and secondary school. His interests lay beyond the schoolyard and perhaps his intellect allowed him to brush off any sneering or jeering. He was far from being one of the popular children in school and behind his imposing frame he was awkward and shy as an adolescent. His height meant he towered over most of his classmates, but that didn't give him added confidence. He was not built for team sports despite his big frame and preferred the study hall over the playing field. Ashok made him play cricket – a sport hugely popular in India – but Leo hated it and played only to keep his father happy.

Despite his somewhat nerd-like credentials (he was also a big *Star Trek* fan), he was not a complete loner and had a small but loyal group of friends. 'I was never kind of popular, either in primary school or secondary school. I was never one of the cool kids or whatever, but I always had friends,' he says.

There was an expectation in the Varadkar household that the children would work hard academically and other activities should play second fiddle. 'Definitely the expectation was around studying hard and being top of the class. It wouldn't have been getting on the rugby team,' Leo says. When it came to his studies, Leo was very competitive with his eldest sister Sophie and always wanted to achieve higher grades. Miriam was keen for Sophie to follow in her father's footsteps and become a doctor. She tried to enrol her daughter in the local secondary school, only to learn the all-girls school did not teach science, which was a requirement for entering medical college.

'My mum was very keen to have Sophie grow up to be a doctor. She went to see the head nun before she was going to secondary school, and the school, which was an all-girls school, couldn't offer physics and chemistry,' Leo says. 'The head nun suggested to my mum that instead of Sophie becoming a doctor perhaps she should write children's stories because she is very good at writing stories,' he adds. Miriam was 'having none of this', according to Leo, and decided to look elsewhere.

One of her friends was sending her children to King's Hospital boarding school in Palmerstown, which was just a few kilometres away from the Varadkar home in Castleknock. There were closer schools, but Miriam wanted her daughter to have the best education the family could afford. Sophie and, later, Leo both attended the school as day students. Sophie went on to become a doctor but never took over the family practice. Instead, she became a consultant paediatrician and moved to London, where she now works in the internationally renowned Great Ormond Street Hospital. Sonia, meanwhile, went to the all-girls Mount Sackville Secondary School before going on to become a midwife.

Miriam raised her children as Catholics, so sending two of them to King's Hospital, which was a Protestant school, presented somewhat of a religious quagmire. Leo and his sisters had both made their Holy Communion and confirmation in the local church. But, as was generally the case in the Varadkar household, medicine won out over faith.

The Varadkars worked hard for their money, and education was a top priority when it came to the household budget. The school fees would have been less when a young Leo enrolled but currently King's Hospital charges €7,190 per year for day students.

Leo was not overly pleased when he learned he was going to King's Hospital. All of his friends from primary school and a lot of his pals from his neighbourhood were attending Coolmine

Community School in Blanchardstown. 'If I had been left up to my own devices, I would have just gone to the same school as them,' Leo says.

Making friends proved difficult for Leo in his new environment. He struggled to engage with other children his own age and becoming an adolescent brought its own problems. He freely admits he was never confident as a teenager or even into his twenties. 'I was never trying particularly to be one of the lads. I wasn't of that personality anyway. Definitely in school I would have been much more shy and reserved,' he remembers.

But what he lacked in interpersonal skills he made up for in his studies and exam results. He was always at the top of his class academically and was not afraid to quiz his teachers. He goes as far as describing himself as a 'swot' and even a bit of a 'smartarse' when it came to questioning teachers during tutorials. Getting lippy occasionally landed him in trouble. But his biggest offence during his schooldays was bringing fireworks, which he had bought in Northern Ireland, into King's Hospital to sell to his classmates. The would-be border smuggler was caught red-handed and his paraphernalia was confiscated by a teacher.

Overall, though, he was far from a troublemaker and generally kept his head down and got on with his studies. 'I was never actually expelled or suspended or anything like that. I insulted a teacher or that sort of thing but never anything huge. Definitely, around fifth or sixth year, I started making more friends and would have gone to nightclubs, underage drinking, that sort of thing,' he says. Leo's height and frame made him look a lot older than he was and helped him convince bouncers outside the Vortex nightclub in Dunshaughlin, Co. Meath, to admit him on occasion.

By his third year of secondary school in King's Hospital,

Leo had become restless. He was eager to finish up his second-level education and begin university. At the time, most students could complete their secondary school education in five years but in King's Hospital there was an additional 'transition year'. Transition year is an optional period between the two main secondary school exams – the Junior Cert and Leaving Cert. It is aimed at giving students practical experience before entering their final two years of schooling. Leo pleaded with his parents to let him move school so he could avoid the additional year. He had his sights set on the Institute of Education on Leeson Street in the city centre. 'Leo would have been eighteen doing his Leaving Cert and he never wanted to do transition year, ever,' Sonia says. 'He hated the thought of it and he said it was the worst year of his life – the year he learned not to study.'

Transition year might have seemed like as an unnecessary waste of time for young Leo, but it was during this school term that he met an ally who would feature prominently throughout his career in politics. Frances Fitzgerald was a Fine Gael TD (Teachta Dála, a Member of Parliament) for the Dublin South East constituency at the time. Fitzgerald was a former social worker who became chair of the National Women's Council before entering national politics. Through a family connection, Leo sought out a week's work experience with Fitzgerald as part of his transition year training. 'There's some weird courses of interaction with Frances over the years,' Leo says.

My parents were friends with her and her husband Michael. And I knew her sons. We've known each other for a long time even though we rarely were politically close. We were personally close at a lot of points in time. I did a week in Leinster House with her. At that time, she was an opposition TD. She was the wrong side of John Bruton at the time. He was the Taoiseach and she had been at the wrong side of that heave. Then I did a week with Susan Denham in the Judge's Library. Susan's husband Brian is a paediatrician and he knew my dad.

Then a justice of the Supreme Court, Susan Denham would go on to become Ireland's first female Chief Justice, while Frances Fitzgerald would serve as Tánaiste under Leo Varadkar and also as Minister for Justice under his predecessor, Enda Kenny.

Fitzgerald also remembers meeting a 'very committed' Leo Varadkar when she took him on for a week's work experience. 'What struck me then, first of all and it's still the case, is that he's always been a very committed political activist since he was very young,' Fitzgerald says. 'He's had a huge interest in politics, in policy, in ideas and he's been like that from very young. The other thing that struck me about him ... is that he was very intelligent in his approach to things,' she adds.

Leo's educational achievements are noted in two separate locations in King's Hospital. A framed picture of him hangs alongside other notable past pupils, who went on to become academics and scientists. His name is also etched into a large decorative wooden board in the school's dining hall in recognition of his final-year Leaving Certificate results.

Over dinner, while watching television or during long family drives, Miriam, Ashok and the children always discussed medicine. It could be interesting cases, the latest innovations or plans to improve the practice. Naturally, having worked long and hard to establish their business, Leo's parents hoped one of their offspring would one day take over. By the time Leo was about to enter university, his two sisters were pursuing medical careers. Neither of the Varadkar daughters was interested in general practice, so the focus shifted to Leo.

There are conflicting views in the family about what pressure was put on the Varadkars' only son once he finished secondary school. In an interview during the 2017 Fine Gael leadership campaign, Miriam cast doubt over whether she and her husband had pushed their son into medicine. 'It's very difficult in a house when there's nothing else spoken about but medicine so maybe we did,' she told RTÉ. Ashok said Leo's decision to take up medicine 'came natural to him' because his father was a GP and his eldest sister had also studied to become a doctor in university. 'It was natural, we didn't force him into anything,' he added.

Leo, however, insisted his parents, especially his mother, wanted nothing more than for him to study medicine and take over the family business. 'By the time they retired, it was very well established,' Leo says of the practice. 'A well-remunerated position because they built it up for over thirty years. And certainly that's what they always wanted me to do,' he adds.

Leo's parents would have been equally happy if Sophie or Sonia had taken over the practice, however, as long as it stayed in the family. It was built from the ground up and a lot of the patients in the community had become reliant on the Varadkars for their medical needs. 'From their point of view, they put so much work into this practice and they would have liked to be able pass it on to one of their kids. Just like somebody would with a family business or family farm or whatever,' Leo says. 'I was never sat down and told "You must become a GP and take over this practice." But I kind of knew that's what they wanted, particularly my mum,' he adds.

But Leo's interests lay elsewhere.

From an early age he was inquisitive in nature. He liked to know how things worked, especially when it involved the arms of the state. Newspapers lay scattered across the coffee table in the waiting room surgery and, as a boy, Leo would often flick through the pages. International events and world affairs always piqued his interest, but so did the more mundane workings of Irish politics.

Debates on electoral systems are commonplace in university lecture halls or debating societies. They do not generally take place around the kitchen tables between twelve-year-old boys and their fathers. Yet this would be the scene on many nights after dinner in the Varadkar household. Leo would set out the argument for Ireland's single transferable vote system of proportional representation, while Ashok made the case for Britain's first-past-the-post regime.

Leo was fascinated by elections, and the kitchen-table debates fed his hunger for knowledge on politics and society. He had a sponge-like ability to soak up information, and bewildered some of his classmates when he would discuss political issues in the schoolyard. Leo thanks his father for his interest in politics. 'It probably does come from my dad. Because my dad is interested in politics, although he was never involved in it,' he says. 'We would definitely talk about politics at the dinner table. We would be discussing Mikhail Gorbachev and the Ayatollah Khomeini's war in Iran, Iraq, [former Taoiseach] Charlie Haughey and whatever else was happening in the news,' he adds.

While Ashok clearly influenced his political outlook, Leo says they are not particularly close. They would rarely embrace or exchange praise or compliments. It is part cultural and part personality. There are no personal grievances between Leo and his father; they get on fine. Rather, Leo puts it down to Ashok's traditional view of the father's role in a household. He says his father saw himself as the provider of the family. He worked hard, earned a good living and ensured his children wanted for nothing. Leo's emotional support came from his mother and sisters.

In an interview for this book, the Taoiseach speaks with remarkable candour about his relationship with his father. 'We're not particularly personally close. It's not that we don't get on or anything like that,' Leo says. 'But he's of that generation, he's in his late seventies. He wouldn't be the kind of modern father. Both his age and because of his Asian background he wouldn't be touchy-feely, give you a hug or say, "Well done son,"' he adds. However, there is a sense that Leo would like a stronger bond with his father.

Friday 2 June 2017 was one of the proudest days of Leo Varadkar's political career. Amid a sea of colourful campaign posters and cheering supporters, he was hoisted shoulder-high above the crowd as he was officially elected Fine Gael leader. After posing for the obligatory victory photograph, he was returned to the floor of the Round Room in Dublin city centre's Mansion House venue, where he embraced his mother, father and partner Matthew Barrett. But despite the emotion of the day and the sense of euphoria, Leo still felt awkward receiving his father's affection. 'It was a weird experience because when I was elected party leader in the Mansion House, he gave me a hug. I can count on one hand the amount of times that happened,' he said later.

There is also an undercurrent of opposing political ideologies between the two Varadkar men. During the Fine Gael leadership campaign, Ashok told *Irish Times* journalist Miriam Lord that he considered himself a socialist, to which his wife added, 'A champagne socialist.' In the same interview, he was asked what advice he would give his son as he prepared to become Taoiseach, and Ashok responded, 'I want him to look after the most vulnerable ... to work for those who need help. He shouldn't forget about those people.' He said his son's outlook had 'matured' since his early years in politics, which saw him criticised for his highly conservative, right-wing views.

While Leo's more socially conservative views have softened over time, his stance on economics still sits to the right of the political spectrum. He is quick to dismiss his father's left-wing credentials and insists Ashok is no more a socialist than he is. Rather, he says his father's views are lost in cultural translation. 'You've probably seen stuff where he describes himself as a socialist but that's total rubbish,' he says.

> Again that probably just comes from the Indian background, where seeking independence from Britain was a form of socialism. It's not that he believes in high taxes or generous welfare, quite the contrary. He's quite right-wing on those sort of things. Nor the nationalisation of the means of distribution of wealth or any of those sort of things.

However, Ron Elliott, a Varadkar supporter and former patient of Ashok's practice, says the two men are more similar than they realise. 'Whether Leo likes it or not, I think his father has had a huge influence on him. There are many traits they share. There are many things about Leo that I think he has inherited from his dad,' Elliott notes. 'His mannerisms. The way he [Ashok] would talk to you is very similar to the way Leo would talk to you. It's not condescending. It's speaking from a base of knowledge,' he adds.

Some of the apparent personal distance between Leo and his father may be down to Ashok's hard-working nature. Setting up a local GP practice takes a lot of work and there are very few days off. The Varadkar surgery was open six days per week from 9 a.m. to midday and then again from 4 p.m. until 7 p.m.

Once the practice closed for the evening, paperwork had to be filed. Ashok also did house calls and, because the practice was attached to the property, patients often called to the house after hours in times of emergency. It was non-stop. 'It might be late before they sat down so they were tired, and Dad might have gone out on house calls in the middle of the night. It was tough, tough days,' Sonia says. 'Even when Dad stopped doing the house calls at night, people would know, on a Sunday, if they are stuck just knock on the door and he'd see you,' she adds.

Overall, the Varadkars had a happy upbringing and are extremely grateful for the opportunities their parents' hard work afforded them. They are grounded in their outlook and do not give the impression of being driven by money. Always standing out from the crowd proved difficult for Leo, however, and at times he struggled with his ethnic identity.

But he would soon be forced to tackle a far greater personal challenge.

CHAPTER 3

POLITICS AND
MEDICINE

It was just weeks into the new academic term at Trinity College Dublin. Leo Varadkar stood awkwardly outside the university's arts building awaiting the start of a Young Fine Gael meeting. In his late teens and slightly overweight, Leo was dressed in a bright red jacket that he would wear throughout his early college days. Aloof and standoffish, Leo tried to strike up a conversation with his fellow freshers.

One of these students was Mark Finan, who would later become one of Leo's closest friends and confidantes. Like many others who met Leo early on during his college days, Finan recalls a student who was at best dull and at worst socially inept. 'He spoke, and he was so boring. There was no liveliness, no charm. Nothing,' Finan says.

Averil Power, who herself would go on to embark on a political career, tells of an individual who was extremely shy. 'He would have been quite quiet. He can be difficult to get to know. But anybody who knew him had a lot of time for him and could see he was a good guy.'

Also introduced to Leo was Lucinda Creighton. Like Leo, Creighton was socially conservative, deeply political and not afraid to speak her mind. She too would soon catch the attention of the Fine Gael talent spotters.

Finan, Creighton and Varadkar struck up a close friendship during their college days. Along with others, the trio bonded over history, debating and especially politics. They were your typical teenage nerds who quickly found that university, unlike secondary school, caters for all social groups.

According to Finan, Creighton and Varadkar were 'like the odd couple' and shared plenty of arguments and fallings out. 'They would be all friends one minute and not so friendly the next minute. That was the way in college,' Finan says. 'If you have two driven people, and they're both driven towards the same goal, they are going to unavoidably clash. But their clashes weren't policy-based, they were personality-based, I think.'

Friends of Leo and Lucinda say they quickly became feared within Young Fine Gael. They thrived on riling up their opponents during debates. Frank Flannery recalls Leo and Creighton as a lethal force for two politicians who were so young. 'There was a pair of them in it and they were quite potent.' Another close friend of the pair, John Paul Phelan, observes, 'They always had their work done and they gave off an air of invincibility.'

Averil Power says that while both individuals stood out from the crowd, Leo always had his eye on bigger things than just college politics. 'They were both very prominent, both of the same generation within Fine Gael. But, I would say, had totally different approaches and different interests.'

* * *

Leo Varadkar was already dabbling in politics before he entered Trinity. At just sixteen, he had attended his first Fine Gael meeting in the upstairs of Myo's bar in Castleknock full of ideas and gusto. But after a couple of hours listening to constituency bickering, Leo almost decided to give up on politics altogether. 'The first meeting was bloody awful. A boring branch meeting with forty people complaining about the days of the week,' Leo says. 'I didn't go back again. I only really got involved properly in college, which is completely different because it's people your own age.'

Leo had previously flirted with the idea of joining the Progressive Democrats (PDs), a small but effective centre-right party. But, in the end, he opted for Fine Gael, having been attracted to the leadership qualities of John Bruton. At the time, Fine Gael was the lead outfit in a rainbow coalition that also included the Labour Party and Democratic Left. Under Taoiseach Bruton and Labour Party Finance Minister Ruairi Quinn, the coalition managed to stabilise the public finances and produce carefully balanced budgets. Fine Gael was particularly focused on being seen as an economically prudent party. Bruton himself was pro-European and less nationalistic on the Northern Ireland question than his opponents in Fianna Fáil. All this appealed to young Leo's political outlook.

Unfortunately for Bruton, the majority of voters were not similarly impressed. In 1997, Fine Gael performed well in the general election; however, the party was outdone by Fianna Fáil, who convinced the electorate to return them to power. Fine Gael was forced to regroup and get used to life in opposition. But Leo now had his foot in the door of a political party and would soon be called to duty.

* * *

For Leo, Trinity College marked the period in his life when he could finally set himself free. For the first time, he was surrounded by academically driven individuals who, like him, had struggled socially in secondary school. He no longer had to pretend to be someone he wasn't. 'College was a liberation because I was meeting people very much like me for the first time,' Leo says. Classmates he tolerated, or despised, became a distant memory and were replaced by a new social circle of friends who shared his interests in politics and law.

Leo became heavily involved in the Trinity College branch of Young Fine Gael, which was headed for a period by Creighton. He was also elected to the Young Fine Gael national executive, where he served alongside the likes of Creighton, political commentator Elaine Byrne and the future head of the Fine Gael national executive Gerry O'Connell.

It wasn't long before Leo would dip his toe into national politics. Aged just twenty, he agreed to put his name forward for the local elections in the Mulhuddart ward in 1999. His potential had been spotted by Joanne Harmon, the party's then national youth officer. 'He was just different to most of his peers and stood out early on. He could talk for Ireland about Ireland and had a huge interest in Ireland's place in the world,' Harmon says. 'He was exceptionally bright and he wanted to get into politics for all the right reasons – he wanted to change the world. He never slacked. That appealed to me straight away and he didn't have any of the baggage of inheriting his politics or doing it because he was expected to for family reasons.'

Fine Gael knew that running Leo in the Mulhuddart ward was far from the ideal option. Firstly, he was a privileged, well-spoken son of a doctor who was being asked to put his name forward in one of the most working-class parts of Dublin. Leo was better placed to take a seat in Castleknock, where his family was based, but another candidate, Jane Murphy, had already been selected by Fine Gael to contest that ward. Murphy narrowly missed out on a council seat in a contest dominated by established councillors Joan Burton and Sheila Terry.

Leo, meanwhile, completely bombed in his first run at electoral politics. He polled a dismal 380 votes and was eliminated on the ninth count behind the Sinn Féin candidate Paul Donnelly. The election proved to be an eye-opener. Leo realised he had approached his first national contest with the wrong attitude. 'I wasn't coerced into running. I wanted to do it. Sure I knew everything,' Leo says sarcastically. 'Knock on doors and people would be overwhelmed by the brilliance of this twenty-year-old... but they weren't. I think I would have got elected in Castleknock. Even [if only] by virtue of my dad,' he admits.

Mulhuddart was at the time a stronghold for left-wing parties and an area where Fine Gael had no real base. Ron Elliott, who canvassed for Fine Gael in Mulhuddart during the election, says it was an area in which the party could not secure a breakthrough regardless of the candidate. 'Leo's vote was around Blanchardstown, around Castleknock. I called to doors up around the Mulhuddart area. It wasn't just "No". There was a sheer hostility towards me because I was Fine Gael,' Elliott remembers. 'And it was hostility not towards Leo but towards the party at the time.'

Despite the result, Leo had the experience of an election under his belt and was on the radar locally as an up-and-coming politician. 'He took his courage in his hand and he stood,' says Joan Burton.

I would say Leo is somebody who had political ambitions probably from the time he was twelve or fourteen. I would say more than that, he probably had ambitions to be

Taoiseach from that age or younger. In the way other kids wanted to be a fireman or a doctor, I'd say he wanted to be Taoiseach.

Fine Gael General Secretary Tom Curran rejects the suggestion that the party was wrong to field such a young and inexperienced candidate in a ward like Mulhuddart. He says the decision to run the likes of Leo was part of Fine Gael's strategy of rebuilding. 'With the 1999 local elections, it became very, very clear to us that we needed to establish a support base for young professional politicians who we believed could in the future make a major impact for Fine Gael,' Curran recalls. 'You can't measure success in terms of one election. Some people have taken several elections to get there; Leo was a case in point. I wouldn't think it was a mistake, I don't think so.'

Despite his defeat, Leo's willingness to run in Mulhuddart caught the eye of senior party bosses once again. Key strategist Frank Flannery notes, 'I thought he had balls for running. I immediately thought he was a very serious young fellow.' Another key strategist at the time, Phil Hogan, says Leo was rewarded for agreeing to bat for the party in difficult circumstances. 'It would not have been strong, fertile, political ground for Fine Gael at the time,' according to Hogan. 'He agreed to go, even though he was a student. That was appreciated at the time. Then he was in a better position in the following local elections to get – I suppose arising from the realignment of the election boundaries – to get more fertile Fine Gael voting ground.'

Leo's electoral failure sparked a similar reaction among his friends in college. He was admired for picking himself back up, dusting himself down and setting his sights on the next political challenge. 'It showed a lot of guts to put himself forward as a student,' remarks Averil Power. 'I know people would have advised him he hadn't a hope of winning. But that wasn't necessarily the plan. He was building a long-term future for himself and that's smart. You could already see those character traits people now associate with Leo were evident a long time ago.'

Leo quickly asserted himself and became a prominent figure in both Trinity College and Young Fine Gael. But it was the scale of his attacks on the Fianna Fáil-led government that both impressed and alarmed senior figures in his party. In September 2000, Leo led a Young Fine Gael delegation – dressed as chickens – to a protest outside the Dáil. The group generated plenty of media coverage as they goaded Taoiseach Bertie Ahern amid controversy over the withdrawal of his nominee to a top EU post. The Hugh O'Flaherty affair, as it became known, was causing considerable damage to the government. There was deep backbench unrest over Finance Minister Charlie McCreevy's attempt to fast-track the appointment of the former Supreme Court judge to the post of vice-president of the European Investment Bank (EIB).

The unrest stemmed from the decision by the judge to resign from the Supreme Court in 1999 after he came under pressure over his role in what was known as the Philip Sheedy affair. This case centred upon Dublin architect Philip Sheedy, who killed young mother Anne Ryan in a high-speed car crash while under the influence of alcohol. A report into the handling of the case was critical of O'Flaherty. Amid allegations of judicial interference in the case, he and another judge resigned. Failure to do so risked leading to impeachment proceedings and the prospect of a constitutional crisis.

Despite the resignation, McCreevy persisted in his attempts to push through O'Flaherty's appointment to the EIB. It led to huge tensions within government. O'Flaherty withdrew his nomination on 28 August 2000 after it became clear he would not get the relevant support from the bank. Young Fine Gael members seized on the controversy. Leo wrote a number of letters to the *Irish Times* in which he lacerated Fianna Fáil and the PDs over the scandal. 'The O'Flaherty controversy has demonstrated that old practices and attitudes continue to thrive in the grand old party. Moreover, the Progressive Democrats' supposed role as the "good guys who'll keep Fianna Fáil honest" has been called into question once again,' Leo wrote in one letter.

But Leo raised eyebrows within the party following the release of a letter to Young Fine Gael members in Trinity, which he sent in his capacity as a member of the officer board of the party's university branch. The letter stated that the Fine Gael campaign against the proposed appointment 'exposed the truth about Bertie Ahern, who Charlie Haughey so appropriately described as the "most devious one of all"'. Leo continued, 'Continuity Fianna Fáil as we called that party hasn't really changed since Bertie's mentor was at the helm. Populism, greed for power, an absence of political principles and a fair spattering of corruption remain hallmarks of Fianna Fáil.'

The issue of Europe and Ireland's place in the EU would soon see Varadkar's prominence grow even further. By this point, he had been elected as vice-president of the youth wing of the centre-right, pro-European grouping the European People's Party (EPP), of which Fine Gael was a member. After Irish voters rejected the Nice Treaty referendum in June 2001, Leo joined forces with a number of fellow college activists in forming Ireland for Europe. The 200-strong organisation was chaired by Ciarán Toland and its officer board included prominent future political and diplomatic figures such as Dara Calleary, Averil Power, Mark Garrett and Adrian Langan. Ireland for Europe was set up following the referendum defeat and amid growing concern that the public were not convinced by politicians on the issue of the Nice Treaty. 'We were all frustrated that the politicians had made a bags of the first campaign. We didn't trust them to go out and communicate with passion,' says Power, adding:

> Leo sees his own reason for being involved in politics as contributing to debate and making a difference and not just going along with the flow. I'm sure at times that hasn't necessarily endeared him to everybody and it is not necessarily an easy quality in the party political system, where often it is easier to put your head down and just go along with things.

The Ireland for Europe campaign quickly became part of a ground war to secure a victory in the second referendum. The group gained a lot of traction in the media and began signing up trainee barristers and soon-to-be political figures including Leo's current chief of staff, Brian Murphy. But it wasn't just a student-led body. The group fed into a wider national campaign that included leading pro-EU figures such as Brigid Laffan, Pat Cox and Garret FitzGerald. Playing a key role in a campaign that had relatively loose structures and rules appealed to Leo. And, unlike in the local elections, this time he was on the side of victory. Nearly eighteen months after the first referendum was defeated, some 63 per cent of the electorate voted in favour of a more integrated Europe.

Varadkar quickly set his sights on a different political challenge; one that would place him and his close friend Lucinda Creighton on a collision course with the Fine Gael leadership.

* * *

During an early morning session at the Fine Gael Ard Fheis at the Citywest, Leo took to his feet and kicked off a debate that caused tensions. He and Lucinda had spent months hatching a plan to change the way the party leader was elected. Their proposals would give significantly more voting rights to the membership, thus diluting the influence of the Fine Gael parliamentary party. Under their plans, there would also be a leadership election every two years. If adopted, the proposals would represent a major shift in the status quo, which saw the leader elected by secret ballot at a private meeting of TDs, senators and MEPs.

At senior level, the move by Varadkar and Creighton was likened to a bold power grab by the younger generation of the party. TDs scoffed at the efforts by the pair, whom they saw as being on a crusade to cause mischief. Tom Curran recalls the unease the proposal caused. 'Suddenly what it meant was a lot of the parliamentary party were going to lose their influence because suddenly, they, behind closed doors, would no longer be choosing the leader,' Curran says.

Phil Hogan notes that Leo's approach to the issue created the impression among some that he and Lucinda were policy troublemakers. 'He thrived on pushing out the boundaries in relation to his opinion on people or policy,' Hogan says. 'I think he thrived on generating some controversy, particularly around policy issues at national conferences and Ard Fheiseanna.' Senior figures within the party, including former leader Alan Dukes, savaged the plan. He said it would create a 'uselessly complicated system'. While party leader Michael Noonan did not publicly shoot down the proposal, he was known to be privately opposed to it.

Leo did get some support from one of his own political mentors, Frances Fitzgerald. 'You will get a knee-jerk reaction from the parliamentary party. It may be a bit impractical, but it should be used as a jumping-off point,' she said at the time.

Leo insisted that the changes were necessary to democratise Fine Gael. 'Tony Blair, Charles Kennedy, Iain Duncan Smith, Ruairi Quinn are elected in this way,' he told the Ard Fheis.

The party's overarching body, the Executive Council, sought to kick the issue into touch pending the publication of a report into the matter. Leo labelled the attempts to block his plan as 'nonsense'. The motion was passed by the Ard Fheis, handing a major victory to the Young Turks.

* * *

Although Varadkar already had a local election run and a successful referendum campaign under his belt, he was still viewed as immature and mischievous. Throughout his college years, Leo lived in his parents' home in Castleknock and travelled into the city centre each morning by train or bus. It meant socialising and bringing people home after a night out was much more difficult – particularly with parents who put pressure on their children to be academically focused. 'I would have come out of myself in other ways a bit sooner if I hadn't been coming home,' Leo said later.

Varadkar was a regular at Young Fine Gael social events, many of which he helped organise. Friends remarked on how he would always insist on a mix of good-quality wine and canapés for those in attendance. The nearby restaurant Dunne and Crescenzi was a popular spot for Varadkar and his Fine Gael pals. Some nights on the town were more memorable than others. Members of the tight-knit group remember one particular evening hosted by a former Fine Gael minister. After several glasses of wine and a couple of bottles of beer, Leo went in search of more alcohol for his friends. He ducked in behind a makeshift bar installed for the event and helped himself to a few bottles of beer. But he was caught red-handed. Just as he was walking off, the minister spotted him and asked what he thought he was doing. Instead of apologising and asking if it was OK to take a beer, Varadkar launched an attack on the minister's personal political performance. He also got stuck into her party colleagues, some of whom were also at the event. 'It was carnage. Leo was worse for wear. The minister was not at all pleased and would remark about the incident for years to come,' says one source present.

*   *   *

After completing his Leaving Cert exams, in which he secured an above-average 555 points, Leo had opted to study law. But just two weeks into his degree, he received notification that his points for college had been upgraded. This meant he had the option of switching degrees from law to medicine. He could now follow his father Ashok into general practice medicine.

However, Varadkar still wonders whether he should have turned down the option of medicine and gone on to practice law. 'I'll never know if it was the right decision,' he says. 'I always think people make these decisions far too young. Who the hell knows when they are eighteen what they want to do?' As his medicine degree progressed, Leo had further doubts about his career choice. 'To be honest, I was a lousy medical student. I did the bare minimum, failed one or two exams along the way and had to repeat them,' he says.

It wasn't that I wasn't able to do it. It probably wasn't really the course I wanted to do. I was quite a lazy student, which is quite different to what I demand of people now. I certainly wasn't getting up early in the morning to make my first lectures or anything like that. So, it really was because I wasn't fully committed to the course.

Friends also thought medicine was out of sync with Leo's personality. After all, he was standoffish and was not particularly personable with patients. But he possessed a photographic memory, which led others to believe he didn't need to push himself hard academically to succeed. 'He has a huge brain. Trinity was no problem to him,' a close friend remembers.

When he was finishing his med [studies], he failed an exam. He was in shock. It had never happened to him before. He didn't have to study really because he just absorbs it. I think Trinity wasn't that big a deal for him. He got to do a lot of the politics.

Eventually, Varadkar and his fellow medical students were sent out into the country's hospitals on work placement. Here, he experienced the many complicated issues that have plagued the Irish health service to this day. Despite being socially awkward, his straight-talking approach to patients made him stand out. He learned how to explain complex medical situations in simple terms. It was an approach he believes has served him well since graduation.

Leo moved to Wexford Town in his fourth year of university, where he rented a room from another hospital worker. It was the first time he had found himself living away from his parents. But he also worked extremely long hours. During later work placements in Crumlin and Beaumont Hospitals in Dublin, he was faced with the everyday realities of hospital medicine. No matter how hard you work, sometimes patients don't make it. Watching patients pass away while in his care deeply affected him, but he forced himself to move on and focus on the next person who needed his attention. 'Those things can't not affect you. But then you also know as a doctor, you kind of have to suck it up,' Leo says.

> Sometimes it was good training for politics in a lot of ways. It teaches you to compartmentalise. So you're dealing with the dying patient and then you're dealing with the person who is not that sick at all five minutes later and they still deserve your full attention. It does teach you to be able to compartmentalise problems and issues.

Leo also picked up another skill during his medical training: how to uncover a hidden agenda.

> It's about looking for that hidden agenda because patients often come in with one problem but it's not the real problem underlying that. They may have headaches but they don't need paracetamol. So you have to get the full story. It could be a brain tumour, it could be exhaustion, it could be stress.

* * *

Leo's Trinity days came during the late '90s and early noughties – the heyday for Bertie Ahern's Fianna Fáil. This period fell in between the middle of then Finance Minister Charlie Mc-Creevy's seven consecutive budgets. Fianna Fáil's mantra at the time was, in effect, 'There's something for everybody.' Ireland was booming economically as the country glided comfortably through the period known as the 'Celtic Tiger'. Leo's generation constantly heard politicians talk of tax cuts and giveaway budgets. Those who knew Leo in college say he regularly expressed concern about this sort of 'one for everyone in the audience'-style politics. Instead, he believed in rewarding people who went out and worked – not those who were comfortably living on welfare.

His arguments against a welfare state led to accusations that Leo was right-wing. Often, over wine, friends of Leo's joked that he would one day be assassinated due to his views. 'There is very little filter in him,' Mark Finan says. 'And certainly, I've been with people who wouldn't know Leo in a social engagement and he would say something and the person would get either offended or shocked because they wouldn't be used to his straight talking or wouldn't know whether to take him seriously or not.'

Although Leo was enjoying his newfound college freedom, he soon discovered the drawbacks of the typical student lifestyle. Having arrived at Trinity weighing around 90kg (14 stone), he quickly piled on the weight. Friends of Leo say his struggle with his weight undermined his self-esteem. They remember that he blamed his weight gains on eating too much Indian food. 'He blames his mother's cooking,' remarks one friend. Leo admits that he lived what he described as a 'sedentary' lifestyle of fast-food dinners and a lack of exercise:

In college, I would have been fat, like. I say I couldn't run 2x100 [metres]. Whereas other people might have gone to the GAA [Gaelic Athletic Association] on Sunday morning or gone to do something active as a family, we would drive over to Deansgrange for this great Indian restaurant and have lunch there and go lie down. So it was very much a sedentary kind of lifestyle, which I now see my sisters are revolting against...

Even during his first elections, senior Fine Gael figures say Leo was anxious about how he would appear on posters. 'He was extremely image-conscious and worried about being viewed as fat and unhealthy,' says one party figure.

But the issue of weight and image was trumped by a far greater anxiety: sexuality. From the start of his third-level studies, Leo didn't show interest in any type of relationship. With his focus on politics and college activities, he wasn't prepared to talk about his sexuality. Not only wasn't he prepared to talk about it, he was in denial himself that he was attracted to men.

Leo's friends say they never had a discussion with him about relationships. They don't recall him ever having a girlfriend or expressing much interest in the opposite sex. But Averil Power remembers how other female students would fancy Leo. 'He is a very good-looking guy and I don't remember him ever having a girlfriend in college even though loads of the girls would have thought he was a good-looking guy.'

Leo admits he did have romantic encounters with one or two girls in college. But he laughs off suggestions that girls were chasing him. 'I've met a few of them since and they were happy to know that it was me and not them,' he laughs. 'I definitely was the problem.'

One person who suspected Leo was gay while he was at college is his sister Sonia. But in typical Varadkar fashion, the blunt manner in which she broached the subject with her younger brother caused him to recoil. 'Probably again, the Varadkar thing, I probably asked him too straight and he probably wasn't ready,' Sonia says. 'But I would have always wondered why such a good-looking boy with a great job, a nice guy, doesn't have a girlfriend and nobody he's interested in. I don't think he was ready when I asked him.'

Though Leo brushed off the questions from his sister, Sonia, so proud and affectionate about her brother, explains how during his college days she had a real fear about his future. She dreaded the prospect that he would always be alone. That he wouldn't find his soulmate, someone to one day share his life with. 'I suppose I am a romantic. I always want happiness,' Sonia says.

> I would hate to think of Leo coming into his apartment and no one being there for him, or an empty fridge, and that used to kill me. Even when he'd come for dinner, and he didn't notice, I have six chairs but I would take one away so he wouldn't feel that there was no one there. I would be there with [husband] Johnny and the two boys and Leo would come for dinner, so I would get rid of a chair and he would never notice.

Leo had managed to keep his sexuality under wraps for the time being. In his own words, he 'suppressed' the fact he was gay during his college days. 'That's obviously what I did. I wasn't aware I was doing this. But looking back on it, I definitely suppressed and concentrated even more on college and politics in Fine Gael.'

For now, Leo's growing passion for politics was his driving force, but an internal struggle over his sexuality would eventually have to be resolved.

CHAPTER 4

SCRUBS AND THE
BAND OF BROTHERS

'Fine Gael should not seek a Messiah to lead it out of its difficulties. There is none and never will be.' This was Leo's blunt assessment of Fine Gael's fortunes, recorded in the immediate aftermath of the 2002 general election. The party had suffered a near-obliteration at the polls, haemorrhaging twenty-three seats.

The booming economy and period of relative stability gave little reason for voters to desert Fianna Fáil. But for Fine Gael to lose almost half of its fifty-four seats, including those held by some of its highest-profile politicians, was nothing short of a disaster for the party. Michael Noonan promptly resigned, having been in charge for just fifteen months. He was replaced by Mayo politician Enda Kenny.

In his letter to the *Irish Times*, published just days before Kenny was elected leader, Leo insisted individual leaders should not be blamed for the hammering at the polls. And he warned of tensions between the party's conservative, Christian democrat base and the liberal wing.

Fine Gael's decline in recent years cannot be blamed solely or even largely on its leaders. It stems from a number of factors – organisational, strategic, demographic and political. Greatest among these is Fine Gael's internal conflict between its conservative Christian democrat base (which it is set on deserting) and its liberal, social democratic base from the FitzGerald era (which deserted it some time ago). Fine Gael's resurgence will come from the realisation that the party must forge a distinct identity in its own right, rather than merely as the alternative to Fianna Fáil.

Enda Kenny's election as Fine Gael leader took place behind closed doors at the parliamentary party meeting, by way of secret ballot. He was one of four candidates; the others were Richard Bruton, Phil Hogan and Gay Mitchell. Kenny knew that the key to victory was winning over the support of the party's fourteen senators. Their backing would in essence elect the leader of the country's second largest party. But the failure to involve the wider Fine Gael membership infuriated Varadkar and Lucinda Creighton, who then held the position of vice-president of Young Fine Gael.

It was a smack in the face for the youth wing of the party, whose motion to change the rules around the leadership had already been passed at the Ard Fheis. The Young Turks made their views known through the letter pages of the *Irish Times*. 'Clearly, the rump 31 TDs and the 14 unelectables from the fag-end of a Senate have learned nothing from Fine Gael's mauling at the polls,' the pair wrote two days before the result was declared. 'The decision of the parliamentary party to decide the future of Fine Gael alone and behind closed doors is a disgrace and demonstrates their contempt both for the loyal Fine Gael membership and the 400,000 or so electors who voted for them. Shame on you all.'

The Fine Gael party was in the doldrums. It had lost its focus and was showing little sign of being brought back on course. For the likes of Varadkar, Creighton, Paschal Donohoe and others, the party just didn't get the scale of the crisis it found itself in. And yet, while others within the party took a different route, these three were willing to put their careers on the back burner in order to rebuild a party that was faltering.

'It's important to say that Leo was one of the up-and-coming candidates at the time the Fine Gael brand was so weak in Dublin,' explains Dublin organiser David McCarthy. 'He had to deal with questions as to why would you associate yourself with this brand? He, Lucinda, Paschal – they changed the narrative as young vibrant voices which Fine Gael needed to change its fortunes around.'

While Leo used the national media effectively to raise his profile, he was also making a considerable mark locally. He quickly aligned himself with Sheila Terry, who had served as a councillor since the early '90s for the now defunct Progressive Democrats before becoming an Independent. Terry then joined Fine Gael in 2000 and began building up the sort of reputation on the doorsteps of Castleknock that Leo would seek to emulate. Despite a sizeable age gap, the pair quickly became close. Members of Terry's campaign team say she perceived Leo as a future star of the party, while he saw her as a political mentor.

At the time of the coming together, the party in Dublin West was demoralised. It had only around thirty active members and no Dáil representation after Austin Currie opted to stand in the new constituency of Dublin Mid-West. The party's councillor Tom Morrissey quit and joined the PDs – taking the polar opposite approach to Sheila Terry. Members were crying out for leadership and energy. It therefore came as no surprise when Leo, then aged just twenty-three, was asked to serve as Terry's campaign manager in the 2002 general election.

Leo almost single-handedly ran the Terry campaign. He canvassed extensively alongside his mentor, personally designed election leaflets and engaged directly with party headquarters. Despite the nightmare result nationally, Terry came excruciatingly close to securing a seat, losing out to the Labour Party's Joan Burton by just over 600 votes. There was, however, a consolation prize waiting for her. Just months later, Terry secured a seat in the Seanad, the upper house of Ireland's Parliament.

Leo was also presented with a prize of his own – but it wasn't without difficulty. New rules brought in under the so-called dual mandate (laws banning politicians from holding seats on more than one electoral body at the same time) obliged Terry to give up her council seat. At the time, Leo – still in medical school – told the party he was willing to allow the seat to be handed to a Fine Gael supporter from Mulhuddart named Declan Kettle. He was in the latter stages of his Trinity studies and felt that he should instead wait until the pending 2004 local elections to once again run for office. But Kettle turned it down.

Despite Leo being the obvious candidate to take over the seat, he was forced to wait a lengthy period before being formally co-opted. Some of his supporters believe Terry may have held up his appointment for as long as possible in order to find a candidate who would pose less of a threat. The long delay frustrated Leo and led to suspicions about Terry's intentions. 'It was an open question for ages. She had been elected as an Independent, so the co-option wasn't automatically Fine Gael's,' says one source, adding, 'In some ways it suited Sheila to be both a senator and councillor as it kept her very well connected to issues locally.'

But by 13 October 2003, four years after bombing in his first local election, Leo had the title of councillor to his name.

His co-option took place upstairs in Myo's, his local pub in Castleknock. Gathered to hear Leo's speech was a different type of audience to the one so often present at Fine Gael events in Dublin West. Young and fresh faces filled the room. Many of those present were Trinity College students whom Leo had persuaded to become signed-up members. He may have inherited Sheila Terry's council seat by proxy, but from the audience in the room that day, party bosses knew that he had brought with him an influx of new blood.

David McCarthy had started his job as Fine Gael's regional organiser the day Leo was co-opted. He remembers the reaction from senior Fine Gael figures in the room. 'I can vividly remember the night because I went up to speak after him. It was my job to tell people that it was my first day and I was tasked with rebuilding an organisation in Dublin that had collapsed,' McCarthy says.

> You could see that Leo had great enthusiasm and energy and was a future potential candidate. I remember saying to myself, 'My job is going to be easy dealing with someone like this.' He spoke, for a young guy, really well. You could tell he was smart, quite direct but clear and that he had ideas as a politician and was clearly able to articulate them.

While McCarthy's main role was to prepare candidates in Dublin for the upcoming local elections, he says Leo and his team needed very little assistance. 'Leo would always be one of the candidates who could pull twenty people on a Saturday to get feedback from constituents, which he realised was important. He was a strategist even back then,' McCarthy says.

By the time of the election, he had organised an active group of people working constantly for him, you could see that straight away. People were hearing from him, reading about him, meeting him on the doors. The saturation of you, your face, your name, particularly at local level, is the only way to do it.

Among Leo's inner circle in Dublin West were Fine Gael members Ron Elliott and Ned Walsh. Elliott went door to door with Leo, organising face-to-face conversations with constituents. He speaks of Leo as a proud father does of his son. Elliott had spotted Leo's talent and was determined to harness it. 'I would have been quite obvious and blatant about it. I would say to him, "Leo, that's a Fianna Fáil house – no need to knock that door, just keep going." I felt I had a responsibility to mind him from that.' Elliott recalls how the team became so active on the doors, they would liken themselves to the well-oiled operation on the north side of the city that built the success behind former Taoiseach Bertie Ahern. 'That was the general tone. That was the feeling,' Elliott remembers.

Ned Walsh, meanwhile, says he was struck by Leo's intelligence and honesty on the doorstep, as well as his grasp of both local and national issues. But he remembers that Leo's own demeanour and stand-offish approach with people was a weakness. 'He would have been perceived as being a bit on the aloof side. He wouldn't be like Enda Kenny or as good as him at meeting people and shaking their hands and moving on,' Walsh says. 'It's just the way he was reared.'

Walsh's remarks reflect what many of Leo's colleagues and indeed friends say about him privately. His awkwardness around people, his sense of shyness, his ability to be condescending and rude at times are often cited as Leo's bad traits. But Tom Curran believes Leo's mannerisms are a strength.

'I think it disarms people,' Curran says. 'His shyness increases his vulnerability, which people really like. People may say he is shy, but he is well able to communicate to people. His vulnerability, I think, is a tremendous asset to him.'

Those who spent the most time with Leo on the doorstep point to an even greater asset, available to him at all times: his family. The Varadkars were pillars of the community, which they served seven days a week through the local GP practice. The family's popularity benefited Leo hugely in his canvassing. While Walsh likens Leo to his father Ashok in terms of personality, he believes his father's role as a family doctor was a significant pull factor in terms of votes. 'He is highly respected as a doctor – that helped Leo quite a bit. You'd struggle to meet anybody who would have a bad word to say about him.'

During his canvassing days, Leo always insisted to his team that he would not promise something to a constituent for the sake of it. The fixing of roads and potholes – parochial-style politics – was not what Leo wanted to become known for. 'Leo would never over-promise,' says Elliott. It's a description also given of Leo by colleagues who sat alongside him on Fingal County Council. 'You wouldn't see him asking about potholes in Dublin West,' according to party colleague and Dublin TD Alan Farrell.

Leo put himself forward for deputy mayor but, not for the first time, he struggled to contain the political workload alongside his long hours at the hospital. Farrell agreed to fill in for him. But Leo's juggling of both his council and his hospital work led to some peculiar occurrences in the chamber of Fingal County Council. His council and now Dáil colleague Clare Daly recalled in the Dáil some years later how he would arrive late into meetings with a Mars bar and a can of Coke in his hand.

Others remember how Leo would travel straight from hospital to the chamber dressed in his medical attire, with a stethoscope around his neck. It generated the nickname 'Scrubs' in the local media. According to his fellow councillor Joan Burton, her now deceased Labour colleague Peggy Hamill was particularly exercised by Leo's attire. 'She was going nuts at someone … coming from a hospital dressed in uniform,' Burton says. 'I presume people had a word with him, and he eventually turned out as he always does: immaculately, beautifully dressed.' Varadkar admits he attended some meetings in hospital scrubs but denies he ever wore a stethoscope.

As a councillor, Leo continued to use his preferred method of recording his somewhat controversial views on national issues: the letters pages of the *Irish Times*. And in the autumn of 2003, he opened himself up to further accusations of holding right-wing political opinions. In an article in response to reports that state funding could be removed from private schools, Leo insisted this would drive out middle-class families. 'Dividing Ireland into a country of those who pay for everything and receive nothing and those who pay for nothing and receive everything, with only a small minority in between, would deal a fatal blow to what is left of Ireland's social contract,' he wrote. 'Rather than taking funding away from fee-paying schools and making them entirely a law unto themselves, why not require fee-paying schools to take a quota of students from disadvantaged backgrounds in return for their State funding?'

A month later, Leo decided to take on his constituency rival Joe Higgins on the issue of bin charges. In a letter published in both the *Irish Times* and the *Sunday Tribune*, Leo wrote that he was 'appalled' at the actions of protesters to the charges: 'Bin collection is a service like any other. Just like electricity, post, television and heating oil, we must pay for it if we can afford to do so. Surely no one would regard paying for these to be double taxation.'

As the 2004 local elections loomed, Leo had a dedicated team around him. Joan Burton calls his supporters the 'Band of Brothers', a play on the hit American war drama produced by Tom Hanks and Steven Spielberg. 'I wouldn't be conscious of an enormous number of women,' Burton says. 'Now, there'd be a circle of women who would be very supportive of him and that. But almost all of his key campaign people with the exception of Lisa, who is his secretary and lives in the constituency, it would be very much a band of brothers.' The Lisa referred to by Burton is Lisa Tavey. She is regularly mentioned as one of Leo's most loyal supporters and went on to become his personal assistant in the Department of the Taoiseach. Another woman central to Varadkar's political success is Mary Donohoe, a long-time supporter who still works with him to this day.

Despite predictions that Fine Gael would struggle to maintain its vote in Dublin, the party returned roughly the same number of seats. But in Dublin West, something remarkable happened. Leo secured 4,894 votes – or 38.2 per cent – almost two quotas and the highest in the country. It's a record that has been beaten on only a handful of occasions since.

'I was the first of a new generation that had grown up in the area. People knew me from when I was two,' Leo says of his massive vote. Others, however, insist that half of the vote secured by Leo can be attributed to the influence of Ashok.

Regardless of the factors, the result was staggering, particularly given that Leo's first electoral contest had seen him secure just a few hundred votes.

Just months after his election, Leo enjoyed a victory of a different kind. Years after the proposals were first mooted, the Fine Gael national executive paved the way for changes to the system of electing the party leader. Under the plans, first spear-headed by Varadkar and Lucinda Creighton, the Fine Gael parliamentary party would now hold just 65 per cent of the overall vote. Some 25 per cent would be held by the wider party membership, with the remainder being assigned to councillors. It was a massive result for the Young Turks and brought about a significant democratisation of the party.

Leo's path to Dáil Éireann (the lower house of the Irish Parliament) was now well and truly marked out. But there was still one person standing in his way.

CHAPTER 5

THE MOST TALKED-ABOUT POLITICIAN IN LEINSTER HOUSE

In February 2005, the upper house of the Oireachtas, known as the Seanad, played host to a heated debate. Senators debated a bill on civil partnership, tabled by the renowned gay rights campaigner David Norris. The bill was designed to pave the way for same-sex couples to enter into a civil union and was the first real step towards marriage equality. Fine Gael had already published a policy document on the area of civil partnership, which proposed giving same-sex couples greater rights in areas such as tax, pensions and property. The document was launched with little fanfare by senator Sheila Terry, a low-key and eloquent performer from Dublin West.

Amid suggestions that the government was attempting to kill off the Norris bill, Terry let fly on the floor of the Seanad on 16 February. 'I do not know if the government's opposition to this bill is born out of indecisiveness or homophobia, but it has let the House down in the way it has dealt with it today,' she said.

The following week, Terry apologised for making the charge of homophobia, having faced criticism from a number of politicians, including former Attorney General Michael McDowell, who would later serve as Tánaiste. Terry continued, however, to apply major pressure on the government to progress the issue of civil partnership.

Six years later, the Dáil passed legislation that was a virtual replica of Terry's initial proposals. She was, in many ways, Fine Gael's champion on equality. Terry's work on civil partnership was an important milestone for LGBT rights. Unbeknown to her at the time, it would pave the way for her constituency understudy, Leo Varadkar, to go on to become the country's first openly gay Cabinet minister.

* * *

In the weeks leading up to the 2004 local elections, Sheila Terry spoke to party officials about candidate strategy. She was the sole Oireachtas member in the constituency of Dublin West and held in high regard by Fine Gael headquarters. Terry suggested a two-candidate strategy that would see a running mate being installed to contest alongside Leo Varadkar. And, in her view, her son Damien would fit the bill.

Team Varadkar was not consulted about the move and suspect that it stemmed from Terry's concern that her constituency colleague was quickly becoming a threat. A Dáil election was on the horizon and Terry knew that it represented her best chance yet of taking a seat. But with Leo now the sole councillor in Castleknock, he was in an ideal position to maximise his support base. Having her son on the council would of course stifle Varadkar's growth and enhance Terry's chances at a future selection convention for the Dáil.

In the end, the proposal fell flat on its face. Varadkar was chosen as the sole Fine Gael candidate on the ticket. If elected, he would have the advantage of being the ward's only Fine Gael councillor.

Terry was present in the count centre on election day when Varadkar polled record numbers. Fine Gael figures in the constituency believe it may well have been the moment she realised she was fast becoming outflanked by her own prodigy.

As Fine Gael geared up for the 2007 general election, tensions in Dublin West increased sharply. Branch members who supported and actively canvassed for both Varadkar and Terry knew there was only one place on the ticket. The experienced senator versus the councillor tipped for much bigger things. As the constituency prepared for a showdown at its selection convention, the pair met to discuss the elephant in the room. Sensing she was fighting a losing battle, Terry told Varadkar he should be the party's general election candidate. She would not stand in his way. She cited his local election result as the factor behind her offer of an endorsement. Varadkar declined, instead telling Terry he would run for the Dáil at a future date. He said his own time would come and, for now, he was happy to support her campaign to win back a seat for Fine Gael.

However, Varadkar soon had a change of heart. He was persuaded that the majority of the membership wanted him on the ticket rather than Terry. Before taking the decision, Varadkar did not pay Terry the courtesy of telling her he was going to run.

His U-turn stunned the Terry camp, prompting suggestions among some of her supporters that he had betrayed the woman who had helped copper-fasten his rise in the party. In essence, the move by Varadkar brought his relationship with his mentor to an end. But relations were about to get worse.

According to well-placed sources, Leo deeply regrets his handling of the affair. He believes in hindsight that he should have sat down with Terry and told her of his change of heart, instead of allowing word to spread back to her camp. Terry and her family felt betrayed. It is an experience that she has refused to speak about publicly ever since.

The once closely knit team of Varadkar and Terry were now at war.

* * *

Sean Sheils served as the manager of the bar in Leinster House for over forty years and lives in the Dublin West constituency. Now in his late seventies, Sheils has known virtually every politician of note since the late '60s. As with his successor, Darren Brady, politicians and journalists would regularly approach Sheils to gather the lay of the land. After all, the head barman in Leinster House is best placed to know and hear everything. Sheils became intrigued when, in late 2006, senior TDs began talking about a newcomer whose name they could barely pronounce.

Leo Varadkar was not yet a member of Dáil Éireann. But after his local election result in 2004, his name was on everybody's lips as a future star of Fine Gael. 'I remember the time well because he was the talk of Leinster House, really,' Sheils says. 'And most people, even senior Fine Gael people, they couldn't pronounce his name. No more than most people at that time, they had great difficulty pronouncing the name Varadkar.'

As was often the case, Sheils was leant upon by senior Fine Gael strategists for his advice. One of these figures was Phil Hogan, who approached Sheils to discuss Fine Gael's election strategy in Dublin West. Sheils's advice to Hogan was simple: a party like Fine Gael would be crazy to ignore a candidate who secured the highest local vote in the country.

'You couldn't blame Leo. Leo stood for the local elections and got nearly two quotas,' Sheils says. 'I said it would be an insult to the Fine Gael people in Castleknock if you didn't run Leo in the general election.'

Sheils was a Fine Gael supporter from Dublin West – although, as manager of the Dáil bar, he kept this under wraps until after his departure in 2006. But he was also a close friend to Sheila Terry. 'Obviously Sheila Terry was the senator and he was the councillor. She thought she had the ground to be nominated on her own,' Sheils says. 'She was staring at a Dáil seat... things were on the up.' But he adds, 'You had to run your strongest candidate and obviously Leo was your strongest candidate.'

The path was now clear for Varadkar to make the leap into national politics – but, first, he still had to publicly face down his mentor.

* * *

Once one of the strongest and most united Fine Gael branches in the country, Dublin West was now at loggerheads. Tensions had been simmering between the Varadkar and Terry camps, culminating in a heated meeting that would leave wounds for years to come. Kavanagh's pub would play host to the battle of Castleknock. Ron Elliott, who campaigned for both candidates for many years, recalls the tense atmosphere in the small lounge located at the Laurel Lodge Shopping Centre. 'It was an uncomfortable meeting. I was uncomfortable,' Elliott says. 'There were sparks flying, some people were quite disappointed at the time. I was disappointed that there was going to be a parting.

I would have preferred if they could have co-existed; I think that would have been the best solution for the party.'

Fine Gael HQ knew the split was potentially damaging, particularly if news of it made its way into the national media. Senior Fine Gael figures at the time – including Phil Hogan, Frank Flannery and Tom Curran – all believe Terry knew deep down that Varadkar was destined for the Dáil. 'You can't stop the inevitability of people with ambition and prospects coming to the top. He effectively succeeded her,' Curran says. 'That left for a short period some bad feeling and bad taste in some people's mouths in the constituency,' he adds. Hogan went as far as to describe Terry as one of the most unfortunate Oireachtas members in Fine Gael history. But he denies Leo shafted his mentor. 'I think she came to the realisation … that there was only going to be one Fine Gael seat in this area,' he says. 'She was pragmatic enough to know that he had received a huge personal vote and a huge Fine Gael vote in those elections in 2004 and there were efforts made to accommodate her in other constituencies.'

Sean Sheils, along with many others in the party, insists Terry was given options that would have ensured she still had a future in national politics. A return to the Seanad was an inevitability if Fine Gael had a decent election result. Terry was also offered the option of moving constituency, according to a senior party source, who insists that at no point would she have been told to step aside. Terry turned down the various approaches, the source says.

Flannery recalls how Terry's supporters insisted she be added to the ticket alongside Leo in the event of his victory at the selection convention. But he was heading up what was known as the Flannery Commission, which was established with the intention of bringing young blood into the party. Terry would have to move aside if she was not prepared to switch constituencies, he explains. 'She was very upset. She felt that was her seat, but Leo got 5,000 votes in the local elections and we were looking for a candidate for the 2007 election. Sheila wanted to run and Leo wanted to run. The constituency chose Leo.'

Leo's supporters believe his main advantage over Terry was the fact he was home-grown. She, in contrast, had switched allegiances on a number of occasions between the PDs, Fine Gael and the Independents. It's an assessment shared by the local Labour TD and former Tánaiste Joan Burton. 'He was on the radar as going to be a Dáil candidate. A force to be reckoned with,' Burton says.

Sheila Terry was very personable, a very nice woman to deal with. Very good performer in the Seanad. But she was not heartland Fine Gael even though she was heartland Castleknock. Because she was someone who came in from the PDs, once Leo asserted himself, I think he had a natural advantage over her.

To this day, the exact events surrounding her acrimonious departure from Fine Gael remain shrouded in mystery. She has refused offers of interviews, with sources close to her family insisting she wants to draw a line under what she views as a difficult chapter in her life. 'She got caught up in a whirlwind of Leo and the tide coming in for Fine Gael,' Sheils says. 'She opted not to stand. I'd say she got bad advice from certain people when she should have gone the other way.'

With Terry finally off the pitch, Leo was selected unopposed at the convention in the Castleknock hotel. After months of infighting and acrimony, the only hitch on the night was the lights going out during his speech.

* * *

Paschal Donohoe, the country's Finance Minister and a close ally of Varadkar's, was another young pretender who Fine Gael bosses were determined should be on the ticket. While Varadkar was admired and respected for his decision to run in the 1999 local election, Donohoe impressed senior party figures by his willingness to put his career on hold for a tilt at a Dáil seat. Donohoe believes the plan that saw him, Varadkar and others brought to the fore in the 2007 election was one born out of survival.

> Fine Gael said to itself, 'if we don't make choices about our future, we won't be around in five, ten years' time'. So there was a realisation from Enda, from headquarters and from the people around us, we could go the way of Nokia. We could go the way of Blackberry. We don't have any divine right to still be around and that really was a real truth about the party then.

Donohoe says this realisation led to two things: the establishment of the Flannery Commission that put both him and Varadkar front and centre, and the decision to move aside long-serving party members. 'Headquarters basically said, "Come convention time, we would do what needed to be done and these people would be candidates,"' Donohoe says. 'Enda went to them… The General Secretary went to them and said, "Look, really appreciate your service, really want you to stick around. Really value what you've done. But we need to get new people in." And Leo and myself were really the beneficiaries of this.'

As the 2007 general election loomed, Fine Gael knew the stakes could not be higher. This was Enda Kenny's first national election as party leader and a major chance for him to become

Taoiseach. But private research conducted by Fine Gael showed Bertie Ahern's Fianna Fáil-led government was very popular with voters. The public were satisfied with the state of the Irish economy – prompting Fine Gael to focus their campaign instead on the need for better public services. 'Our approach to 2007 was we had all the research that showed the government was very popular. Bertie was probably one of the most popular Taoiseachs we've ever had in Ireland over a long period of time,' Flannery says.

Healthcare formed a huge part of the election campaign as Fine Gael hammered their opposite numbers over waiting lists. Government incompetence quickly became an election theme too. The issue of electronic voting machines – which cost the taxpayer tens of millions – was hammed up by Fine Gael. 'We got great value out of those. Government incompetence, waste of public money and disastrous services while the fat cats are creaming off money for themselves,' Flannery says. But, like in most elections, Flannery admits the party over-promised. 'I think we promised to build five new hospitals. If we got elected that would have been a fair old challenge.'

* * *

Leo approached the 2007 general election in a position few first-time candidates find themselves in. To say the odds were stacked against him is an understatement. Dublin West was a three-seat constituency made up of some of the biggest names in Irish politics. To this day, it remains a constituency suffering from division. Take a walk down the estates of working-class Mulhuddart and you will encounter people who insist the recovery has yet to spread to their community. Yet take the short drive to leafy Castleknock and you will experience a Dublin suburb that fits the definition of Celtic Tiger Ireland. Head to the north of the constituency to the likes of Hollystown and you will meet the young couples who commute to the city centre each day for work. They've moved out here because house prices and rent are cheaper. Building a family is on the cards. Not too far away is the village of Ongar, whose residents enjoy a quiet life away from the hustle and bustle they experienced during their twenties and thirties. It's a constituency very much split between left and right.

This is the battleground that faced Leo during his first general election. For a 26-year-old, it was a daunting task. But what made it even more overwhelming was the calibre of the field of TDs already in situ – one of whom Leo had to take out.

* * *

Joe Higgins was the leader of the Socialist Party and a champion of the far left. He managed to cultivate a significant following not only in Dublin West but among working-class groups across the country. For a TD like Higgins to create a solid base in Dublin West at a time of economic prosperity is an illustration of his ability to connect with people on the ground. His profile grew significantly in 2003 when he was jailed alongside his colleague Clare Daly for their role in the anti-bin-tax campaign. To this day, he is seen as a force of Irish socialism.

Next was Joan Burton, one of the most impressive debaters in Leinster House, who had narrowly defeated Sheila Terry to the third seat in 2002. Burton was one of the faces of the success story of the Labour Party in the early 2000s. But Burton's support base had been volatile over the years, causing her to lose her Dáil seat in 1997 before regaining it in 2002.

The people of Dublin West were also represented for more

than three decades by one of the most respected and influential dynasties in Irish politics. The Lenihan family were a tour de force. Brian Lenihan Sr was a leading figure in the Fianna Fáil party and served in various Cabinet positions over twenty-five years. He also held the position of Tánaiste. In 1990, Lenihan was famously sacked by the then Taoiseach Charles Haughey following a controversy that erupted during the presidential election. Upon his death in 1995, Lenihan's Dáil seat was taken over by his son Brian Jr following a closely fought by-election. Lenihan Jr was a popular political figure despite being landed with the unenviable task of overseeing the Department of Finance during the financial crash.

Varadkar's camp knew Lenihan's seat was safe; to be elected, he needed to take out either Burton or Higgins. But he was certainly the underdog in a 'group of death' constituency. While there was a national swing to Fine Gael under way, he still needed to increase the party's support from the 2002 base of 12 per cent to at least 20 per cent. Leo's team decided that flooding the constituency with leaflets and other election material would be key to their success. 'High visibility, high number of leaflets being dropped, presence of candidates and actively asking everyone for their vote,' friend and supporter Mark Finan recalls. Varadkar personally drew down a bank loan of €50,000 to fund his campaign. He took four months' unpaid leave from the medical profession in order to campaign on a full-time basis. He employed quirky tactics such as handing out Lion chocolate bars at traffic junctions each morning in a bid to target commuters and families on school runs. 'Vote No. 1 – Leo the Lion', the election gimmick read.

And, as many of his key supporters at the time observed, it was his own family and the Varadkar name that would prove to be his secret weapon. Many people were willing to lend their vote to a young man whose parents had for years provided top-class medical care to the community. Ronan Melvin, a key figure in Leo's campaign, says the role of his family was pivotal: 'Without a doubt, Leo realised the family were an asset. A nice family, ran a business, knew everybody, there was a huge network there.'

With polling day approaching, Varadkar and his team put in one last major canvassing effort, targeting commuters at train stations. At a local level, the issue of school places for children emerged as a contentious issue on the doorsteps. Varadkar was vocal on the subject in the knowledge that it would generate support. Describing him as an 'electoral hoover' and a 'political juggernaut', political pundits were backing the first-time Dáil candidate to take a seat.

The fight for the third seat in Dublin West was being pitched as a battle between Varadkar and Burton. On the Monday before polling day, however, one newspaper constituency profile predicted Varadkar would perform well but would ultimately be pipped by Burton for the seat. It was the last thing his campaign needed. 'We were like, "Oh God, we are getting a good response on the doors, we think it is going well." And I particularly remember us all looking at the paper saying, "Oh god." There was so much work gone in,' Melvin says. 'I think we went canvassing in a new area that afternoon where every house said they were voting for us.'

On 24 May 2007, Varadkar was joined at the count centre at the Coolmine Community School by family and supporters. Early tallies indicated Higgins was struggling to pick up transfers and his seat was very much in jeopardy. Team Varadkar hoped their man could take advantage of the drop in support for Higgins, but as the declaration of the first count approached, they realised he was challenging for the second seat, behind Lenihan, who topped the poll for the third consecutive general election. Leo secured 6,928 first preference votes – almost double the number Sheila Terry had managed five years previous. He was declared a TD after the fifth count. Joan Burton, who was outflanked by Joe Higgins in 1997, reversed the fortunes and took the third and final seat.

Team Varadkar were ecstatic. In response to questions from the media about his election success, Varadkar said he was determined to make an impact on politics. 'I'm not going to be sitting around the Dáil bar for the next five years,' he said. Higgins left the count centre that day in the knowledge that he had been defeated by a new kid on the block.

Nationally, Fine Gael secured fifty-one seats – an increase of nineteen. Despite entering into a pre-election pact with Labour, it wasn't enough to topple the Ahern-led Fianna Fáil party. Fine Gael was going back into opposition once again. As one key strategist involved in Fine Gael's campaign observes, Kenny was simply no match for the Ahern machine. 'Fianna Fáil were in complete command. Enda was regarded with a certain degree of cynicism at that time. If Bertie was the city slicker, Enda was the country bumpkin and the media never got too attracted to him.'

After a short period of negotiations, the government of the thirtieth Dáil was made up of Fianna Fáil, the PDs and the Green Party. In June, Leo wrote a letter to the *Irish Times* in which he lambasted the Green Party for its decision to enter government, saying the party was nothing more than a mudguard for Fianna Fáil.

With the new Dáil term set to commence, leader of the opposition Enda Kenny was preparing to unveil his new front bench. Varadkar had been linked with the health portfolio after the party's health spokesperson Dr Liam Twomey had been a surprise casualty in the election. Kenny knew Fine Gael needed to boost its image, particularly in Dublin. Leo was just twenty-eight and one of the youngest TDs in the Dáil. Paschal Donohoe, who had not managed to get elected in 2007, says Kenny's decision to appoint Leo showed experience and foresight. 'His approach was always: how can I have the best people around me? He would have identified Leo certainly as someone who went from one of the worst local election results in 1999 in Mulhuddart, to sticking at it for five years and then getting almost 5,000 votes in Castleknock.' In a meeting in Leinster House, Kenny offered Leo the position of enterprise spokesperson and handed over the portfolio. It was a proud and memorable occasion for any young TD. There was no such offer for Varadkar's close friend Lucinda Creighton, who was also elected to the Dáil first time out.

But before Varadkar accepted the portfolio, and indeed the new job, he had a request for his party leader. The first-time TD was studying to become a GP and needed to dedicate at least one day a week solely to his studies. He wasn't willing to take on the role of enterprise spokesperson if it would jeopardise his medical training. Kenny accepted the request and Varadkar took over a brief he would quickly make his own. But his next major act would also capture the surprise and attention of people in Leinster House.

* * *

The election showed senior Fine Gael figures that their belief in Varadkar's talent was well founded. They also knew that he had a craving to be noticed and the ability to get under people's skin. But what they did not expect was for any new TD to twist the knife so soon after the election result.

Just over three months later, Varadkar penned a letter to the *Irish Times* in which he issued a severe critique of the party's performance. The piece, published on 11 September 2007, was penned in a personal capacity. But it was highly critical of the campaign itself, particularly in relation to its messaging. 'We did not win the policy debates. We showed an unwillingness to take clear positions. We did not demonstrate competence to run the economy,' Varadkar wrote. Varadkar singled out Kenny for demonstrating 'immense passion, stamina and ability' during the campaign itself. But he said that when push came to shove, Fine Gael struggled when its policies were attacked:

When our policies came under scrutiny we were, on occasion, unable to stand over our own promises – how and when would we deliver medical cards for every child under five; who would benefit most from our tax policies; how would we deliver 2,000 extra beds; whether the 2,000 extra gardaí were really extra at all etc.

The letter from Leo caused unease at senior level within the party. This was a man just elected first time out. Why was he not more focused on learning the ropes than commenting on an election that was now in the past, senior bosses wondered. For Phil Hogan, the letter demonstrates that Leo had yet to fully mature:

It took him a while to graduate from being a conference speaker at an Ard Fheis to being a member of the parliamentary party. I think he would recognise that himself but that's part of the opportunity that Enda Kenny as leader of the Fine Gael party gave to young people. He put him on the front bench on day one.

Brian Hayes says it demonstrated courage: 'This was a fellah who clearly wanted to be on the front bench but had no difficulty saying to Enda, "Basically, you ran a crap campaign in '07."'

Leo had already positioned himself as one of the most talked-about politicians in Leinster House. But his next move would see him taking on the most talked-about politician in the country.

CHAPTER 6

BECOMING AN OPPOSITION TD

Drug dealers, pimps and political scandals. A marital break-down. A money trail with no apparent start or finish. Dig-outs and whip-rounds from friends in Dublin and Manchester. Briefcases full of UK sterling and Irish punts. It had all the hall-marks of a television drama. But it was in fact the extraordinary story behind the financial affairs of Taoiseach Bertie Ahern.

Just weeks into the new Dáil term, the Fianna Fáil-led gov-ernment was in disarray. The Mahon Tribunal, a judge-led in-quiry into allegations of planning irregularities, had cast major doubt over the credibility of Ahern's account of his personal finances. The controversy had been part of public discourse for well over a year but opposition parties, particularly Fine Gael, shied away from criticising the popular Taoiseach and his pri-vate affairs. Varadkar, however, bucked this trend. In September 2006, months before being elected a TD, he began to publicly question Ahern's credibility. 'I have plenty of friends but I do not know anyone who would be willing to pay my mortgage, decorate my apartment, pay for my holidays, or take on my legal bills,' Varadkar wrote in a letter published in both the *Irish Times* and *Irish Independent*. 'I wonder if the Taoiseach has ever asked himself why he has friends like that when the rest of us do not?'

In September 2007, Ahern's story began to unravel. The Fianna Fáil leader was forced to give eighteen hours of sworn testimony about his personal finances in front of the tribunal. With every answer Ahern gave, more questions arose. His credibility was very much on the line. As pressure mounted, the opposition decided to swoop. A motion of no confidence was tabled, forcing Ahern to come before the Dáil to fight for his political career. The Taoiseach told the Dáil that he had been going through a 'dark period' following the break-up of his marriage. He had been Finance Minister at the time and had turned to friends for assistance. Ahern admitted his memory of certain details was hazy. But he insisted he had done nothing improper and was cooperating with the tribunal. One by one, Fianna Fáil deputies got to their feet and issued a staunch defence of their leader. Bertie Ahern was not perfect, they said, but his contribution to Irish politics was unrivalled. They insisted the public had already cast their judgement on this matter on election day when they returned Ahern as Taoiseach. But amid hostile exchanges, the opposition claimed Ahern was no longer fit for office. Fine Gael and Labour piled pressure on Fianna Fáil's partners in government, the Green Party and the Progressive Democrats, to pull the plug. The stakes could not have been higher.

Fine Gael's young bloods, including Simon Coveney and Lucinda Creighton, were among those launching the most scathing attacks on Ahern. But it was Varadkar who drove home the message that, in his mind, Ahern was a liar. He likened the personal scandal to the one that had engulfed then US President Bill Clinton a decade earlier. And, not for the first time, he pointed to notorious remarks made about Ahern by his predecessor Charles Haughey, saying, 'Sadly, this dark affair will darken the Taoiseach's record in the same way as Tony Blair's involvement in Iraq or Bill Clinton's corruption and personal scandals darkened theirs. History will judge the Taoiseach as being both devious and cunning, in the words of his mentor, master and, clearly, role model.' It was a solid blow, more so because it was landed by one of the Dáil's youngest and most inexperienced members.

Brian Hayes, who had contributed to the debate minutes earlier, says Varadkar's decision to 'go for the jugular' was both brave and strategic. 'I thought that was very calculated. He sensed Bertie's best days were behind him,' Hayes says. But did Leo risk biting off more than he could chew? 'I remember talking to him in the car that day and saying, "God, I hope you haven't gone too far,"' remarks key supporter Ronan Melvin.

Two days later, as the House prepared to vote on the no confidence motion, an incensed Ahern responded to the attacks from Fine Gael's Young Turks – or Young Tories, as they were described by some TDs. The Fianna Fáil leader singled out Leo as he predicted he would not last long in politics. 'Unfortunately, I felt that some of the new Fine Gael people were bringing a new low into it,' Mr Ahern said.

> At one stage they wanted to talk about cleaning up politics, and then they brought in the gutter comments. ... I'm big enough to take it, but when you hear a new deputy who isn't a wet day in the place not alone castigating me but castigating Tony Blair and Bill Clinton, I wish him well. I'd say he'd get an early exit.

Varadkar now accepts that his decision to go after the country's most popular politician was a strategy that divided opinion.

'There were some people in the party who took the view that it was ungentlemanly or I had gone too far or you shouldn't be so strident or whatever,' Leo says. But he admits that by opting to play the role of 'attack dog or Rottweiler', it ensured that he was now getting noticed. Being outspoken was a key element of Varadkar's strategy to stand out among the new breed of Fine Gael TDs: 'Every opposition party needs one and I was happy to play that role.'

Bertie Ahern's response in the Dáil chamber suggests he saw Leo as an upstart and a bit of a smartass. In Fine Gael headquarters, General Secretary Tom Curran was forming a different view entirely. Curran watched the unfolding events closely and recorded his observations of the party's new TDs in a small black notepad. Every move made by Leo and others would be accounted for in what became known internally as 'Tom's little black book'. 'I think what we were seeing was the start of another golden generation in the party,' Curran says.

* * *

2008 brought with it the news of some extremely bleak jobs figures. The rate of unemployment had almost reached a five-year high, with more than 170,000 people signing on the Live Register in December 2007 alone. A new set of economic troubles signalled an end to the Celtic Tiger. As fears grew about a possible economic recession, Varadkar accused Fianna Fáil of killing off the Tiger and warned that job losses, particularly in the construction sector, would skyrocket. It was a warning that would be repeated by many others in the coming months.

But Ireland's looming economic disaster remained on the undercard while controversy still surrounded the Taoiseach's finances. In January, there were reports that some Fianna Fáil

TDs wanted to publicly criticise the Mahon Tribunal over its costs to date and its alleged failure to prevent leaks to the media. But within the Green Party – Fianna Fáil's coalition partner – a deep sense of malaise was setting in. The party publicly expressed its confidence in the tribunal to do its work. But party leader John Gormley refused to do the same when it came to Ahern. 'I've said what I said. I'm very happy with the performance of the Green Party in government,' he said when asked about his confidence in the Taoiseach.

The opposition scented blood and upped the ante with regular attacks on Ahern's credibility. In a surprise admission, Varadkar said publicly that Fine Gael had been too slow off the mark when it came to scrutinising Ahern's finances. He admitted that an opinion poll released before the 2007 election, which indicated that the public was not concerned over the revelations, had 'spooked' his own colleagues. 'I think it is fair to say that ultimately we made an error in not sticking by our guns that time and standing by a fundamental principle for Fine Gael, and what has always been a big difference between Fine Gael and Fianna Fáil, which is a commitment to ethics and integrity in public office,' Varadkar said.

Just days later, fresh questions about Ahern's financial affairs emerged when he admitted he was unable to secure a tax clearance certificate until after the publication of the Mahon Tribunal report. Fine Gael lodged a complaint with the Standards in Public Office watchdog, asking that it investigate whether Ahern was tax-compliant following the 2002 general election. Ahern insisted he was. It then emerged that suppliers to the Taoiseach's own office had been told they must supply a tax clearance certificate for payments of €1,000 and above. The story again generated negative headlines for the Fianna Fáil leader. With Ahern's position looking more tenuous by the day,

Leo immediately came out of the traps. 'The political head of the country, who can't get a tax certificate because of outstanding tax liabilities from the 1990s, is insisting that the toilet roll, kitchen roll and rubber band supplier to the department must have just such a tax certificate,' he said. 'This highlights the ridiculous nature of the Taoiseach's situation. It is not normal. It is not acceptable and it is simply incredible that a political leader does not have a tax certificate.'

Pressure mounted further on Ahern after his former secretary Gráinne Carruth contradicted him at the inquiry, accepting that payments she had lodged in his account on his behalf had been in sterling. Her admission contradicted both Ahern's evidence and her own previous testimony. Ahern would later claim that some of the lodgements emanated from bets he had placed on horses. His time was up.

In May, Ahern resigned as Taoiseach and leader of Fianna Fáil, saying that the controversy was overshadowing the work of government and the pending Lisbon Treaty referendum. The move to ratify the Treaty of Lisbon was defeated in the June 2008 referendum, in what was a highly embarrassing development for the government and Ahern's successor, Brian Cowen.

In the blame game that followed, Varadkar claimed that the race card had been quietly used by the No campaign. 'It was about immigration. All the way along that was the elephant in the room that nobody spoke about. Some of the No campaign used xenophobia,' he said. He also accused Minister for Justice Brian Lenihan Jr, his constituency colleague, of failing to do enough to ensure the referendum was passed. Varadkar, who had quickly become Fianna Fáil's harshest critic, said the lack of trust in politics caused by the Ahern controversy also contributed to the referendum defeat. And he saved his most cutting remarks to date for Ahern himself. 'We have a former

Taoiseach who is essentially giving the John Gilligan defence that he won the money at the horses,' Leo said, referring to the notorious gangland criminal. 'This is a defence for drug dealers and pimps and not the kind of thing that should be tolerated from a former Taoiseach and a member of this House.' Using Dáil privilege, Leo made an impassioned plea for a clean-up of the political system:

> People have such a low opinion of politicians because we won't root out the rotten apples in our own barrel, and we allow them to contaminate our entire system. We need to get real. Politics in this country is falling apart. We have to make ourselves relevant to show the people that we work hard and we have to start to restore trust in politics.

Phil Hogan, who was a mentor to the Young Turks, says Leo had demonstrated to the party that he was prepared to push the boundaries. Leo's actions, Hogan says, played out well among the Fine Gael backbenchers:

> At the end of the day he was a robust debater in the Dáil. He generated a lot of goodwill with backbenchers in Fine Gael by taking on Fianna Fáil in a very strong way and, you know, if Fianna Fáil were willing to say difficult things about Fine Gael policy or individuals, well then, you could rely on Deputy Varadkar that he wasn't going to pull back.

It was not until March 2012 that the Mahon Tribunal published its final report into alleged planning corruption. The three judges found that Ahern gave untrue evidence about the source of over 165,000 Irish punts. Fianna Fáil leader Micheál Martin threatened to expel Ahern over the findings but he resigned voluntarily. Ahern has always rejected the tribunal findings. In an interview with RTÉ's Miriam O'Callaghan in July 2015, Ahern said of the Mahon Tribunal, 'They're wrong, they were wrong then, they're wrong now and they'll be wrong 'til the day I die.'

* * *

With the economic downturn quickly manifesting into a full-blown recession, opposition spokespeople enjoyed plenty of air time and column inches. But some of the proposals floated by Varadkar reaffirmed the view that he was one of the most right-wing politicians in Leinster House. Among the cohorts he decided to target through his seemingly ad-hoc contributions were prisoners and immigrants. In December 2007, a peculiar question tabled by Leo appeared on the Dáil order paper: 'To ask the Minister for Justice, Equality and Law Reform if he will charge prisoners for the cost of their time in prison, where prisoners can afford to meet this cost, and if he will make a statement on the matter?'

Junior minister Conor Lenihan, the brother of Leo's constituency colleague Brian Lenihan, decided to go on the attack. 'To my mind Deputy Varadkar's proposal is rather loathsome, because I believe any person with an understanding of our prison system could easily inform him that the people incarcerated in our prisons tend to be from very poor backgrounds,' Lenihan told the Dáil. Charlie Flanagan, the Fine Gael justice spokesperson, distanced his party from Leo's comments, saying they were made in a personal capacity.

It's often the case that a TD goes into hiding after their solo run proposal is shot down by party bosses. Varadkar stood firm, however, insisting he would pursue the proposal with the Fine

Gael front bench. 'It's been said the idea is right-wing, maybe it is. But this is a government that wants to charge sick elderly people for long-term care, while prisoners don't [pay]. Who's right-wing there?'

But accusations of being right-wing were soon followed by accusations of being a racist. In September 2008, Varadkar suggested at an Oireachtas committee hearing that unemployed foreign nationals could be paid six months' worth of social payments to go home. He said the plan had been pioneered by the socialist-led government in Spain. 'Foreign workers could be given a lump-sum payment of up to six months' unemployment benefit if they agree to return home,' he said. 'It would be entirely voluntary and with 40,000 on the Live Register it would save a lot more than it would cost to finance their way home as we do at the moment for homeless migrants and failed asylum seekers.'

Friends of Leo say he saw the proposal discussed on TV and merely floated the idea to create a debate. But coming from the Fine Gael enterprise spokesperson, it was quickly perceived that the proposal was party policy. The Minister for Social and Family Affairs, Mary Hanafin, said the plan was verging on being racist. Opponents and sections of the media attacked Leo, likening the proposal to a policy that might be put forward by the British National Party.

The controversy led to concerns among senior Fine Gael figures that Varadkar was all of a sudden becoming a liability. But, once again, he stood firm, hitting back at his critics. 'Racism gets thrown around in Ireland no matter what you say. I think it is a sad day when you can't ask a question about welfare reform without being called a right-wing racist Nazi,' he said. 'If I am [racist] then so is Bill Clinton, so is José Luis Rodríguez Zapatero in Spain, so is Brian Cowen, because we already operate many voluntary repatriation schemes in Ireland funded by the state. So me and 98 per cent of the world must be racist and that's it.'

Phil Hogan believes putting out these sorts of controversial proposals was part of Leo's bid to distance himself from the establishment. 'Perhaps he could have been more inclusive by bringing these matters to the front bench and the parliamentary party, but one of the most attractive features of his political career was that he was seen as slightly semi-detached from politics and not part of the mainstream,' Hogan says. 'He used policy ideas in his early days to show he was different than the established political viewpoint, that he was different in the way he wanted to convey them.'

*   *   *

Leo's enterprise portfolio ensured he was well placed to become a strong voice on economic issues and Ireland's deteriorating banking system. But it would also place him head to head with Brian Lenihan, one of the hardest-working and most likeable ministers in Irish politics. Tipped as a future leader of Fianna Fáil, Lenihan was appointed to the finance ministry in May 2008, replacing the new Taoiseach Brian Cowen. Little did Lenihan know he was taking on the toughest job in Irish politics at a time when the banks were concealing massive losses on loans to property developers. Very quickly, Lenihan would go on to tackle one of the greatest dilemmas ever faced by a Minister for Finance in the history of the state.

On the night of 28 September 2008, Lenihan was among a small group of people who gambled with Ireland's future in order to prevent a collapse of the banking system. The bank guarantee, which covered €440 billion worth of deposits and borrowings, was signed. But Ireland's problems were stacking up. On budget week in October, Lenihan warned that the country was now facing 'one of the most difficult and uncertain times in living memory'. With Ireland now officially in recession, Lenihan delivered his budget speech, in which he said the world's financial system had been 'turned upside down'. The country now faced a 'historical task' [*sic*] in returning to stability.

Varadkar had had previous run-ins with Lenihan's brother Conor, but he had always had a lot of respect for Brian. In the wake of the budget speech, however, he quickly moved to capitalise on the unenviable task facing the Fianna Fáil minister. In a letter to the *Irish Times*, Varadkar castigated Lenihan for the depth of his 'denial' about the economic crisis. Lenihan, he said, was displaying a great degree of ineptitude. 'We are in the midst of a deep domestic recession and are about to be hit by the effects of an impending recession in Western economies. There will be no global recession. The Minister for Finance really needs to understand this.'

In November, and with unemployment continuing to rise, Varadkar told the Dáil that Ireland was quickly becoming a 'third world' country. 'Ireland is sliding into the economic abyss,' he said. 'The economy is shrinking. The public finances are starting to make Ireland look like a country in the developing world, not Europe, and unemployment is set to soar.' Days later, at the Fine Gael Ard Fheis in Wexford, Varadkar gave another sobering account of our economic standing: 'Even if we were to close all of the schools and universities in Ireland, disband the gardaí and defence forces and close down the Department of Agriculture, we would not be able to balance the budget.' At the same conference, Varadkar laid out eight proposals in his capacity as enterprise spokesperson that he said would help rebuild Ireland's economy. They included tax breaks for businesses to take on new employees, re-examining the national pay deal and recapitalising the banks on the condition that they provide credit to businesses and households.

In July 2009, Varadkar – reacting to the latest jobs figures – declared that Ireland had finally been met with 'the darkest day of the worst recession in living memory'. However, that day would in fact arrive over a year later when Lenihan formally applied for a financial bailout from the European Troika, made up of the International Monetary Fund, the EU Commission and the European Central Bank.

Despite often being opposite numbers in the Dáil chamber, Varadkar and Lenihan shared a respect for each other and often spoke privately about the state of the economy. They enjoyed each other's company and would attend events together in the constituency. In fact, as Varadkar now admits, Lenihan was a bit of a gossip in Leinster House and would often brief him about confidential government matters. 'One thing I do distinctly remember – the time when they were doing the first round of the public sector pay talks. The idea was floated around that there would be twelve days of unpaid leave or something like that,' he says. 'He was absolutely scathing about that and said this deal wasn't going to be done. Obviously I shared that [with Fine Gael].'

The twelve days' unpaid leave for civil servants in lieu of pay cuts was discussed between the government and unions during talks aimed at finding €1.3 billion worth of savings from the public pay bill. Lenihan was vehemently opposed to the proposal.

Around this period, Varadkar dedicated much of his energy to highlighting wastage within the state training agency FÁS. Over several months, revelations of serious misspending would prompt him to call for 'heads to roll' at FÁS. The agency was under the auspices of Varadkar's opposite number in government, Minister for Enterprise Mary Coughlan. Unlike Lenihan, Varadkar didn't rate Coughlan, who was also the country's Tánaiste. He targeted her in the same dogged fashion as he did Ahern. During an appearance on RTÉ's *Questions and Answers* programme in October 2008, Varadkar described Coughlan as Ireland's version of the US Republican politician Sarah Palin, labelling his counterpart 'Calamity Coughlan'. He ridiculed Coughlan after it emerged that the Office of Public Works (OPW) had forked out €47,000 to repair a toilet leak in her office. 'It seems a bit expensive that it would cost so much to repair a toilet unless it was a particularly valuable toilet or was something special. I just hope that the minister doesn't keep it to herself and shares it with her officials,' Varadkar said.

But the verbal exchanges between the pair quickly became vicious. In January 2009, Coughlan gave an interview in which she bemoaned the lack of a 'honeymoon period' upon taking office: 'I didn't even have time to say "howya" to the girls in the office.' Coughlan, then aged forty-three, also questioned whether some of the criticism levelled at her was due to her age. Varadkar didn't hold back. 'She spent the first six months hiding behind her gender and now she is hiding behind her youth,' he said.

The FÁS expenses scandal soon resurfaced and, this time, politicians such as Mary Coughlan were dragged right into the centre of it. Revelations that hundreds of thousands of euro had been spent on lavish holidays to the US for executives prompted the resignation of FÁS boss Rody Molloy. The controversy deepened when it emerged that Molloy received a golden handshake pension worth €892,000 after he stepped down. The revelation placed intense pressure on Coughlan.

Her decision to sit on a report into the matter for a number of weeks prompted Varadkar to accuse her of a cover-up. 'The Tánaiste has had this report for a number of weeks. I believe her decision to release the report at this time was a deliberate attempt to stifle its findings. Calamity Coughlan has turned into Cover-up Coughlan,' he said.

In early 2010, with a Cabinet reshuffle looming, there was speculation in political circles that Coughlan's department could be split. Media reports suggested that she used vulgarities in a meeting with the board of a firm in the US and that Irish officials were embarrassed to go abroad with her. Varadkar went in studs up, telling Coughlan she brought the 'cringe factor' to overseas trips. 'Others said you are unable to talk to business people and when you do the language you use is often inappropriate and vulgar,' he said. 'What do you say to those who level the charge at you that you are not suitable to represent Ireland overseas?'

Coughlan was visibly shaken. She hit back at Varadkar and accused him of making 'many nasty' and 'politically motivated' comments. 'My personality is a matter for others to decide. My job is to represent this country abroad when I do so, and I do so with pride and the privilege that has been bestowed on me by the Taoiseach.'

Varadkar went further, suggesting any move to restructure the department was due to the Taoiseach being afraid to sack her. 'But it seems to me the real reason why the government is considering a reform of your department is because the Taoiseach doesn't want to dismiss you; his personal loyalty to you means that he is actually considering abolishing the department from underneath you,' he said.

Varadkar was accused of being sexist – accusations he was having none of. 'If anything, I went easier on her because she was a woman,' he said. 'She's accused everyone of sexism. Nobody that I know would ever say that I'm sexist. Most people would accept it was the last line of defence for Mary Coughlan.'

* * *

By the spring of 2010, it was becoming increasingly likely that Fine Gael would be returned to power after fifteen years in the political wilderness. Varadkar, now one of the most feared opposition TDs, was destined to be handed a ministry under Enda Kenny. But there were still people within the party who believed his brand of politics could potentially damage Fine Gael. On 23 March, Varadkar made a contribution in the Dáil that confirmed many of those fears. It was a speech that, to this day, he views as one of his greatest miscalculations.

During a debate in the aftermath of Taoiseach Brian Cowen's ministerial reshuffle, Varadkar opted to trample on the reputation of one of the fathers of Fine Gael: Garret FitzGerald. Accusing Cowen of making a hames of his reshuffle, Varadkar declared, 'This is an appalling botch job. The Taoiseach is no Seán Lemass, Jack Lynch or John Bruton.' He continued, 'He is a Garret FitzGerald. He has trebled the national debt and effectively destroyed the country.'

Varadkar left the chamber following his extraordinary remarks completely oblivious to what he had just done. To this day, FitzGerald is idolised by Fine Gael members and is credited with turning the party's fortunes around during a difficult period in the '80s. He mentored some of the party's shining lights, including John Bruton, Alan Dukes, Michael Noonan and Ivan Yates. Serving as Taoiseach for two terms, FitzGerald drove some hugely significant policy decisions, including a liberalisation of the country's contraception laws. He played an important role in restoring peace in Northern Ireland and in 1985 he signed the Anglo-Irish Agreement with Margaret Thatcher, giving the Irish government an advisory role in Northern Ireland's governance.

Leo's remarks caused hurt both to the family of FitzGerald and to the wider Fine Gael party. As one of Varadkar's closest friends puts it, 'Leo reminds me a bit of Roy Keane. When Roy Keane is doing well, he's brilliant, but when he puts his foot in it, it's shocking. You are just waiting.'

It didn't take long for the fallout. Varadkar's own front-bench colleague, Louth TD Fergus O'Dowd, labelled the criticism of FitzGerald as 'disgraceful'. Various other TDs and senators distanced themselves from the remarks, including Lucinda Creighton, who spoke to Varadkar in the aftermath. 'Coming from Dublin South East, where Garret served as a TD and a Taoiseach, I know people were upset about the remarks, but I think we need to move on now,' she told RTÉ. 'I think that Leo should make a statement in the Dáil. I know he regrets it and he needs to put that on the record.'

Surprisingly to some in the party, Fine Gael leader Enda Kenny stuck by his young TD despite the hurt he had caused. 'Enda believes the party is big enough and bold enough to allow people to express personal opinions. And Leo Varadkar was expressing a personal view,' a spokesman for the Fine Gael leader said. Supporters of Kenny say he wasn't prepared to publicly rebuke one of his most inexperienced, yet talented, politicians. 'Kenny knew Leo fucked up – but as a leader, you have to stand by your team,' one minister remarks.

Would Varadkar come out and apologise or stick to his guns? He veered towards the latter, telling the *Irish Times*, 'I stand over my view on Garret FitzGerald's performance as Taoiseach and his rolling criticism of Fine Gael. What I said in the Dáil was over the top. He wasn't responsible for the crisis in the 1980s but [Brian] Cowen is responsible for the one now. That's the difference.'

Mark Finan says Varadkar did not go into the debate intending to criticise FitzGerald. 'But there's no filter mechanism there,' Finan notes.

> I would imagine that as soon as he said it, he had an idea in his mind the message he wanted to convey, but that is not the message that people understood the words to be. You have somebody that dedicated his life to the state. And you have somebody who is young, who hasn't achieved the same level of success and failure, criticising them for what they are doing. Rightfully, he was criticised for it.

Brian Hayes, however, provides a different outlook on Varadkar's actions. 'I took him to one side on the Garret stuff and said you have mucked up on this, you should go in and apologise. It was wrong what he said. It was petulant,' Hayes says, adding:

> There was a large part of Leo, me as well, who resents how the Garret FitzGerald government didn't do the things they said they'd do to fix the economy. There were a lot of people in Fine Gael who were very disappointed [with the FitzGerald government] and he was trying to articulate that.

Tom Curran says the experience helped shape Varadkar into a better politician:

> A lot of people saw that as 'Here is a guy learning on the job.' He is prepared to speak his mind and people saw a number of things that he said, which he may have now regretted, they

saw it as part of the learning process. But the authenticity of the guy is not taken away by those lapses.

Varadkar admits that he later apologised to the late Garret FitzGerald both via a letter and in person. Asked now whether he regrets his actions that day, he replies, 'Jesus, if there were twenty seconds of my political career that I could delete, that would be it. No, no, it was terrible, crass and disrespectful.' He continues:

> I wasn't even supposed to speak that night. Whatever happened, I was in the restaurant and Deirdre Chambers, who was in the whips' office at the time, said, 'We need someone to go in.' So it was a total accident in that sense. And I just saw Cowen sitting there and into my mind came the unsuccessful reshuffle of '86 and it just kind of all came out.

As Varadkar would later discover, his remarks towards Garret FitzGerald were not easily forgotten within certain sections of the party. But he had now cemented his reputation as a straight and honest talker who was prepared to take on anyone in politics – even his own party leadership.

CHAPTER 7

THE 2010 FINE GAEL HEAVE

Fine Gael director of elections Frank Flannery was walking along Grafton Street in Dublin City Centre when he bumped into the veteran RTÉ broadcaster Charlie Bird. A few months earlier, Flannery had been central to convincing Bird's colleague George Lee to run as the Fine Gael candidate in the upcoming Dáil by-election in Dublin South.

Lee had made a name for himself during the financial crash as the station's economics editor. The TV star represented something fresh and different. He was trusted by the public – at a time when voters had little faith in the ability of their politicians to pull the country off its knees. Lee felt it was his civic duty to take up the offer to enter politics and use his talents to help drag the country back from economic collapse.

It was a risk that paid off, as Lee received a massive 53 per cent of the vote, which took place on 6 June 2009. It was a particularly significant coup for Enda Kenny, whose leadership of the party was under intense scrutiny at the time. But after the dust settled on Lee's by-election success, the reality of life as a backbencher soon set in. During that chance encounter on Grafton Street in early 2010, Charlie Bird warned Flannery that his new recruit was unsettled and agitated. Flannery thought little of the remarks at the time. But just a few weeks later, on 8 February 2010, Flannery was sitting in a hotel room while on his holidays in the Far East when he received a phone call that left him dumbstruck.

Lee had resigned from the party, Flannery was told, only eight months after his election victory. Lee complained he had 'virtually no influence or input whatsoever' in shaping Fine Gael's economic policies and said he found the job 'personally unfulfilling'. Flannery had put a trojan effort into convincing Lee to join Fine Gael in the first place and had great hopes for the Dáil's newcomer. He, and many others, felt both embarrassed and betrayed. 'I didn't pay any more attention to George Lee. When he left, he was gone and didn't mean anything more to me. Politically speaking, he wouldn't get two seconds of my time or attention at that point, but we are still good friends,' Flannery says.

Lee soon felt the full wrath of Fine Gael's top brass. And it was Leo Varadkar who was first out of the traps in attacking his former colleague. Varadkar said the departure marked a 'sad day' for Fine Gael and Irish politics, adding that Lee could have contributed significantly if he hadn't bowed out so soon. Varadkar went on to claim the broadcaster had been offered a position on the Fine Gael front bench but had turned it down. He also noted that Lee was appointed chair of a Fine Gael policy committee, which never sat once. Lee's reasons for quitting Fine Gael were being openly tested.

The next day, Varadkar went even further and publicly stated that Lee's 'ego wasn't satisfied by the reality of the job'. He also dismissed suggestions that Lee quit the party over policy differences. 'I think Lee is trying to change the rules now, trying to say it was about principles, trying to say it was about policies,' Varadkar told the media. 'I spent eight months watching George in the Dáil. I don't know what policies he has or what principles he has. There weren't many at all.'

Varadkar wasn't the only Fine Gael politician who chose to attack Lee over his decision. Brian Hayes, Lee's campaign manager in the by-election, suggested he quit because he was forced to take a wage cut as a TD. Others weighed in too, and behind-the-scenes briefings to the press were even more vicious. Nonetheless, George Lee was gone. Fine Gael TDs could brief the media all they wanted but it would not camouflage the damage the resignation had caused the party.

Soon, the pressure would shift over to Enda Kenny. Questions about Kenny's leadership had been festering in the months leading up to Lee's resignation. Ironically, the leadership issue arose despite the fact Fine Gael was the country's most popular party and on the cusp of being returned to power. Fianna Fáil, no longer trusted in the eyes of voters, saw its support plummet. An election was imminent and Fine Gael politicians could taste victory. They knew they'd be in government after the next election, most likely with the support of the Labour Party or Independents. But questions about Kenny's leadership continued to niggle. There was a group of TDs in the party who had never rated Kenny's leadership style and wanted him gone. They had been agitating for years but now others – even some of Kenny's long-time supporters – were beginning to agree with them.

Opinion polls placed Fine Gael in pole position as the election loomed. But, significantly, Kenny trailed behind Labour leader Eamon Gilmore in terms of personal support. Kenny was a natural when it came to pressing the flesh with voters or working a room at party events. But in a live television or radio studio, he was a liability. Botched media performances, including an exceptionally awkward interview on *The Late Late Show*, did Kenny no favours. And it led to further doubts among backbenchers about his ability to perform in the role of Taoiseach. During one interview on Newstalk, Kenny failed to coherently set out Fine Gael's position on water charges. The performance was raised by Brian Hayes at a testy front-bench meeting soon after the broadcast. Hayes remembers Varadkar, then a first-time TD, backing him up when he criticised Kenny over his dismal media performances. '[Kenny] was asked his view on water and didn't want to commit the party on water. I actually raised it at the front bench,' Hayes says.

> I said, 'Enda you just cannot do that again, you cannot be so all over the place on an issue that is as fundamental as that and on an issue where we are as a party, where our supporters would expect us to be strong on.' And I remember Varadkar at the front bench when the rest of them looked down into their socks and he said, 'Enda you can't get away with that in future.' This was a fellah only on the front bench a wet week.

Kenny, not for the last time in his political career, found himself apologising to his party colleagues for his media performances and promised to up his game.

Publicly, TDs and senators said Kenny had their full support, but after the Lee resignation, rumblings about his leadership were surfacing. It wasn't long before prominent party TDs, including Varadkar, began to consider Kenny's replacement. Richard Bruton, the party's deputy leader and finance spokesman, was seen as a leader in waiting. Bruton's clear and articulate understanding of the financial crash meant voters saw him as a trusted voice at a precarious time for the economy. He was more than able to take on Minister for Finance Brian Lenihan. In the aftermath of the George Lee debacle, focus shifted to Bruton, who – in a timely intervention – confirmed to reporters his leadership ambitions. Reluctantly, however, Bruton said he remained 'absolutely loyal' to Enda Kenny. Kenny was then forced to deny his leadership was under threat from a potential move by Bruton. Nonetheless, the pieces on the chess board were beginning to be moved.

Even at this early stage in his political career, Varadkar was asked if he would like to one day lead Fine Gael. 'I'm in politics because I want to change things and to change things you need to be in power. I'm thirty-one. Of course I'd love to lead Fine Gael,' he responded. However, it was Simon Coveney, Leo's future leadership rival, who was particularly strong in his criticism of Kenny. Coveney said the Fine Gael leader 'doesn't always lead from the front' and warned that Kenny 'needs to step up to the mark and if he can't … then there's the obvious consequences of that'.

A leadership contest was brewing. All that was required now was for a challenger to step forward.

* * *

The controversy over the Lee resignation eventually died down and Fine Gael continued to do well in the opinion polls. However, Kenny's personal satisfaction rating remained poor. The research showed the public didn't take to him. No matter how hard he tried to endear himself to the average voter, it just wasn't enough. And, much to his dismay, the challenges kept stacking up for Kenny. His proposal to introduce gender quotas was voted down by his own parliamentary party. In

March 2010, following an internal Fine Gael vote, party chairman and Kenny loyalist Tom Hayes was replaced by Galway TD Pádraic McCormack, who had a tense relationship with the leader. Senior figures around Kenny knew that disquiet about his leadership was becoming a major issue. They knew, too, that his popularity among the voters needed to improve. In the same month, while speaking at the Fine Gael conference in Killarney, Co. Kerry, Kenny asked the public to put their trust in him and allow him to lead the country out of the economic abyss. Unfortunately for Kenny, his own party didn't trust him.

As he made his pitch to become Taoiseach, manoeuvrings were taking place behind the scenes to oust him. But Leo wasn't part of them. John Carroll, his then parliamentary assistant, insists the Varadkar camp were not among the plotters. 'The bit I can say hand on heart is that Leo wasn't involved in anything of that nature. His activity was focused on producing policy papers [and] private member's bills and challenging ministers,' Carroll says.

For the next couple of months, Fine Gael concentrated on selling their message, in the expectation that an election would be called within the year. Open criticism of Kenny died down temporarily as the party focused on Taoiseach Brian Cowen's failure to grapple with the scale of the financial crisis.

On Thursday 10 June 2010, the pressure on Cowen intensified. In the weeks previous, the government had published two independent reports on the financial crash. The reports found that decisions taken by successive Fianna Fáil administrations were key factors in creating the housing bubble that resulted in the collapse of the banking system. Fine Gael had had enough. The party tabled a motion of no confidence in Cowen.

It was not a vote Enda Kenny would win, but, nonetheless, it rallied Fine Gael backbenchers. Very soon, however, the pressure shifted back onto the Fine Gael leader. On the evening the motion was tabled, an *Irish Times* opinion poll spelled disaster for Kenny. The Labour Party was four points ahead of Fine Gael and was now the country's preferred choice to lead the next government. How could Fine Gael, on the cusp of power just weeks previously, find itself lagging behind Labour? To make matters worse, Eamon Gilmore's personal rating was almost double that of Kenny's. The dissenters believed it was time to pounce.

By chance, Richard Bruton was due to appear on RTÉ's *Prime Time* that night. The poll results were naturally raised. 'Do you, Richard Bruton, have confidence in your leader?' asked presenter Miriam O'Callaghan. 'It's not about me,' Bruton responded. O'Callaghan tried again: 'It's a straight yes or no.' But, much to the dismay of Kenny's inner circle, Bruton refused to back him. 'I am just as much in the dock in terms of Fine Gael's failings. We are all in the dock. We have to look at our performances,' he said. An hour later, Bruton appeared on TV3's *Vincent Browne* programme. Again, he refused to directly express confidence in his party leader and less than subtly expressed his own ambitions to lead. 'In the swag bag of every corporal is a lieutenant's baton,' he told Browne.

Panic broke out in Fine Gael. No one knew if this was an orchestrated campaign to oust the leader or merely a solo run by Bruton. If it was in fact organised, the leadership and the dissenters wanted to know who was involved. They were about to find out.

* * *

The next day, Varadkar was one of the first TDs out to defend the party leader. 'Enda has been leader of the party when we were on 19 per cent and also on 38 per cent in the polls – we don't change our leader on the basis of any one poll,' Varadkar said. 'We've been ahead in twenty-five polls in a row for two years, including one only ten days ago which had us in first place and Labour in third. I would not be talking about a seismic shift in the political landscape based on this one poll,' he added.

John Paul Phelan, then a senator and close friend of Varadkar's, said his colleague may have been publicly supporting Kenny but his words in private were somewhat different. Phelan says Leo sympathised with a group of TDs who were losing confidence in their leader's abilities. 'A clique kind of formed, I suppose. It was a clique so much as there was a group of people who were dissatisfied with the party's progress under "Castlebar",' Phelan says, in a reference to Kenny (Castlebar is Kenny's home town). 'He [Leo] would have been party to that. He wouldn't have been ringleader or anything, but he would have been very sympathetic. The ringleader types were Brian Hayes, Denis Naughten, Billy Timmins and Simon Coveney,' Phelan adds.

Over that weekend, Kenny called Bruton and asked him to issue a statement to the Sunday newspapers expressing confidence in him. Bruton refused. He told Kenny directly that he would no longer be able to express confidence in him if asked to do so. It was the clearest indication yet that Kenny was facing a battle for survival.

Meanwhile, anti-Kenny TDs privately briefed the media that they were encouraging Bruton to make a move. The lead headline of the *Sunday Independent* read, 'Fine Gael revolt as knives come out for Kenny'. The briefings were intended to let the leader know his days were numbered. Fine Gael frontbench TDs were quoted in the article as saying, 'I like Enda, but the game is up. End of story,' and 'I've supported Enda before, but I can't any more. Jesus, we're behind Labour.'

Bruton was actively building support that weekend, and Leo Varadkar was on his list of TDs to call. 'He rang me that Saturday and asked me for my support and I said I'd give it to him,' Varadkar confirms. John Carroll was among a group of Fine Gael staff taking part in a hillwalking challenge when Varadkar called to tell him he was prepared to back Bruton if a leadership challenge arose. 'My recollection was he made up his mind on the Saturday or Sunday,' Carroll says. 'He said it was in the best interests of the party and then committed himself to it. It wasn't something we were talking about beforehand. This wasn't something that was there. There wasn't any great game plan.'

By Sunday morning, the message was loud and clear – the rebels wanted Kenny gone and they expected him to step aside by Tuesday's parliamentary party meeting. The mood in the party was tense. Senior figures knew they were on the cusp of taking charge of the country and returning to government. But now it all seemed to be falling apart over an internal power struggle. The rebels were preparing to oust their own leader on the same day that a vote of no confidence in the Taoiseach was scheduled. It was a farcical act of self-harm by Fine Gael. But this was nothing new for a party which has a historical reputation for internal blood-letting.

Frank Flannery says the coup d'état took him by complete surprise. 'I couldn't believe the party could be so daft,' Flannery recalls. 'Fine Gael was running at the pace of a leadership coup a year and here they were starting again as they were coming up to battle. We had a good local election and we were going to have a good general election,' he adds.

On Monday, Kenny took decisive action and sacked Bruton.

He had no other option. On announcing the sacking, Kenny said party members had done 'huge damage' to the party through their 'anonymous comments to the media'. He accused TDs of seeking to bring Fine Gael back to the 'bad old days' when internal conflict and leadership challenges mired the work of the party. Kenny said he planned to put down a motion of confidence in himself that week. Phil Hogan, Paul Kehoe, Michael Ring and Alan Shatter, along with around twenty other party members, came out to bat for Kenny and insisted there was no need for leadership change.

Within an hour of his sacking, Bruton said Kenny did 'not have the capacity' to deal with the challenges posed by the economic crisis. 'He has done tremendous work. His efforts cannot be criticised but unfortunately he has not been able to convince people that he can manage the difficulties that lie ahead,' Bruton said.

But for Bruton to succeed in overthrowing Kenny, he needed a plan. And, above all, he needed a strong team behind him.

At 7.30 a.m. on Tuesday, Varadkar joined a group of front-bench TDs at what was supposed to be a secret meeting in the Green Isle Hotel on the outskirts of Dublin. Along with Varadkar, six other members of Kenny's front bench attended the meeting. They were Michael Creed, Olivia Mitchell, Denis Naughten, Billy Timmins, Fergus O'Dowd and Brian Hayes. Olwyn Enright took part by speakerphone. Simon Coveney was expected to attend but didn't – which led to speculation that he was supporting the other side. Varadkar was concerned about Coveney's no-show and called him as soon as the meeting ended. 'I rang him on the way into the Dáil that morning just to make sure he was still on side and he said he was,' Varadkar says.

Before the meeting, Varadkar had taken soundings from his

local supporters to see what appetite there was for a change of leadership. Sources in the room that night say there was a definite split and several diehard Fine Gael members in Castleknock insisted now was not the time for a leadership battle. Back in the Green Isle Hotel, Brian Hayes recalls how Varadkar told Bruton that while most of his supporters wanted Kenny gone, they didn't necessarily believe Bruton was the right man for the job. 'Leo was very honest at the meeting,' Hayes says. 'He came in and he said, I will never forget this, in front of Richard and in front of everyone, he said, "Well, they all want Enda out, all our members in Dublin West want Enda out, but they are not convinced you are the right man for the job."' Varadkar, however, says he personally was 'very much for Richard'. He adds, 'I genuinely thought Richard at the time would have been the person I would have supported.' As the meeting ended, the Green Isle Hotel conspirators prepared to attend the front-bench meeting scheduled for later that morning and call for Kenny to go. But when they showed up to the meeting room in Leinster House, things didn't go quite as planned.

Kenny came out swinging and admonished them all. He told them they were useless, lazy and insisted it was their fault the party was performing poorly in the polls. He accused them of holding the party back before sacking the entire front bench. It was a chaotic set of events. Before the rebels could respond, Kenny closed down the meeting and walked out the door, followed by his supporters. The rebels were left stunned. They retired to Olwyn Enright's office and discussed their next move.

Later that morning, Varadkar was among the same nine TDs who marched up the plinth of Leinster House to speak to the media. He hung to the back of the group, but his towering figure was there for all to see on RTÉ's *Six One News*. Denis Naughten told the media the group were 'putting their careers on the line' by declaring they no longer had confidence in Kenny. Naughten insisted, however, that they were doing it for the good of the party and the country.

For Varadkar, the move represented the biggest gamble of his political career to date. He was turning his back on the only leader of Fine Gael he had served under since taking up professional politics: the man who had appointed him to the front bench straight after being elected for the first time. Leo believed Kenny's days were numbered. But the clock was ticking for the plotters to execute their plan. The TDs had less than two days to convince their party colleagues to purge Fine Gael's leader of the past eight years.

Leo played a very public role in the campaign to oust Kenny. He did not shy away from media requests during the heave and was blunt and honest in his criticism of the leader. Frank Flannery remembers pleading with Leo to reconsider his position. 'I said to him, "Leo make sure you go with your head on this occasion, we can't afford any mistakes or slip-ups,"' Flannery says.

> He texted me back and said after long consideration he was comfortable with what he was doing and both his head and his heart were fully aligned on the matter. That was the end of the conversation as far as I was concerned. I texted him back and said, 'That's good, Leo. Now the one other thing I would ask you for is for the duration of this campaign don't say anything that will make your political life more difficult in the future.'

Varadkar clearly didn't heed the advice. Later that evening, he went on RTÉ's *Prime Time* and delivered a devastating appraisal of Kenny's abilities by paraphrasing Hillary Clinton's 2008 US presidential attack advert about Barack Obama:

I have to ask myself that key question – the 3 a.m. question – that if we are in government and if there is a national crisis and if there is a sovereign debt crisis for example and Patrick Honohan [the Governor of the Central Bank] lifts up the phone at 3 a.m. and rings the Taoiseach, who do I want to answer that phone?

He also suggested that Kenny could perhaps – as a consolation prize – be appointed Minister for Foreign Affairs should Richard Bruton go on to become Taoiseach. The mere suggestion infuriated Kenny.

Amid the fallout from Varadkar's interview, Kenny's team of supporters were also working the phones. Consideration was given to whether some of Bruton's backers could be persuaded to change sides. But Varadkar was not one of them. Phil Hogan, Kenny's director of elections during the heave, says the leader's camp saw little point in approaching Varadkar to bring him on side. 'There was a hardcore on each side of this motion of no confidence that … were not going to be changed, no matter how many phone calls you made, and Leo would have been one of the people that were written off from the word go,' Hogan says.

Kenny's camp also knew that Leo was an upcoming star in the party, however. He appealed to the traditional, centre-right Fine Gael voter who may have felt left behind in the Kenny era. He was an intellect, had bright ideas and was a very able media performer. They knew his support for Bruton might convince party members who were sitting on the fence to vote for the challenger. 'We would have made sure to see who he was talking to, who was he attached to, who he was friendly with,' one of Kenny's key lieutenants says.

Despite Kenny's conviction that Varadkar wasn't for turning, the pair did have a conversation during the heave in which the

Fine Gael leader tried to persuade the young TD to switch sides. Varadkar explained to Kenny his reasons for not supporting him and insisted he wouldn't be moved. But what Kenny did next came as a major surprise to Varadkar. 'What he said to me in the meeting when I told him I wasn't supporting him – he said no matter what happens I'll be back on the front bench,' Varadkar says. But Varadkar did not believe Kenny would be true to his word. He thought the promise was merely part of the leader's strategy to hold on to power.

Other senior Fine Gael figures also tried to change Varadkar's mind during the drama, which lasted six days. Varadkar's long-time mentor and family friend Frances Fitzgerald, who was backing Kenny, met him for coffee in Leinster House. 'We had a very pleasant conversation about it. Leo was questioning my view and I was questioning his and telling him why I felt he was wrong,' Fitzgerald says. 'We had totally different views at the time. He's never aggressive. I had my view and he had his and we had a conversation. Of course, everyone was trying to convince everybody,' she adds.

Wednesday 16 June 2010 was a day of intense activity within Fine Gael. Phone calls and texts were being exchanged non-stop. People were being dragged into private corners of Leinster House to be grilled on their voting intentions. While Kenny was doing much of his own groundwork, he was supported hugely by Phil Hogan and Paul Kehoe. Hogan was a master of psychological warfare. He knew the party inside out. He preyed on each TD's and senator's hopes, fears and ambitions to lock down their votes. Every tactic possible was deployed to shore up support for the leader. 'The strategy was to concentrate on the people who were available to be persuaded. We were very confident from the word go we had a majority of the people, particularly the backbenchers and the senators,' Hogan says.

Bruton's camp, on the other hand, didn't seem to know what they were doing. Support for the rebel candidate was building and it looked at one point as if they could have the numbers. But the campaign was too leaky and there were too many people involved in devising the overall strategy. 'As the saying goes, "Too many chefs spoil the broth,"' remarks one minister of the Bruton campaign. Hogan believes the Bruton faction put too much emphasis on winning over front-bench votes and underestimated the influence of backbench TDs and senators:

> There were people in the parliamentary party who may not say a lot in the Dáil or parliamentary party or Senate but had the same voting entitlement and voting weight as the key people in the Fine Gael front bench. That was a big mistake that was made by the people that were opposed to Enda Kenny.

Suspicion and paranoia also began to creep into the Bruton camp. They believed there was a leak in the camp and all fingers pointed at Simon Coveney, without any concrete evidence. The Cork TD failed to show up for the infamous Green Isle Hotel meeting and there was talk that he may have tipped off the media to the whereabouts of the 'secret' rendezvous. A suggestion also emerged that Coveney would challenge Bruton in a leadership contest if Kenny lost the motion of confidence. Coveney denied he was prepared to enter the fray as a third candidate – but the suspicion remained.

John Paul Phelan insists there was certainly a spy in the Bruton camp but said he did not believe it was Coveney. 'The Kenny camp were able to screw to the ground four or five backbenchers in the last few days that they would not have known about were it not that they had somebody on the inside providing them with information,' Phelan says. Varadkar also says he did not believe Coveney was playing both sides. 'This is one of the stories nobody really knows the answer to. I don't think he was,' he says, adding:

> I think Simon was just being Simon and he tends to believe the best in people and can be very optimistic almost to a fault sometimes and I think he was trying to sort of reason with people, and listen to both sides, maybe try and convince them to step down or whatever, maybe more in that space.

Varadkar says he does believe at least one TD was pushing Coveney as a compromise candidate at the time of the heave. 'I think some people genuinely thought he would be the third option,' he says. In an interview for this book, Coveney said putting his name forward was 'never a serious proposal' but refused to comment on who was backing his candidacy.

Coveney also addressed for the first time the attempt by his own party members to taint his reputation by claiming he was playing both sides in a leadership campaign. 'There was a very devious story which I remain very upset about because I know where it came from. That was an attempt to undermine my reputation in the party,' he said.

> I was very upfront with leaders and leadership contenders, so it really stung me that someone would spread a rumour that I was playing both sides. It did have the desired effect of undermining the influence I had on a certain group within the party and it was a very clever strategy but a very nasty and devious one.

Coveney declined to reveal who he believes spread the rumour, adding that he did not want to be 'personalised and bitter about it'.

All this was playing on the rebels' minds as they walked into the Fine Gael parliamentary party room at 11.30 the next morning, Thursday 17 June. A tense and heated five-hour debate followed, with most TDs and senators setting out their stalls on the motion of confidence. Contributions were emotional and heartfelt. Those who spoke believed strongly in the candidates they were backing. They were making their choice only in the interests of the party.

But it is Enda Kenny's speech that is most remembered by those who sat in the stuffy party room in Leinster House on that summer afternoon. Even walking into the meeting Kenny seemed in a jovial and confident mood, telling reporters he planned to 'raise the roof'. The party leader was the first speaker to take to the floor and he delivered his speech like his political life depended on it, which it did. He banged the desk with his closed fist, dismissing opinion polls before setting out his political achievements. Kenny insisted he would be the man to lead the party into the next election and said he would come out the other side of that vote as Taoiseach.

The next move by Kenny would be remembered for years to come. He eyeballed several 'traitors' in the room, including Varadkar, and excoriated them for their disloyalty. He told them they would be nothing without him. They would still be voting on county council motions if he had not taken a chance on them and given them their start in national politics. Varadkar admits Kenny's 'powerful' speech may have swung votes at the last minute and he also concedes that he deserved the dressing down he received from the leader. 'Enda is able to turn on the emotion. He did it really well with his delivery at that time, but he had a go at a few of us,' he says.

I think I offended him on *Prime Time*. I suggested he could be Minister for Foreign Affairs or something like that. He kind of called me out on that and criticised me for it, said it was arrogant or disrespectful or whatever – which it was so I wasn't particularly hurt by it.

When it was his turn to speak, Bruton said he was a politician of conviction who sat on neither the left nor the right of the political spectrum. In a clear attack on Kenny's personal popularity, he pointed to the need to improve the party's standing in the opinion polls. Coveney was among the next TDs to speak. He praised Kenny for his years of service but said the party needed to look to the future. Varadkar soon followed. He said the public had lost confidence in Kenny and the party needed to prepare for a three-way race in the next election, in reference to Fianna Fáil and the Labour Party. TDs and senators who backed Kenny paid tribute to his electoral successes, which had seen the party increase their number of seats at consecutive elections. They also warned it was the wrong time to change the leader as the country was on the verge of a general election that Fine Gael could potentially win.

After a highly charged meeting, voting finally took place. Paschal Donohoe, then a senator, and party chairman Pádraic McCormack counted the votes in an adjoining room. Kenny was victorious. The official result was never made public, but the Fine Gael leader walked out of the meeting that afternoon to the cheers of dozens of supporters who had travelled from his home county of Mayo. Flanked outside Leinster House by his supporters, Kenny vowed to unite the party before leading Fine Gael into the fast-approaching general election.

The plotters were deflated. Their political careers now looked to be over, or at least stalled until Kenny was gone. Varadkar was as disheartened as anyone. He said those long six days of infighting were 'scarring' for the party and for him personally. Varadkar took particular issue with the TDs who had sat on the fence. 'The only people who annoyed me were the ones who were ambiguous. Who were on one side and the other side,' Leo remembers. 'I had no problem with Phil [Hogan] because you knew where Phil stood. There were one or two who could have been a bit braver. There was certainly at least one who – if you put it that way – was egging people on and then subsequently backed the other side.'

John Carroll says Varadkar was resigned to spending the foreseeable future on the back benches. The team even discussed what projects he could pursue as an ordinary deputy. 'He had no expectation of being reappointed after the heave. We were looking at things we could do from the back benches but there was no mourning,' Carroll says. Varadkar's close friend Mark Finan remembers the aftermath of the failed coup quite differently. Over bottles of red wine and chateaubriand in the Castleknock Hotel, Varadkar confessed to Finan and their mutual friend Nollaig Crowley that he was having doubts about his political future. He had earlier spent the afternoon sitting on the couch watching detective drama *Midsomer Murders* and was feeling sorry for himself. But, after a few glasses of wine, Finan says, the trio got 'absolutely trollied'. He says Varadkar was in a 'difficult place and the advice we offered was just to take time and do nothing'. Finan adds, 'It was just to wait and see what happened, and he did.'

Varadkar's case for reappointment was not helped by his declaration during the short-lived heave that it would be hypocritical for him to accept a front-bench position in the event of a Kenny victory. A week later, Varadkar received a call from the Fine Gael leader. In his office, Kenny sat across from Varadkar and reminded him of the conversation they had had during the heave. Kenny had told Varadkar he would not sack him even if he voted against him. He said he was honouring that commitment and offered Varadkar the communications, energy and natural resources portfolio. Varadkar was taken aback. 'In my mind at the time when we lost in the heave, I wasn't going to serve in the front bench,' Varadkar says.

Varadkar would be one of three rebels to retain their positions on the front bench. Simon Coveney and Richard Bruton were also welcomed back to the top table despite their roles in the heave. 'Kenny realised after the heave there were certain people you have to accommodate,' says John Paul Phelan. 'There are certain people who are dispensable. Varadkar was too big a star to be left out despite his perceived treachery. There would have been a bit of an outcry now if he hadn't been reappointed.'

Phil Hogan insists no one had to convince Kenny to bring Varadkar and the others back into the fold, as the leader was focused on uniting the party after a vicious leadership battle:

> To be fair to Enda Kenny, he got on with the business of bringing people like Richard Bruton, Simon Coveney, Leo Varadkar back on the front bench, giving them the responsibilities, and they equally understood that they were fortunate to have a leader of the party that was prepared to forgive them.

Hogan adds, 'The best thing to do was try and heal the wounds and bring people from both sides of the argument onto the front bench and get ready for the general election, which was coming anyway within the following year.'

And Kenny didn't have long to wait.

As the economy continued to implode and unemployment soared, it became increasingly obvious that the Fianna Fáil-led government could not last much longer. Kenny, once a dead man walking, was now a leader in waiting. Some of those who had betrayed him would spend a long time in the political wilderness. But as the election campaign would show, Leo Varadkar was far too valuable to disregard.

CHAPTER 8

GENERAL ELECTION 2011: LEO BECOMES A MINISTER

An exhausted Leo Varadkar arrived home to his empty apartment in leafy Castleknock following a long day knocking on doors. It was the middle of the 2011 general election campaign. Fine Gael could sense victory was on the cards. The party had spent weeks urging voters to kick Fianna Fáil out of government and 'take our country back'. In Castleknock, Varadkar stood staring at a supermarket ready meal rotating in his microwave as he impatiently waited for it to be heated. He hadn't found time in between hours of canvassing and media appearances to stock his fridge.

The images were captured by the RTÉ documentary *Naked Election*, which followed six candidates throughout the duration of the campaign. Not for the first time, Varadkar stood out. The footage painted a lonely picture of a man who was quickly becoming one of the country's most established politicians. It was also the sort of image that would compound the fears of his family and friends, who suspected, in Varadkar's own words, that he was suppressing his sexuality.

But while Varadkar struggled on one hand with this internal battle, he excelled on the campaign trail. Now the party's spokesperson on communications, Varadkar found himself pushed to the forefront of the Fine Gael campaign. What he lacked in one-on-one social skills he made up for in abundance with his understanding of the realities of the deepening economic crisis. With families being ripped apart by an unemployment crisis and emigration, Fine Gael knew the campaign would be underpinned by emotion. People felt hurt and betrayed by Fianna Fáil's disastrous handling of the economy. Voters were looking for leadership and reassurance – about their jobs, their homes, their livelihoods, their children's future.

Making the case for tackling forced emigration, Varadkar used a press conference to promise the creation of some 45,000 work experience and education places. 'I've been struck by the number of people who have told me about their sons and daughters who have had to emigrate to find work,' he said. 'Fine Gael is not prepared to lose this talent without a fight.' During the press conference, Leo made an impromptu admission about his own political style. 'I am not someone who is really a natural canvasser,' he said. 'I probably should not be in politics at all; I am not really a people person.'

Meanwhile, Fianna Fáil was in meltdown. The party's loyal support base was eroding at a phenomenal pace. Years of constituency work evaporated overnight as angry voters turned their backs on TDs once considered local heroes. This was a bruising campaign experience for even the most battle-hardened members. From day one of the campaign, Fianna Fáil struggled to escape the fact that the party was responsible for handing over the country's financial sovereignty to the EU and IMF.

Both Fine Gael and Labour had a clear position throughout the campaign that they wanted to re-negotiate elements of the deal agreed with the Troika. And so remarks during the campaign by Alan Dukes, the former Fine Gael leader and chairman of the bailed-out Anglo Irish Bank, prompted a swift intervention from Varadkar. Dukes claimed that the banks may need a further €50 billion capital injection – far exceeding the level of funding already set aside for the bailout. It was an astonishing and frightening prediction. 'It is indeed scary. The whole situation is scary. It's realistic I think,' Dukes said.

Along with the Labour Party, which was enjoying a strong campaign, Fine Gael had ruled out any further bailout of the banks. 'Not another cent,' Varadkar assured voters. 'There will be a new government in six weeks and the banks aren't getting another cent.' Brian Hayes, who played a key role in the campaign, says Varadkar had the ability to speak directly to voters in a language they understood and appreciated. 'It was a key moment in the campaign ... because he got the language right,' Hayes says. 'He has a great way with language. Some politicians waffle on – he just gets to the point quickly.'

Within Fine Gael headquarters, Varadkar was being talked up as one of the party's best assets. He had shown a strong grasp of policy and was able to sell it to the electorate with precision. He was, as one senior Cabinet member puts it, 'no longer just saying things for the sake of it'. But while Varadkar was quickly becoming the face of the party's national campaign, his team of foot soldiers were working the constituency. Dublin West had shifted from a three-seat to a four-seat constituency as a result of boundary changes. Team Varadkar believed their candidate would hold his seat but this did not mean they could ease off the throttle. They knew groundwork was the key to a successful election campaign. Early morning canvasses of commuters and door-to-door campaigning could not be neglected simply because Varadkar was enjoying national exposure. 'I've heard him say several times there's no avoiding the graft. There's no avoiding knocking on doors,' remarks Varadkar's close friend and supporter Ted Leddy.

Varadkar had a running mate in councillor Kieran Dennison, but Fine Gael knew realistically the party could only take one seat here. He agreed to split the constituency and allow Dennison to canvass solely the area of Mulhuddart. By doing so, he consented to steering clear of the part of the constituency that had rejected him twelve years previously. Towards the latter stages of the campaign, Varadkar wrote a letter to constituents around Mulhuddart asking them to give their no. 1 preference to Dennison. 'The Mulhuddart ward took in a lot of leafy areas at the time, such as Lucan North,' says one Leo strategist. 'The days of Leo being toxic here were long gone. There were some good Fine Gael areas there where people would have been delighted to see Leo on the doorsteps. Yet they were getting a letter from him saying "Please vote for Kieran".'

Fianna Fáil, meanwhile, were braced for an electoral drubbing, particularly in Dublin. Brian Lenihan contested the election despite having been diagnosed with pancreatic cancer. As Varadkar's supporter Ronan Melvin observes, there was a sympathy factor behind Lenihan's campaign this time round. 'Fianna Fáil were losing seats everywhere,' Melvin says. 'Brian, due to his personal support and the terrible news he had as well… there was a huge sympathy factor. That's why Brian kept that seat – the only seat kept in Dublin.'

As the campaign entered its third week, the focus switched away from whether Fine Gael would win, towards the identity of their bedfellows in government. All the indications pointed to Labour, who were flooding the country with posters carrying the slogan 'Gilmore for Taoiseach'. Party leader Eamon Gilmore was riding the crest of what became known as the 'Gilmore Gale'.

As polling day neared, Fine Gael began to stretch its lead on its rivals, despite a late attempt by Labour to portray Varadkar as a Margaret Thatcher-style politician leading a 'stealth tax' party. 'What he [Leo] wants to do is take money out of the pockets of families in this country that are struggling to survive,' said Labour's social affairs spokesperson Róisín Shortall.

In Dublin West, Labour's deputy leader and finance spokesperson Joan Burton proved too much of a match for Varadkar and topped the poll on the first count. Varadkar was elected on the second count with just under 20 per cent of the vote. Joe Higgins of the Socialist Party secured his return to the Dáil, along with Lenihan, who watched on as dozens of his friends and colleagues had their seats wiped out.

25 February 2011 represented the worst day in Fianna Fáil's history. Lenihan could barely believe the scale of his party's demise. After the final votes were counted, Fianna Fáil ended up with just twenty seats – its lowest ever Dáil representation. The result represented a political earthquake, one that is unlikely to be repeated for decades. Fianna Fáil, punished for its chaotic handling of the economy, was forced to hand the keys to Government Buildings to Fine Gael and Labour. It was now over to Taoiseach Enda Kenny to decide the makeup of his Cabinet as the thirty-first Dáil commenced.

On 9 March 2011, Kenny received his seal of office. It was an extraordinary moment for a politician who less than twelve months earlier had been forced to fend off attempts by Varadkar and others to oust him in a bloody coup. Kenny hadn't forgotten those who sought to overthrow him. But his advisers stressed the importance of healing the wounds and urged

Kenny to appoint key Bruton backers to Cabinet. As the ministerial appointments loomed, Varadkar privately told colleagues he was not expecting anything more than a junior ministry. Kenny reappointed him to the front bench after the heave but Varadkar believed there was little or no chance he would be made a Cabinet minister. There was a long list of Kenny loyalists who would be ahead of him in the queue. But at the back of Varadkar's mind was the conversation he had shared with Kenny during the heave. Before the parliamentary party vote of confidence, Kenny had told Varadkar he had no intention of sacking him even if Richard Bruton's coup failed. But Leo was still surprised to get a call from Enda Kenny's office on the day Kenny was appointing his Cabinet.

When he arrived, the Taoiseach offered Varadkar the portfolio of transport, tourism and sport. Varadkar couldn't believe his luck. Fine Gael figures who spoke to Kenny that day say he was influenced particularly by Mark Mortell, a trusted party strategist. Mortell believed Varadkar had a star quality that simply could not be ignored. Frank Flannery and Tom Curran also lobbied Kenny to appoint Leo to Cabinet. 'If you believe in the idea of Fine Gael transforming itself and bringing on waves of new potential leaders – when you get them elected and are in government, you need to give them power,' Curran says. Phil Hogan, who was also handed a Cabinet post, says youth and geography shaped Kenny's thinking: 'I would say it was important Leo was brought back because he represented a youthful and dynamic and energetic segment of the population, which was an image important to convey to the Dublin electorate.'

Kenny also appointed Richard Bruton and Simon Coveney to Cabinet, in a move designed to further heal divisions. But there was no place for a number of other key Bruton backers, such as Michael Creed, John Deasy, Fergus O'Dowd, Brian

Hayes and Lucinda Creighton. O'Dowd, Hayes and Creighton would, however, be rewarded with junior positions. According to Hayes, Kenny could have ignored Varadkar but chose not to for one key reason: 'Because he [Leo] is very, very talented and he's a 24/7 politician. Being a 24/7 politician … is a huge advantage because it's a 24/7 business. So you're not distracted by family and all this kind of stuff.'

Other senior figures say the decision to appoint Leo straight to Cabinet annoyed those who lost out. 'We had a very large parliamentary party at the time and you had people who came into Fine Gael in the '90s who were always waiting for their time to be appointed as a minister,' says one figure close to Kenny. 'All of a sudden you have this guy, elected in 2007, and five years later he was sitting at the Cabinet table? And during that five-year period he was trying to take out Enda Kenny? Of course there were noses out of joint.'

While Creighton was handed the key junior ministry of European affairs, influential party figures believe the week marked a significant moment for the Young Turks faction. Varadkar had stolen a major step on his closest political ally. The relationship began to change that day. 'I think the greater difficulty between Leo and Lucinda would have happened at the point when he became a Cabinet minister. It was at that point the paths of both of them really began to differ,' says one senior government figure. Tom Curran believes Creighton's difficult relationship with Kenny played a factor in her being overlooked for Cabinet. 'Lucinda was much more playing the media. Leo was less so. He would make some interventions which were often a lot more telling and incisive,' Curran says. 'She had a very different type of relationship with Enda.' Another key party figure close to the pair says Creighton was upset that Leo had been handed an opportunity over her. 'It wasn't that she felt she should have been there – but that he was there ahead of her. He played the game so much better than she did and he learned.'

* * *

One of Varadkar's first decisions upon being promoted would prove to be among the most important of his career. The youngest member of Cabinet appointed a team of trusted advisers who quickly set about laying out the necessary pieces for a future tilt at the leadership. Leading this team was Brian Murphy. Affable and intelligent, Murphy is highly respected within the Fine Gael organisation, having held a number of key positions. He quit a lucrative job in the private sector to work as Varadkar's chief adviser. In 2012, Varadkar found himself at the centre of controversy after it emerged that he had lobbied Minister for Public Expenditure Brendan Howlin to secure a €135,000 package for Murphy. At the time, special advisers were paid just over €80,000 but Varadkar insisted on a more lucrative salary for Murphy. A salary of €105,837 was eventually sanctioned – still significantly above the agreed cap. The fact that Varadkar personally lobbied for a breach in the pay cap at a time when the public purse strings were extremely tight illustrates the value he placed on Murphy. Murphy would go on to serve as Varadkar's most trusted aide and, at key moments, would prove to be a mentor.

Varadkar also poached Nick Miller from the Fine Gael press office and appointed him as press adviser. The softly spoken Miller is seen as one of the most effective spin doctors in the country and is well respected by TDs and political journalists. For Tom Curran, these two appointments sent a message to the wider Fine Gael family that Varadkar was serious about moving up the political ladder. Curran describes the Murphy appointment in particular as 'one of the most politically astute moves I have seen'. He says Miller helped build Leo's profile nationally. 'Leo now had huge credibility in the organisation through Brian Murphy and huge credibility in the press through Nick Miller, who people saw as a very straight guy. Those two appointments told me this is a guy who is really planning for the future,' Curran says. 'He became the most accessible minister in terms of the organisation. He, as such a young man, could see what was necessary and appoint the best possible people. They are unrivalled. They don't have ego. It's a great way to be.'

Murphy and Miller joined a team that already included three of Varadkar's closest aides. John Carroll had been his parliamentary assistant since 2011, while Lisa Tavey and Mary Donohoe handled the constituency work. It was a close-knit inner circle where trust was the rule of thumb at all times. Meanwhile, the air of celebration surrounding Fine Gael and Labour following their election victories quickly evaporated as ministers grappled with the stark economic reality facing the country. Varadkar and colleagues soon realised the condition of the state's coffers meant difficult choices would have to be made immediately.

Just weeks into his tenure, Varadkar announced that the government would consider selling off a crown jewel: its stake in the national airline Aer Lingus. And in April, he told the Dáil that the multi-billion-euro Metro North and DART underground projects would be put on the long finger pending a review of capital spending. But it didn't take long for the government to face accusations that it was reneging on key election promises.

The latest round of stress tests found that the banks would need an additional injection of capital of €24 billion. Minister for Finance Michael Noonan moved quickly to announce a restructuring of the banking system, describing the previous government's bank guarantee on 30 September 2008 as 'the blackest day in Ireland since the Civil War broke out'. But opposition TDs accused the government of a spectacular U-turn, reminding the public of Varadkar's pronouncement during the election that 'not another cent' would go to the banks.

In media interviews following the major restructuring announcement, Varadkar denied that he had made a false promise, saying the European Central Bank (ECB) had put its foot down: 'We would have liked to impose losses on senior bondholders, but Europe has ruled it out. We are certainly ruling it out for AIB and Bank of Ireland, because Ireland will never get back to normal if we do impose losses on senior bondholders at these two institutions.'

But it wasn't the only election pledge made by Fine Gael and articulated through Varadkar that would become unstuck. During the campaign, Varadkar had coined the phrase 'bonfire of the quangos' as his party promised to scrap dozens of state-funded bodies. The plan never came to fruition. Labour's Joan Burton says it was clear to her that both Varadkar and Simon Coveney were competing to champion proposals without thinking them through. 'For both him and Simon, there was a competition over the "bonfire of the quangos". Now, you might say when both of them went into government it was a bit of a learning curve,' Burton says, pointing out that no such cull took place. 'That was one of the great catchphrases of the right at the time. I would say again Leo and Simon were on a very sharp learning curve.' Varadkar argues that the government did significantly reduce the number of state agencies.

Just weeks into the new Dáil term, the coalition was finding it extremely tough to renegotiate its bailout conditions. As the Cabinet met to discuss its next move, Varadkar tempered public expectation about the prospect of an improved deal. 'It's a long way to go. I think it's fair to say that renegotiating the EU/IMF agreement is going to be a lot harder than we thought it was going to be,' he said. 'We still think we're going to get the interest rate reduction, but that is nowhere near as easy to achieve as we thought it was going to be.' Those difficulties were perhaps best laid bare not by any government minister, but by the man who had signed Ireland up to its bailout deal in the first place.

On 24 April, Brian Lenihan told the BBC that Ireland had been forced into the bailout. He said he came under pressure from the ECB to agree to a bailout in November 2010 – before he had even secured government approval. He said the European Commission was less forceful than the ECB on the need to enter into a bailout programme. 'I believed that I had fought the good fight and taken every measure possible to delay such an eventuality, and now hell was at the gates,' Lenihan said.

In May, the government said it was preparing to seek a 1 per cent cut in the interest rates attached to its bailout in order to bring the country in line with Greece and Portugal. Varadkar firmly rejected a call from economist Morgan Kelly, who famously predicted Ireland's crash, to walk away from the bailout deal entirely. 'In my view, that's not a solution. If you do that, first of all you impose personal bankruptcy on a lot of people, horrendous social consequences on working people and people on social welfare,' Leo said.

Despite the financial constraints facing the coalition, certain measures were introduced in the summer of 2011 aimed at stimulating the economy. One of these measures was cutting the VAT rate for the tourism sector to 9 per cent in a move that would go down as one of the government's most significant stimulus measures. Varadkar was learning quickly on the job and had impressed the Taoiseach's team since his appointment as minister.

He joked that his high profile had meant his social life was 'totally dead. It's awful actually. It's really awful. It's actually very hard to go out because I'm just too feckin' well known,' Varadkar remarked in an interview with the *Irish Independent*.

But in May, the Young Turk had another foot-in-mouth moment that caused consternation throughout government. In an interview with the *Sunday Times*, Varadkar opened the door to the prospect of a second financial bailout. He said that he did not believe Ireland would be in a position to return to the bond markets in 2012 and that a further international loan could be required. 'I think it's very unlikely we'll be able to go back next year. I think it might take a bit longer... 2013 might be possible but who knows?' He continued, 'It would mean a second programme [of loans from the Troika]. Either an extension of the existing programme or a second programme. I think that would generally be most people's view.'

Unfortunately for the young minister, it wasn't most people's view. Or, if it was, they didn't want to express it publicly. The mere suggestion that Ireland would require a further bailout infuriated Enda Kenny and Michael Noonan. And it would lead to Varadkar being subjected to a series of spectacular slap-downs, undoing the view within the party that he had shed the liability tag. In the Dáil chamber, Fianna Fáil leader Micheál Martin said the comments had been picked up by 2,000 international outlets as he criticised what he described as 'solo runs' by ministers. In a clear rebuke to Varadkar, the Taoiseach said he had had words with ministers about making statements that could inflict damage on the economy.

Leo Varadkar sharply divided opinion both at Cabinet and within the wider Fine Gael parliamentary party. Colleagues encountered a man they found to be awkward, unapproachable and utterly unsociable. He was still viewed as one of the most right-wing TDs in the party and was held in deep suspicion by Fine Gael's coalition partners, Labour.

Joan Burton, then the Minister for Social Protection, recalls various encounters with Varadkar during the dark days that followed the bailout. She says she always suspected Varadkar was influenced by his time working as an intern on Capitol Hill. Both Leo and his friend Mark Finan had interned with Republican congressman Jack Quinn during their younger days. Burton suggests Varadkar may have been influenced by right-wing US politics initially, before moving closer to the centre as he matured. 'When Leo was going into government and into the run-in to that election, he wanted all the social welfare adjustments done in two years, as demanded by the Troika,' Burton says. '[That] would have been horrendous and would have devastated the economy because it would have cut the heart out of social spending,' she adds.

According to Burton, Leo was forced to soften his position on social welfare cuts following encounters with her colleague Brendan Howlin. But, she notes, he became less vocal at Cabinet as the coalition's term progressed. 'I think Brendan Howlin, I did as well, tried to persuade him that savage social welfare cuts were in nobody's interests,' Burton says. 'I think when he went into Cabinet first, he was quite a strong contributor. He became more silent then as time was passed.'

Fine Gael ministers at the Cabinet table during the coalition period have expressed differing views about Varadkar's performance. Phil Hogan recalls how Varadkar – along with James Reilly and Alan Shatter – supported him strongly when the parties were at odds over the handling of the introduction of water charges. 'I appreciated that a lot because it was a difficult time for me when I was implementing government policy and very few ministers were prepared to come out and publicly back me.'

Varadkar was also involved in a strange encounter at the Cabinet table over the issue of ministers using bus lanes for official government business. In May 2011, the coalition honoured an election pledge to scrap the use of garda-driven Mercedes for senior politicians with the exception of the Taoiseach, President, Tánaiste and Justice Minister. Ministers were instead told they could hire civilians to drive them around in their own vehicles. As Minister for Transport, Varadkar was responsible for the ministerial order required to enact the decision of Cabinet. Fine Gael figures present at the meeting recall how Varadkar was opposed to the idea of allowing civilian drivers to use bus lanes. He 'threw a strop', sources present say, telling his colleagues he would note on the order paper his opposition to the bus lane proposal. 'Fucking hell, all people wanted was to get to work on time and, to do that, we needed to use the bus lanes,' says one source present at the meeting.

> But Leo didn't want to. Then he did. Then he said he's writing on the side of the ministerial order that he didn't agree. What was that about? Afterwards he went around telling everybody he didn't personally agree. Big fucking deal, like – a bus lane. It saved a lot of money. The bill reduced by two thirds.

Meanwhile, within the parliamentary party, TDs were beginning to group into different cliques. The most notorious – yet exclusive – of these social circles became known as the Five-A-Side Club. Dublin Bay South TD Eoghan Murphy was responsible for setting up the group of new TDs in 2011. They included backbenchers such as Pat Deering, Brendan Griffin, Noel Harrington, Anthony Lawlor, Paul Connaughton, Seán Kyne and Seán Conlan. The sporting term used for the group was a front for what they really did: plot, drink pints and gossip.

As the Dáil term progressed, the Five-A-Side Club garnered a reputation for being anti-Enda Kenny. They were viewed as being both troublesome and rebellious and were instantly blamed for leaks from parliamentary party meetings. But, for Murphy, it was important that there was a cohesive group of TDs within the party who could exert influence as a unit whenever a leadership contest arose.

The Five-A-Side Club would meet for pints, often continuing until the early hours of the morning, in the Ginger Man pub just around the corner from the Dáil. The issue of the leadership was regularly discussed. It was often joked that in the event of a contest, the majority of the group would back Simon Coveney, leaving Murphy as the sole member in Varadkar's corner. Although Murphy found Varadkar socially awkward at times, the pair struck up a close friendship. He would often invite the minister to join the group for a pint. By doing so, Murphy opened the door for Varadkar to develop relationships with this cohort of strong-minded TDs who were looking beyond Kenny for their next leader.

Unbeknown to Varadkar, a support base was slowly being built around him. But as the Five-A-Side Club plotted their next move, another group of Fine Gael politicians was engaged in a conversation of a completely different kind.

* * *

The political silly season brought with it a sense of optimism for the government. Despite the myriad of challenges, the coalition had survived its first term and was relatively stable. Senior ministers were also quietly confident of the prospect of striking a deal with the Troika that would allow the country to exit its bailout programme. This scenario began to materialise in July when Enda Kenny announced that Ireland had secured a larger interest rate cut than previously envisaged. Some €800 million would be knocked off the cost of the country's debt as a result. It was seen as a significant victory.

Days later, Varadkar told RTÉ's *This Week* programme that it was time to be optimistic again. 'Really, for the first time in three years, for me, I'm starting to see the light at the end of the tunnel,' he said candidly. The pronouncement was followed by the unveiling of a new year-long initiative by the government known as 'The Gathering'. The proposal, spearheaded by civil servant John Concannon, was designed to attract the Irish diaspora home to celebrate their national identity. The initiative would lure 350,000 back to Ireland, Varadkar said, in what would be a major boost to tourism and the economy.

Ironically, the proposals were followed by remarks about holidaying that landed Varadkar in hot water once again. In December 2011, unemployment figures were still rising, and half a million people were jobless. Speaking at a tourism conference in Dublin, however, Varadkar suggested families would soon be in a position to take a holiday again. He also said the only financial hits families would suffer would be the recently announced €100 household charge and the VAT charged on household appliances such as televisions and fridges. 'The only people whose pay is being cut are ministers and senior civil servants. That means incomes will be the same next year,' Leo said. 'You'll have to pay €100 for your house and 2 per cent on a new TV or fridge, but that's it. That means people will be able to take a holiday, which they might not have been able to afford this year.'

Varadkar notes that official figures show the number of people taking domestic or foreign holidays actually increased that year. 'I was right if insensitive,' he adds. Once again,

Varadkar opened himself up to accusations of being out of touch. But soon afterwards, the political focus shifted away from economic issues.

The death of an Indian woman called Savita Halappanavar in October 2012 left the country stunned and created media headlines around the world. 'Ireland murders pregnant Indian dentist' read the headline of the *India Times*. Savita, aged thirty-one, was seventeen weeks pregnant when she presented herself with back pains at University Hospital Galway. She quickly developed sepsis, which put both her life and the life of her unborn baby at risk. Savita was miscarrying but, as a result of Ireland's strict abortion laws, she was denied a termination. She died on 28 October surrounded by her husband Praveen and a number of friends. Praveen claimed he was told by hospital staff that his wife could not be permitted a potentially life-saving termination because Ireland is 'a Catholic country'.

As two separate investigations were launched, anger about Ireland's strict abortion laws spilled out onto the streets. The focus was on Article 40.3.3 of the Irish constitution (Bunreacht na hÉireann), otherwise known as the Eighth Amendment. The clause, introduced by way of a referendum in 1983, gives equal rights to the mother and the unborn child. Critics say the amendment has been catastrophic and has forced thousands of women to travel to the UK to access safe abortion services. Savita would become an icon. How could Ireland fail this beautiful, pregnant woman, and indeed her family, in such desperate fashion, pro-choice advocates asked? Anti-abortion groups, however, claimed Savita's death was seized upon by the opposing side in order to further their campaign to liberalise the country's abortion laws.

As politicians struggled over what action to take, a real sense of unease grew within Fine Gael. Several TDs and senators were intrinsically pro-life and deeply opposed to any move to repeal the Eighth Amendment. The group included Lucinda Creighton and her husband, senator Paul Bradford. The amendment had divided the nation for over three decades. It was now causing serious tension within political parties, including Fine Gael, Fianna Fáil and Sinn Féin.

The situation for Fine Gael was made even more complex by the fact that the party's coalition partners, Labour, were opposed to the Eighth Amendment and were demanding change. In late October, as calls for abortion legislation mounted, Varadkar intervened, saying he did not believe in allowing TDs a free vote when the issue came before the Dáil. 'There's no real tradition of having free votes in Ireland,' he said. Within Fine Gael, the group of TDs led by Creighton were considering their next move. They were not prepared to vote for any legislation that would permit abortion, even in limited circumstances.

But as Fine Gael ministers tried to buy time, a Dáil bill tabled by Dublin North TD Clare Daly brought the issue to the fore. Daly's bill would provide for terminations in cases where the mother's life was in danger. As the bill was being debated, Fine Gael politicians attended a three-hour meeting of the parliamentary party in Leinster House, during which Varadkar clashed with Enda Kenny over the prospect of a future referendum on abortion. Kenny ruled out the idea as he moved to dampen the unease within his parliamentary party. The Daly bill was defeated – but it was now inevitable that something had to be done in response to Savita's death. Kenny said the Cabinet would make a decision on the issue by the end of the Dáil term – prompting Varadkar to quickly back down on his call for a referendum. It meant the abortion issue was kicked into touch for much of 2012 and 2013 as the economy retook centre stage. In July 2012, Ireland backed the EU fiscal treaty following a referendum. The government said it would use the result to try to strengthen Ireland's hand at securing a debt writedown.

In September 2012, Varadkar was appointed Fine Gael director of elections for the children's referendum, which proposed placing a greater obligation on the state to care for children. But he and Children's Minister Frances Fitzgerald came under fire after a court ruled prior to the vote that the government had wrongly used taxpayers' money to promote the Yes campaign. Amid fears that the controversy could jeopardise the referendum being passed, Leo pleaded with voters to consider the importance of introducing constitutional protections for children. 'The government is collectively responsible and if we've made a mistake, we accept that, but don't take it out on the children,' Varadkar said. The vote was passed, albeit by a much smaller margin than the government would have hoped.

At this point, Varadkar had settled well into his role as Minister for Transport, but he had scarce budgetary resources at his disposal. 'He didn't get to do a whole lot in the Department of Transport because he had no money,' says Phil Hogan. 'But that was the position with everybody. The housing programmes, the health programmes and the capital investment programme in transport were all effectively put on hold until we sorted out the nation's finances.'

Varadkar's colleagues believed he was now hitting the right balance between statesman and man of the people. He had become an experienced TD and Cabinet minister who was being spoken about across the political divide as a future leader. Unfortunately, he was still too gaffe-prone, too liable to cause offence, albeit inadvertently at times.

Ahead of the introduction of a new insolvency scheme, in March 2013, Leo suggested that some working mothers who entered into the new scheme would have to choose between their careers or paying the mortgage in cases where childcare costs exceeded the mother's income from work. 'I know one or two women who probably don't make very much money at all from working, but they do it to keep their position on the career ladder, if you like, and that is a legitimate thing to do,' Leo said. 'But if you can't pay your mortgage as a result, or buy your groceries as a result, then that is something that needs to be taken into account in any insolvency arrangement.' The remarks caused a public backlash and led senior figures such as Enda Kenny and Lucinda Creighton to distance themselves from the remarks. Varadkar eventually apologised for the comments, which he suggested were misunderstood within some quarters.

*   *   *

November brought the clearest signal yet that the abortion issue was set to rip Fine Gael apart. During an interview with Pat Kenny on RTÉ radio, Creighton said she would struggle to support any legislation brought forward by the government that would liberalise the regime. 'There are deep concerns that if we get it wrong, this could lead, for example, to abortion on demand,' Creighton said.

Senior party figures were braced for trouble coming down the tracks. They knew that the unease within the party had the potential to spread like wildfire. But they were also conscious of appeasing Labour – the driving political force behind the proposed changes to the country's abortion laws. Minister for Health James Reilly began drawing up the Protection of Life During Pregnancy Bill. Varadkar knew that his closest ally in the party, Creighton, was determined to stick by her convictions. Phil Hogan, who was aware of the prospect of a bitter split, says there was a recognition that the likes of Varadkar were also struggling over the issue. 'He would definitely have been uncomfortable with that agenda item, in relation to the Protection of Life [Bill], as were many others in the parliamentary party,' Hogan says. 'But I think he looked at it very deeply, sincerely and came to the conclusion that this legislation was about tightening the parameters of what the X case had been in the Supreme Court some years previously.' The X case related to a complex legal battle involving the state and a fourteen-year-old rape victim who was denied the right to travel to the UK for an abortion. In 1992, the Supreme Court ruled that the distressed teenager should be permitted to travel to the UK for an abortion on the grounds that she was suicidal. However, a subsequent referendum rejected allowing rape as a ground for abortion in Ireland.

* * *

Back in May 2010, a thirty-year-old Leo Varadkar gave a wide-ranging interview to the *Sunday Independent* in which he spoke openly about his views on abortion. He said he wouldn't be in favour of terminations but accepted there is a 'grey area' in cases where there is a genuine threat to the life of the mother. In relation to providing abortion services in the case of rape, this was a non-runner for Varadkar. 'I wouldn't be in favour of it in that case, and, you know, first of all, it isn't the child's fault that they're the child of rape,' he said. 'You can say the same thing about disabled children. You know, some people would make that argument in favour of abortion. It's not their fault they're disabled. I wouldn't be in favour of it in those circumstances either.'

Asked next whether there was no double standard in forcing thousands of women to travel abroad each year for a termination, Varadkar replied:

I don't think that's double standards. People travel overseas to do things overseas that aren't legal in Ireland all the time. You know, are we going to stop people going to Las Vegas? Are we going to stop people going to Amsterdam? There are things that are illegal in Ireland and we don't prevent people from travelling overseas to avail of them.

Indeed, Varadkar's remarks were indicative of his deeply conservative disposition and also his own support base in the Fine Gael branch in Dublin West, which was predominantly pro-life. So when the issue came to a head in May 2013, there was initial concern at senior level in Fine Gael that Leo and others might not support the proposed changes to the law.

The scale of the chasm within Fine Gael was laid bare at a parliamentary party meeting. Enda Kenny and James Reilly had just published the Protection of Life During Pregnancy Bill, which would allow for terminations in cases where there was a real and substantial risk to the life of the mother. Varadkar spoke in favour of the bill, which was due to be enacted before the summer recess. Paschal Donohoe recalls the impact of his contribution, which he said was drawn from his experience as a doctor:

He stood up and talked about being a doctor, and clinically what all this means, and I remember the effect that had on the room. My judgement would be that ultimately what was decisive for him in that period was his medical training in Holles Street Hospital, [which] fed through to the views he ultimately had across that period.

But on the opposing side were some of his closest friends in the party. The group included Creighton, Paul Bradford, Billy Timmins, Peter Mathews and Terence Flanagan. There were a number of others who told the meeting they had serious difficulty with the proposed changes. As Fine Gael looked poised to lose at least half a dozen TDs, Leo and others moved to try to persuade the rebels from jumping ship. Brian Hayes, who was also extremely close to Creighton, says he recalls giving a radio interview in which he pleaded with the group to remain in the party fold:

> I remember going on radio and reaching out to Billy and reaching out to Lucinda and saying, 'A fractured Fine Gael is no use to anybody.' And Leo rang me immediately and said, 'That's exactly the message we want. To try and keep them on side.' He didn't want to see them gone. Nobody wanted to see them gone.

As the Dáil prepared to vote on the legislation, Varadkar appeared defeatist, clearly having resigned himself to the fact that his colleagues were about to defy the party and inevitably be stripped of the whip. 'I really think that those who are voting against this bill from a pro-life point of view are making a very big error, they will be proven wrong by history and they are making a big mistake in that regard,' Varadkar said.

Despite the warning, four TDs and three senators were expelled. It was an extraordinary moment for the party as its leader Enda Kenny held firm on his refusal to allow a free vote. Varadkar was devastated, remarking afterwards, 'It's always hard to lose colleagues and it's almost like losing a member of the family to see somebody lose the whip.'

However, he would quickly realise how expendable political careers can be.

CHAPTER 9

THE 'DISTINGUISHED' GARDA WHISTLEBLOWERS

Garda Sergeant Maurice McCabe was nervous as he drove along the quays of Dublin's river Liffey. His experience with politicians, particularly those in government, had not been positive to date. But, as he made his way into the heart of the city, McCabe felt determined to put his prejudices aside. He was willing to give the politicians – or one, at least – a final chance.

McCabe parked his car in a multistorey car park and tucked a large file, which had been sitting on the passenger seat, under his arm as he walked towards the Department of Transport on Kildare Street. The meeting with Minister Leo Varadkar had been arranged a couple of weeks previously – but even getting to this point had been a hard-fought battle. For the past seven years, McCabe had worked tirelessly to highlight what he viewed as serious misconduct within the Irish police force, An Garda Síochána. He followed all the necessary protocols in order to air his grievances and at all times abided by the chain of command that exists within the force. But McCabe just kept coming up against a brick wall. His superiors didn't want to hear that serious crimes were not being investigated properly. They didn't seem to care that thousands of penalty points handed down to motorists for dangerous driving were being illegally cancelled. No matter how often McCabe raised his concerns, he found he was always being beaten back down.

Years earlier, a high-level internal review of allegations relating to McCabe's division in Cavan-Monaghan found that there was little to see. In fact, McCabe felt the report created the perception he was the problem, rather than the serious alleged misconduct he had raised. But he was not prepared to give up.

The abuse of the penalty points system was McCabe's greatest source of frustration. Under Irish law, drivers who clock up twelve points are taken off the road and there is also a financial penalty for each infringement. But, as McCabe discovered, senior officers were cancelling points without explanation. The beneficiaries were not strangers. They were colleagues, friends and family. Some drivers even saw their penalty points wiped despite committing multiple breaches of road safety law. McCabe was trying to blow the whistle on a corruption scandal. And he was doing so from within An Garda Síochána.

Having failed to convince his superiors to listen, McCabe felt he had no choice but to take a different route. He had made personal contact with the Department of Justice as far back as 2009, when he wrote to the then Minister for Justice Dermot Ahern detailing his grave concerns. After the Fine Gael and Labour coalition came to power, McCabe began writing to Taoiseach Enda Kenny and Minister for Justice Alan Shatter. He wanted to meet them so he could outline the problems he had spent years trying to highlight within the secretive confines of the police force. McCabe thought politicians would not be beholden to the Garda Commissioner, nor shirk their elected responsibility to uphold the law. Despite his efforts, the officer felt his allegations were not given the credence they deserved by the people in high office. Shatter was perceived as a highly intelligent but arrogant minister who did not like to be told how to do his job. He was close to Kenny, having proven his loyalty during the 2010 Fine Gael leadership heave. Similarly, Kenny took counsel from Shatter and trusted his management of the Department of Justice.

An internal garda review of McCabe's penalty point claims was ordered when they were first raised but it reported back very little evidence to substantiate his allegations. The report found there were only a couple of hundred cases involving penalty points being wrongly quashed by officers – a far cry from the tens of thousands of points allegedly erased. McCabe couldn't believe it. The report, which was signed off by the then Garda Commissioner Martin Callinan, satisfied Shatter, who in turn briefed the Taoiseach on its findings. McCabe, though, was far from satisfied.

He decided to get in touch with Independent opposition TD Clare Daly and her colleague Mick Wallace, a Celtic Tiger property developer turned politician. Daly and Wallace were highly supportive of McCabe's campaign. But McCabe needed his support to come from a more senior source. He needed the government to listen too.

* * *

Leo Varadkar had always impressed McCabe. He saw him take a different line from his Cabinet colleagues even when it proved to be an unpopular decision politically. He wasn't afraid to speak his mind. McCabe thought if he could speak directly with Varadkar, then maybe he could convince him to take his allegations seriously. As Minister for Transport, Varadkar had skin in the game when it came to the penalty points issues. Road deaths had been a serious issue in Ireland for decades, but high-profile safety campaigns and the introduction of penalty points had resulted in a significant drop in fatalities.

After the internal garda report was published, McCabe made contact with Conor Faughnan, a senior official with the Automobile Association (AA). Faughnan was well known for his traffic broadcasts and involvement in road safety campaigns. McCabe hoped Faughnan could help him get in contact with Road Safety Authority (RSA) chief executive Noel Brett. By doing so, he would be one step closer to making his case to Varadkar.

In a rare interview for this book, McCabe described how he persevered in his bid to highlight the abuses in the penalty points system despite what he believed was a whitewash report from the force. 'Even when I wasn't getting anywhere and after they came out with these 200 points, I still knew I was right,' McCabe said.

That meeting took place at an Applegreen service station on the N4 motorway in October 2012. McCabe explained his situation and said he'd like to speak with Brett. Faughnan said he would see what he could do. A few days later, McCabe's phone rang, and it was Brett. They arranged to meet in the Longford Arms Hotel in Longford Town.

McCabe had been told by an official in the Department of Transport a few weeks earlier that he had the authority, as a garda, to detail his concerns to Brett. McCabe said Brett was 'taken aback' by the information he showed him about the cancelled points and appeared to believe his claims. It was a significant moment for the garda. At last, McCabe thought, someone is taking me seriously.

Brett did believe him and relayed the details of the conversation to Varadkar. In the New Year, McCabe called the Department of Transport again and was offered a meeting with the minister. Upon his arrival at the department, McCabe was brought to a small meeting room, where he met Varadkar and his political adviser Brian Murphy. The conversation lasted over an hour.

McCabe talked them through his files. He showed examples of motoring offences where points had been quashed, often without explanation. McCabe insisted investigations into his allegations had been at best insufficient and at worst corrupt. 'I went through a number of examples I had with me and I was able to show what was going on. He [Varadkar] asked a number of questions but I was able to answer them all,' McCabe says.

Varadkar and Murphy were impressed but equally worried by McCabe's presentation. It was clear the penalty point system was being abused by some of those charged with enforcing road safety. Importantly, they believed McCabe to be a very sincere and serious individual whose complaints should be acted on. Varadkar and McCabe would not speak again for more than three years. But their paths were entwined throughout that period.

On 11 June 2013, the *Irish Independent* reported the first meeting between the whistleblower and the minister – with a spokesman for Varadkar saying the minister found McCabe to be 'credible'. On the same morning, Varadkar appeared on RTÉ Radio 1's *Morning Ireland* programme and confirmed the report. He said he found the meeting 'very useful and very interesting'. He also weighed in behind the RSA's call for an independent examination of the penalty points controversy, which had been the subject of many Dáil debates. In a significant intervention, Varadkar said he believed the internal garda review did not get to the 'underbelly' of the problem. He prefaced his remarks by saying he did not want to 'intrude' on Minister for Justice Alan Shatter's area of responsibility. But intrude he did.

Despite serving together in Cabinet, Varadkar never had a good relationship with Shatter. But the garda controversy would turn the two outspoken politicians into bitter enemies. Several Cabinet ministers who sat around the table with the pair say there were always tensions. Both are highly intelligent and effective ministers with big personalities. They also share a reforming outlook on politics. Neither got elected for the state car and the six-figure salary. But they certainly had their differences. At the Cabinet table, Varadkar had a view on most areas of policy even if they were outside his portfolio, while Shatter tended to stick to his own brief. This inevitably caused friction between two territorial ministers. 'Leo and Alan Shatter had a fraught relationship, a very fraught relationship,' one Fine Gael minister says, adding:

> I would almost say from day one because Alan Shatter would have seen maybe some of his colleagues who had been around for years not get a ministry and then this young guy was being appointed to Cabinet. Alan thought he was the smartest man in the class but actually he wasn't because we had a guy now like Leo Varadkar who was equally as capable.

The differences between the two regularly spilled out into the public arena and Varadkar was not shy in expressing views that would contradict or undermine Shatter. On several occasions throughout the garda scandals, which plagued the coalition's time in power, Varadkar backed Sergeant McCabe rather than garda management, the Department of Justice or even Shatter. For instance, Varadkar insisted the Garda Ombudsman should examine the penalty points allegations, while Shatter said another oversight body, the Garda Inspectorate, should handle the investigation. Varadkar also publicly endorsed a decision by the Public Accounts Committee (PAC) to hear evidence from McCabe, while a spokesman for Shatter said 'it would not be helpful' for Minister Shatter to comment on McCabe's proposed appearance. The then Garda Commissioner, Martin Callinan, was completely opposed to the planned appearance and sought legal advice in an effort to prevent the whistleblower from giving evidence.

Varadkar was clearly the most sympathetic minister in government to the whistleblower's cause. His support for action placed intense pressure on Shatter, who tried to defuse the situation by relenting to calls for a Garda Ombudsman investigation. But the controversy only deepened after McCabe attended a private meeting of the PAC despite the objections of the Garda Commissioner. The events that followed would turn a controversy into a full-blown crisis for the government and the police force.

Around the time of the PAC hearing, false allegations that McCabe was a child sex abuser began swirling around police and political circles. The chair of the committee, John McGuinness, would later claim he met the Garda Commissioner in a car park, where he was personally told the whistleblower was a paedophile and not to be trusted. Commissioner Callinan has denied he made these comments.

The level of distrust between Varadkar and his Cabinet colleague intensified as Shatter became embroiled in a string of controversies linked to the police force. The Data Protection Commissioner investigated the Justice Minister for revealing details of an interaction between gardaí and Independent TD Mick Wallace on live television. Shatter was initially found to have committed a breach by the Commissioner, but the charge was dropped on appeal. Shatter was also at the centre of an inquiry into allegations that the Garda Ombudsman's office was bugged. A report found he had acted appropriately.

On top of this, Shatter was the subject of constant opposition criticism in relation to his handling of garda whistleblower complaints. He was forced to withdraw a claim that Sergeant McCabe and his colleague Garda John Wilson, who had also turned whistleblower, did not cooperate with the original garda review of their penalty points allegations. Shatter came under pressure from the opposition and was called to correct the Dáil record during a sitting in March 2014.

The ex-Justice Minister to this day insists he has been vindicated of any wrongdoing during his time in office. But over a period of many months, he became a lightning rod for attacks from opposition politicians and, while seen as a brilliant TD, was disliked by many in his own party. Sources close to Shatter regularly blamed Varadkar for negative briefings against him in the press. Varadkar's camp deny this. However, the media coverage did not help Shatter as he fought against a constant wave of controversy.

Varadkar certainly didn't help matters when he appeared to gloat after Shatter capitulated to demands for a Garda Ombudsman inquiry into some of McCabe's complaints. 'I don't want to get into a conflict with the Garda Commissioner or with my colleagues in government,' he told Today FM. 'But the record does show, and I was asked this question on radio probably about a year ago now, as to whether I thought that the investigation should go to the Garda Ombudsman Commission and I said at the time that I did,' he added. These interventions grated on Shatter. Even if Varadkar was correct, ministers believed he should have shown loyalty to a colleague and kept his views private.

This was far from the last time the pair would clash over the operation of the justice system. Arguably, the defining moment of Varadkar's time in the Department of Transport came during an early morning road safety conference on 20 March 2014. Two months before this event, Commissioner Callinan told a Public Accounts Committee hearing he found it 'quite disgusting' that two gardaí would make allegations of serious misconduct against other officers while there was not a 'whisper' of evidence showing corruption. Callinan was referring to McCabe and Wilson over the quashed penalty points allegations.

Varadkar was in his ministerial office with Brian Murphy watching the Commissioner's comments on RTÉ's *Six One News*. Neither could believe what they had just heard. 'Disgusting' certainly was not a word either would associate with McCabe, whom they viewed as an honest garda wronged by the system. The comments also shocked the public and most opposition politicians. McCabe had all but been vindicated by a report by the Comptroller and Auditor General which contradicted the findings of the internal garda audit of penalty points. A later report from the Garda Inspectorate would also back up McCabe's allegations. But at the committee hearing, he had his reputation dragged through the mud by his own boss, the Garda Commissioner.

The night before the road safety conference in Dublin Castle, Varadkar discussed his speech with his close advisers. He believed the time had come to stand shoulder to shoulder with whistleblowers and the road safety agency, which was calling for the penalty points scandal to be properly addressed by the government. However, he also knew it would make life deeply uncomfortable for Shatter and the rest of his Cabinet colleagues who accepted the line that all was well in An Garda Síochána. 'He was of the view and I was of the view that you couldn't go to an event like this before the road safety community and not say something,' one Varadkar aide says. 'It was a conscious decision and he knew he was stepping outside the norm. He thought about it deeply and he decided this is the thing to be done,' the adviser adds.

Walking into Dublin Castle on a rainy spring morning, Leo knew he was making one of the most important decisions of his career. After taking to the podium, he said, 'I want to thank Sergeant McCabe and Mr Wilson for their service. There have been many words to describe their actions in recent months but if I was to use one word it would be "distinguished".' There was a brief applause after the speech, but the tension in the room was palpable. 'There was four or five of the senior guards in front of him when he said that. Obviously, the atmosphere after that got very intense,' an adviser says.

Speaking to reporters following his speech, the Minister for Transport went further and called on the Garda Commissioner to withdraw his remarks about the whistleblowers. McCabe says he was delighted when he heard the comments on the radio but had no idea it was about to happen. 'I was as surprised as everyone else when he came out with the "distinguished" comments,' he remembers.

But while McCabe and Wilson were pleased, Varadkar's intervention was causing ructions within government. Taoiseach Enda Kenny was blindsided by the move. The Taoiseach opted to stand firmly behind the Commissioner – knowing that failing to do so would have tremendous consequences. In the aftermath of Varadkar's speech, Kenny quite pointedly said that he would prefer if his ministers raised their issues at Cabinet rather than in the full glare of the public. It was as close to a slapdown as there could be.

In the hours that followed, there were several phone calls between angry advisers in the Taoiseach's office and the Varadkar camp – but Leo refused to budge. No other Fine Gael minister supported Varadkar's comments – leaving the young minister considerably isolated. In fact, most ministers were furious that he had reignited a scandal that had recently been defused after a tumultuous few months.

In an attempt to kill off the controversy, Fine Gael headquarters directed their TDs to contact the press office for a briefing on the garda scandal before making any comment in the media. But Fine Gael could not control the actions of its coalition partners, and it wasn't long before the Labour Party weighed in behind Varadkar. Education Minister Ruairi Quinn promptly called on Callinan to bring an end to the controversy by apologising for his remarks.

EU Commissioner Phil Hogan, who was in the Cabinet at the time, says he disagreed with Varadkar's approach to Shatter and the garda whistleblower controversy. 'I think his public exchanges and his views in relation to the manner in which Alan Shatter was discharging his functions as Minister for Justice are on the record,' Mr Hogan says. 'I would not have done so, as a Cabinet colleague. The job is difficult enough, you have to attempt to be as collegial as possible,' he adds. Hogan says it was clear Varadkar believed the whistleblowers and was comfortable backing them – even if it meant upsetting Shatter. 'Obviously Leo Varadkar felt very strongly about this issue. He met the whistleblowers and he came to the view that their side of the story was the true one,' Hogan says. 'I believe Alan Shatter was an outstanding Minister for Justice. Of course, he would be somebody who would stand strongly and robustly in terms of standing high in terms of his viewpoint. In the same way Deputy Varadkar would stand high in relation to his viewpoint.'

Shatter was on state business in Mexico at the time of Varadkar's speech, but it didn't matter, as the pair were barely on speaking terms anyway. Those close to Varadkar said he regularly tried to contact Shatter to speak about the termination of penalty points but found it difficult to organise a meeting or even get a response. Shatter turned down an opportunity to be interviewed for this book.

In an attempt to defuse what was becoming an all-out war between the two ministers, Enda Kenny instructed them to sit down and thrash out their differences. Before that meeting could take place, Kenny met Varadkar to discuss his actions. The Taoiseach was far from enamoured of his Transport Minister's speech and asked that he be more supportive of his Cabinet colleague. He wanted an agreed position held firm by his ministers and he did not need civil war breaking out within his Cabinet. But it was too late. The Minister for Transport and the Minister for Justice could barely stomach each other. Their relationship was non-existent, and the pair had in truth passed the point of reconciliation.

On Monday 24 March 2014, Shatter and Varadkar finally sat face to face to air their differences. However, the talks would be overshadowed the following day by one of the most shocking political developments in years: Garda Commissioner Martin Callinan stepped down from his post, in a move that stunned Irish politics.

Later that Monday night, following his meeting with Varadkar, Shatter had attended a meeting with the Taoiseach, the Attorney General Máire Whelan, Secretary General to the government Martin Fraser and Secretary General to the

Department of Justice Brian Purcell. They had met to discuss what they expected to become another garda scandal: the emergence of secret recordings of telephone conversations in garda stations. They feared the unauthorised recordings could collapse criminal trials and result in criminals walking free from prison.

Purcell, who knew Callinan best, was dispatched to the Commissioner's home to make him aware of the Taoiseach's 'grave concerns' about the recordings and to let him know the issue would be brought before Cabinet in the morning. Callinan would later tell a state inquiry into the events that led to his retirement that he had felt he had no option but to fall on his sword after Purcell's visit. Kenny later faced accusations that he had unconstitutionally sacked the Commissioner without the Cabinet's approval. He continues to deny this charge.

News of the Commissioner's resignation filtered through around 10 a.m. on Tuesday 25 March. Before the magnitude of the resignation could be digested, the government announced it was setting up a commission of investigation into the secret recordings. There was pandemonium in political circles. Nobody knew what was going on. Most ministers, never mind TDs, had been unaware of the extraordinary revelations around the recordings. The government had come under mounting pressure from the opposition to sack Callinan in the months leading up to the disclosure. But the coalition had stood firmly behind him throughout every scandal.

It was hoped that the Commissioner's departure and the establishment of the inquiry would be seen as the government taking decisive action: the political equivalent of amputating a leg to stop a disease spreading. But the cancer had taken hold. The avalanche of political pressure had only just begun, and the treatment of Sergeant McCabe by the police force would result in many more resignations.

Among those under the most pressure was of course Alan Shatter. The day after Callinan's resignation, Shatter publicly apologised for claiming McCabe and Wilson had refused to cooperate with an internal garda inquiry into their penalty point claims. 'It was never my intention to mislead the House and I believe it is appropriate that I apologise to both and withdraw the statements made,' Shatter told the Dáil. 'It was never my intention to cause any upset and, if any upset was caused, I hope that my correcting the record of the Dáil today will put this matter to rest.'

The opposition scented blood, and calls came for Shatter to follow in Callinan's footsteps and resign. Earlier that morning, Varadkar said he had 'absolute confidence' in the Minister for Justice when questioned by the media outside an event in Dublin. Ministers from both Fine Gael and the Labour Party weighed in behind the under-siege minister, but his days were numbered. Just six weeks later, on 7 May 2014, just before the publication of an independent review of the Department of Justice's handling of McCabe's complaints of garda misconduct, Shatter stood before the Dáil and announced his resignation. Shatter later had the findings made against him in the Guerin Report overturned by the Court of Appeal following an unsuccessful High Court challenge. He argued successfully that he was not given a fair hearing by barrister Sean Guerin before he compiled his report. Mr Guerin has lodged a challenge to this Court of Appeal ruling with the Supreme Court. A Commission of Investigation established on the back of the Guerin Report also found Mr Shatter acted appropriately in his handling of Sergeant McCabe's complaints.

The episode – in which Varadkar played a central role – caused significant damage to the coalition. Kenny knew he had to set his political ally adrift to secure the stability of the government. In a meeting with Shatter, Kenny made it clear his time was up. Varadkar's long-time political confidante Frances Fitzgerald replaced Shatter in the Department of Justice.

Varadkar turned on the civil service after Shatter's downfall. He branded the Department of Justice as 'not fit for purpose' and insisted 'big changes' would have to happen to bring it into order. 'One of the difficulties for Alan Shatter was he accepted [what] former Commissioner Martin Callinan was telling him was the truth and that his officials would brief him properly and that didn't happen,' he said. Fitzgerald took her lead from Varadkar and refused to express confidence in the Department of Justice Secretary General Brian Purcell. An independent review of the department gave political cover for a few weeks, but Purcell ultimately stepped down from his position and moved elsewhere in the civil service. The purge of the justice system was almost over.

All that was left to do was establish a raft of state investigations and inquiries into the matters that had arisen from the garda scandals. The inquiries would run for many years and in most cases raised more questions than answers. They would also prove to be very costly and at times it seemed the only beneficiaries of the investigations were the well-paid lawyers pocketing legal fees.

However, McCabe's plight was far from over and the treatment of the whistleblower would dog the government for years to come.

CHAPTER 10

HEALTH

Relations between Fine Gael and Labour were bordering on toxic by the winter months of 2013. The coalition was barely two years old and already trust was eroding rapidly. Budget talks were dogged by infighting and hostilities as ministers used the media to brief against each other. With suspicions heightened and relations deteriorating, health became a political football. Major decisions taken in this period would have catastrophic consequences. During heated negotiations, it was decided to slash the state's medical card budget by €113 million. The cards provide people on low income with state-funded access to free medical services.

To this day, the blame game for the budgetary decision still plays out between Fine Gael and Labour figures. In 2013, the decision to target medical card holders almost brought the coalition to the brink of collapse. And the lightning rod for the public anger that followed was, inevitably, Minister for Health Dr James Reilly.

Behind closed doors, senior Health Service Executive (HSE) bosses mounted staunch opposition to an initial proposal to pitch the austerity measure as a move to tackle 'medical card fraud'. After much to-ing and fro-ing, it was eventually agreed to use the term 'medical card probity', which would involve the introduction of stricter criteria for entering the system Reilly, a doctor and the deputy leader of Fine Gael, openly clashed with Labour's Brendan Howlin, the Minister for Public Expenditure.

The scale of the row can now be revealed for the first time. Reilly was so incensed at the decision to target medical card holders that he threatened to quit his portfolio. In late 2013, while out walking on the beach near his home in Rush, north County Dublin, Reilly rang his adviser Sean Faughnan. Reilly did not see the point in continuing in the role if his budget was to be completely slashed. He was prepared to resign as both minister and deputy leader in protest over his treatment and the proposed cuts to his budget. If he did so, the government would fall, Faughnan warned him.

Following late night meetings involving both his own officials and the Taoiseach's, Reilly was persuaded not to resign. In order to keep him in line, he was promised a bailout for health, which sources put at €400 million. The sum would be paid to Reilly's department if the decision to slash the medical card budget resulted in dire consequences. And so, tens of thousands of medical card holders were subjected to a review that would be followed by one of the most damaging 'smash and grab'-style approaches seen in Irish politics in years.

HSE officials involved in the talks say the move to raid medical cards was approved in order to appease Labour. Senior figures insist they were told the cost-cutting measures would ensure a greater budget could be afforded to the area of social protection, which was under the control of Labour's Joan Burton. 'We pointed out to them in order to take €113 million out of medical cards, you'd have to take away hundreds of thousands of medical cards over the course of a year,' says one high-ranking HSE figure. 'We didn't believe that was possible and it wasn't possible. We also said the effect of putting that into the budget would be to create fear and alarm on behalf of everybody who was being reviewed, which is what subsequently happened.' The advice from the HSE was ignored. But as the coalition broke for their Christmas holiday, they were oblivious to the fallout that would soon follow.

In the meantime, Fine Gael backbenchers were already lining up a replacement for the embattled and bruised James Reilly. And it was Leo Varadkar they were turning to as a successor to take over the poisoned chalice of health.

* * *

As the 2014 Dáil term arrived, further cracks began to show within the coalition over a different health proposal. Reilly's bold plan to introduce universal health insurance (UHI) was drawing the ire of Labour due to the proposal's astronomical cost. The health budget was already heading towards a €500 million black hole, and calls for Reilly to be sacked were becoming louder by the day.

But it was the medical card issue that would soon raise its ugly head once more and eventually result in the minister's downfall. Personal stories of sick children and people with chronic illnesses being warned by the HSE that they would be stripped of their entitlements caused political pandemonium. TDs were getting it in the neck. Never before had Fine Gael and Labour backbenchers experienced such anger from their constituents. With crucial European and local elections looming, more and more TDs turned to Varadkar to intervene.

May and June saw a series of embarrassing U-turns and apologies from a government now under intense pressure. The public made their discontent known at the polling stations, as Fine Gael lost a massive 105 council seats, with Labour haemorrhaging eighty-one. It was an election mauling for the coalition partners, while both Fianna Fáil and Sinn Féin enjoyed significant gains. Health was the underlying factor as ministers rued the disastrous handling of the medical card issue. Reilly's time was up.

Enda Kenny had already signalled a Cabinet reshuffle and his Minister for Health was widely tipped to be replaced by Varadkar. There were major tensions between Reilly and Varadkar, dating back to a bizarre exchange in January 2010, followed by a much more serious row in September 2012 over the issue of primary care centres. During the 2010 debate, when Fine Gael was still in opposition, Reilly had raised the need for a greater reservoir of salt to deal with freezing conditions which had led to transport chaos: 'Will the minister take the opportunity to appoint an easily identifiable central figure who will be responsible for making sure there is a sufficient reservoir of salt in the country, much as we do with our oil reserves?' Just moments later, Varadkar responded. While backing the substance of his colleague's claim, he decided to nit-pick at his use of the term 'reservoir'. 'If we had a reservoir of salt it would not be very useful because it would be in liquid form. We need a silo of it. I echo the sentiments of my colleagues in that regard,' he said. The clash prompted Enda Kenny to quip, 'Doctors differ.' Sources familiar with the exchange say that afterwards Reilly pulled Varadkar up and told him, 'What was that about, you point-scoring idiot? Go and check the dictionary.' The following day, Varadkar is understood to have approached Reilly and accepted that his colleague was in fact right about the use of the term. Reilly is believed to have replied, 'Yes, including a reservoir of goodwill.'

But in 2012, a much more severe rift developed between the pair. This time, it was over the issue of the designation of locations as primary care centres. Varadkar broke the party line, saying the decision to add two primary care centres in Reilly's Dublin North constituency appeared to be a 'stroke', a term referring to a cynical political manoeuvre.

The primary care centres issue led to major political tensions between Fine Gael and Labour and prompted the resignation from government of Reilly's junior minister for health, Róisín Shortall. Reilly had amended an original list composed by Shortall so that Swords and Balbriggan – towns in his constituency – were included. Varadkar didn't buy the explanation given, telling RTÉ that the move appeared to be a stroke. 'It does look like it. I don't know if it is or not,' he said.

As one key confidant notes, Varadkar simply was not prepared to remain quiet, even though the move proved hugely damaging to his party colleague. 'He couldn't understand the explanation for how that list was composed and maybe there was an explanation [from Reilly] but it was a very convoluted one, so he was then asked a question and he gave an answer,' the source says. Reilly, to this day, rejects outright the suggestion that he amended the list for political gain. 'On the issue of the primary care centres, I think it was opportunist and disloyal,' Reilly says.

Other members of that Cabinet have also remarked on the relations between Reilly and Varadkar. 'There was always a bit of tension between the then Minister for Health James Reilly and Leo Varadkar,' according to Phil Hogan.

Both of them are in medicine and I would suspect have a different view of the world in relation to what solutions are required to solve the problems of the health service. The context of the times has to be taken into account when you look at the challenges in the Department of Health. In specific terms about this issue, I think James Reilly in good faith wanted to do something for an area that was in urgent need of a primary care centre.

Joan Burton goes as far as to say that the new National Children's Hospital may have been built in her and Varadkar's constituency of Dublin West and specifically on the local Blanchardstown Hospital site if it weren't for the bad relationship between the pair. 'With James Reilly, I certainly was of the view [that] the Children's Hospital might have gone to Blanchardstown,' Burton says. 'It certainly should have in terms of access and site availability. Had [Blanchardstown] been selected, it probably would have been have built by now. But put it this way, the row between himself and Reilly didn't help the case for Blanchardstown in any way.'

* * *

As reshuffle day arrived, Reilly and Varadkar were called in by the Taoiseach. Kenny wanted Reilly to go quietly and offered him the more junior position of Minister for Children. Reilly had two outstanding demands that he wanted fulfilled if he was to vacate health. Firstly, he wanted a special redress scheme provided for victims of symphysiotomy, a controversial surgical procedure carried out on pregnant women in Ireland between the 1940s and the 1980s which involves breaking the cartilage of the pelvis. Secondly, he wanted the medical card issue – which had left his reputation in tatters – addressed once and for all. Both of Reilly's requests were eventually met.

Reilly left health for the Department of Children and Youth

Affairs as damaged goods. Phil Hogan, now European Commissioner, is not alone in believing Reilly was unfairly treated: 'I think the entire government let James Reilly down in relation to the amount of money that was expected to be reduced … from the Department of Health.'

But even before Reilly and Varadkar could settle into their new briefs, further tensions flared. On the day of the reshuffle, Reilly left his meeting with Kenny under the impression that he would be allowed keep certain areas of public health policy in which he had taken a keen interest. These included introducing plain packaging for tobacco products and minimum pricing laws for alcoholic beverages. But Varadkar was having none of it. Reilly was given ownership of new anti-smoking measures, but overall his portfolio was not beefed up to what he believed he had been promised. It was a further embarrassment for Reilly, who paid a high price politically despite sticking by his convictions.

For Phil Hogan, the decision to move Varadkar from transport to health was an obvious one. 'I think that Leo Varadkar was somebody the Taoiseach felt was up to a challenge; as a medical person, he surely was well aware of what was required in terms of structural reform of the health service,' Hogan says. 'But of course he saw, when he became Minister for Health, how difficult it was with many vested interests.'

* * *

Varadkar entered the Department of Health knowing that it was a job in which so many before him had failed. The list of his predecessors is nothing short of a Who's Who of Irish political heavyweights. Micheál Martin, Michael Noonan, Brendan Howlin, Brian Cowen, Mary Harney and James Reilly all tried with limited success to resolve the problems plaguing the country's health service. They all struggled to make a difference in a department that former Taoiseach Cowen described as Angola, in reference to the once war-torn African country.

Within hours of being appointed, Varadkar phoned several of his predecessors. He wanted advice on how to avoid the pitfalls that blighted their careers. 'I think he likes to float things by people to get their opinion,' Harney says. 'They may never change what he's going to do but he likes to hear another perspective and I think that's a strength.' Harney advised Leo that health can leave political careers damaged. She warned him, '"I went to health at the end of my political career. I'm not sure what impact it will have on you if you did it at the start of your career." I remember saying that to him. Because it leaves its wounds on people,' she adds.

Varadkar's move to health was in no way a punishment. Members of his inner circle say the promotion did not come as a surprise, given his experience as a doctor. He had also built up a reputation as a straight talker – which was seen as an essential attribute in tackling the huge financial and organisational crises within the portfolio.

Senior health officials, including the HSE's former Director General Tony O'Brien, noticed an immediate change in approach after Varadkar took office. The ideological focus by Reilly was replaced with a more politically based strategy. Varadkar knew that a general election was less than two years away and that the prospect of introducing major health reform was impossible. He immediately made it clear that despite the toxic reputation of the HSE, he was not going to seek its abolition. But there would soon be personnel changes at a senior level in the department, most notably involving the Secretary General, Dr Ambrose McLoughlin. McLoughlin was seen politically as being close to James Reilly. And, like

Reilly, he had developed a strained relationship with the HSE. McLoughlin offered the option to step aside early and allow Varadkar to appoint his own Secretary General. Three months later, McLoughlin stepped aside and took up the position of CEO of Healthy Ireland, an agency within the department that advises on physical and mental health. Jim Breslin moved from the Department of Children and Youth Affairs to take over the position of Secretary General. For Varadkar it was important to have a personally appointed Secretary General. It meant a trust and a bond could be developed with the head of the department from the off.

Varadkar's next move was far more significant. Just weeks into the brief, he decided to drop a key component of Fine Gael's health policy and a central measure of the Programme for Government agreed with Labour: universal health insurance. The plan, contained in a government White Paper on health, would see equal access to healthcare for all, regardless of income or insurance status. UHI was designed to bring an end to the two-tier system that has underpinned Irish healthcare for decades. In his early meetings with Tony O'Brien and senior HSE officials, however, Varadkar made it clear that he did not believe the system was a runner. Varadkar knew that UHI had become a major distraction. He was also conscious of the absence of political consensus within the coalition to see it through to fruition. But to kill it off brought huge political risk.

'UHI involved compulsory private health insurance for everyone, a plan that was uncosted,' Varadkar says. He adds, 'The country was in revolt over the introduction of water charges so what would the response have been to compulsory health insurance?'

UHI wasn't the brainchild of Varadkar's new foe in Cabinet, James Reilly. It was in fact a proposal driven by former Fine Gael leader Alan Dukes and a central tenet of Fine Gael's 'FareCare' plan, launched in 2009 by Enda Kenny. The UHI proposal had underpinned Fine Gael's election strategy in 2011, with the party flooding the country with posters of Kenny above the slogan 'I will end the scandal of patients on trolleys'. Earlier in 2014, Kenny and Reilly had pushed the deadline for UHI back to 2019. However, Kenny had rejected repeated suggestions that it was unachievable. The former Taoiseach had placed his political reputation on delivering UHI and ending the trolley crisis. But Varadkar had different ideas, having been handed a briefing document that suggested the plan was unworkable.

To suddenly drop UHI weeks into being appointed to health by Kenny was a major judgement call. The announcement was made through an opinion article in the *Irish Independent* in August 2014. The new Minister for Health wrote that delivering the radical scheme within the next five years was 'too ambitious'. He also confirmed that abolishing the HSE was off the table, despite it having been another part of the Reilly plan. 'The HSE should remain in place at least until all of this has bedded down,' he wrote.

Cabinet sources claim Varadkar failed to notify colleagues before announcing his plan to ditch one of their key policies. But, as senior members of Varadkar's team observe, dropping UHI was a decision that could not be avoided. 'A decision had to be made. This wasn't the direction we wanted the country to go down, so we just had to stop the bus and say sorry,' one key aide says.

Reilly still insists UHI is the only way proper healthcare can be delivered. 'In relation to UHI, I've only seen things deteriorate since we've moved away from that,' he says. However, Varadkar's decision to axe UHI went down well with backbenchers who were already talking him up as a potential future leader. As the October budget loomed, Varadkar soon found himself subject to the ire of the Taoiseach.

* * *

With the Dáil due to return from its summer recess, Varadkar gave an interview to RTÉ's *Morning Ireland* programme, during which he was asked about the coalition's third budget. The economy had now stabilised and there was an expectation among the public that this budget would finally put money back in their pockets. Varadkar told the programme that the budget would indeed restore the income of workers – but to a modest degree only. 'Whatever tax package happens, it's going to be relatively modest. It's going to be an extra fiver or tenner in your payslip every week and that would be very welcome,' he said. He also said he did not know if he would be able to introduce free GP care for under-sixes before the end of the year or free GP care for over-seventies the following year – remarks that were out of sync once again with government policy. But it was remarks about health spending that infuriated Enda Kenny and his officials. Varadkar confirmed that the HSE was facing an overrun in the region of €500 million and that any additional health spending would result in tax cuts being offset.

The comments led to a humiliating slapdown at a meeting of Fine Gael ministers that week. Kenny warned Varadkar to desist from airing his budget woes in public. Ironically, Kenny then went public himself to express his dissatisfaction with his Health Minister. 'I am far more interested in hearing how you set about achieving what the government's targets are instead of giving endless, endless volumes of [recommendations] telling me why things can't be done,' Kenny said.

The controversy rumbled on for days, with Varadkar telling

reporters in Cork that he was a 'big boy' and didn't mind 'being slapped down or scolded' by his leader. The solo run over the budget also prompted Finance Minister Michael Noonan, a Kenny loyalist, to pull Varadkar aside for a dressing down. Fianna Fáil leader Micheál Martin pounced on the opportunity to criticise the coalition following the spat. 'Enda Kenny is clearly frustrated and uncomfortable with the new Health Minister's attempts to distance himself from the government's failure to reform the health service and protect frontline services,' Martin said.

But within Fine Gael, the decision to humiliate Varadkar so publicly was having the opposite effect. Backbenchers and ministers alike expressed their unease at Kenny and Noonan's treatment of Varadkar. There was now a growing view within the party that Varadkar was a Cabinet minister prepared to go against the grain and break ranks.

Senior HSE bosses believe the minister's approach to the health budget was in many ways politically motivated. 'He recognised every year that James Reilly was a minister who got screwed,' one source says. 'Leo didn't want that to happen to him. We knew he had long-term ambitions.'

Despite a couple of hiccups, the budget in October 2014 passed comfortably, marking another milestone for the Fine Gael–Labour coalition. The health budget saw its first increase in seven years, with €13.1 billion being set aside for health spending. Nonetheless, Varadkar issued a stark and immediate warning, telling the HSE that the country was not 'awash with cash' and insisting that tight reins would have to be kept on health spending. Varadkar's team knew that the overall approach to health spending was a disaster and would lead to further problems down the track. 'Every year Health and DPER [the Department of Public Expenditure and Reform] had pointless conversations, beat each other up, and then there would be the pretence that there would be more money later,' one source says.

One of the most pressing issues now facing Varadkar and his team was the sense of distrust they had for the HSE. Varadkar became highly suspicious, even somewhat paranoid, that senior HSE bosses were deliberately presenting misleading figures as to the state of the health service. 'The figures financially were different and they didn't add up and they didn't make sense,' says one close aide. 'You're sitting there thinking, "Well, you can't believe what you're told by the HSE because it's just lies," and we could never rely on figures and we could never rely on information coming through because it just wasn't true,' the adviser adds.

Furthermore, Varadkar soon found himself at the centre of a fresh spat with the country's doctors. He suggested doctors wanted him to fail in his role – prompting a sharp rebuke from the Irish Medical Organisation (IMO), which accused the minister of being 'out of order' and engaging in 'malice'.

As 2014 drew to a close, the hospital trolley crisis erupted. The number of people on trolleys was more than double the number recorded a decade previous – when the situation had been deemed a national emergency. Varadkar decided to play hardball with health bosses – a move that would lead to a serious kickback from senior civil servants.

In January 2015, Varadkar took a last-minute holiday to Florida, where some of his family are based. He had initially intended to travel in late December, but a tragic case involving a pregnant woman who had been diagnosed as brain-dead prompted the minister to remain at home. However, his decision to go abroad in the New Year landed him in hot water. Figures produced in early January showed trolley numbers had reached a record high, with 600 people languishing on hospital trolleys on a single day. Fianna Fáil seized on the minister's absence, accusing him of showing a real lack of political leadership. But the failure to secure progress on trolley figures also led to deep tensions between Varadkar and senior HSE bosses. In private conversations with HSE boss Tony O'Brien, Varadkar made it clear that there could be no repeat of the trolley figures and insisted senior executives should be held accountable. In emails sent often late at night, the minister put pressure on O'Brien to take a more forceful approach with underperforming bosses.

One piece of correspondence in particular led to deep tensions between the minister and the country's most senior health official. In September 2015, a newspaper published the contents of an email Varadkar sent to O'Brien. He had written that 'heads will have to roll' due to the overcrowding crisis. The email made front-page news and led to ructions in Leinster House. Fianna Fáil leader Micheál Martin accused Varadkar of leaking the email himself to the media. It's a claim he has always denied.

Varadkar maintained he sent the email to Brien because he was extremely frustrated with the HSE's response to the trolley crisis. The HSE had told Varadkar that investment in the state's nursing home support scheme, known as 'Fair Deal', would drive down trolley numbers. But the statistics were as bad as ever. And so he pressed send on an email that laid bare the tense relationship between himself and the HSE. 'I have no reason to believe it won't be worse than last year, and that really means a head or heads will have to roll,' he said. 'The people or Dáil or Taoiseach can take mine in the election or thereafter, but we'll need an official/executive head to roll before that or there is no accountability.'

O'Brien was furious, according to well-placed sources, and feared that such comments only served to undermine the morale of health workers. One source with knowledge of the exchanges adds, 'When workers hear the media and politicians saying, "These people aren't trying," are they going to keep coming in until ten o'clock at night?' A stand-off emerged between Varadkar and O'Brien. The HSE chief held his ground, telling the minister that only he had the power to sack senior executives. It was a high-stakes move by the HSE boss, particularly given Varadkar's reputation for taking political risks.

It never reached a point where Varadkar asked O'Brien to quit. But he believes the email was leaked to damage him, as one well-placed political source notes: 'Leo was always aware that he did not have the power to dismiss any HSE staff member. He did become increasingly frustrated at the lack of accountability when it came to hospital managers, finance directors etc. Really, there are no rewards for good performance and no consequences for poor performance.' The pair's relationship had deteriorated rapidly. But it was about to get worse.

In the run-up to Christmas 2015, an interview given by O'Brien to the *Sunday Business Post* ran under the headline 'HSE chief: no plan, no money and no vision for health'. O'Brien claimed in the interview that the HSE had been on 'death row' since 2011, when Reilly had indicated it would be axed. It was the type of straight talking that Varadkar himself had built a reputation for. Although O'Brien was privately unhappy with the headline, his strategy in making the stark assessment about the health system was simple: send a message to the politicians. There was a general election looming and O'Brien felt his remarks might ensure health was at the forefront of the campaign. A clear message had been sent to the government and indeed the Minister for Health. O'Brien was willing to call it how it was. 'What he was saying is we need a long-term vision for healthcare and we haven't got one,' says a highly placed source. 'Leo knew O'Brien was saying it with a view to maybe somebody picking that up in the upcoming general election.'

Varadkar was furious. This was not the way a public servant should act, he told colleagues. Varadkar believed that O'Brien's stunt was designed to damage him politically. The timing of it – just three months out from an election – was particularly suspicious. Varadkar weighed up what to do, consulting his close aide Brian Murphy. The pair believed O'Brien was gearing up to resign. Varadkar had a major dilemma on his hands: would he come out in support of O'Brien and his extraordinary remarks, or would he criticise his health chief, knowing that doing so would bring his exit one step closer? He decided to opt for the former and stood by O'Brien. 'If you read beyond the headline it's actually a very interesting interview in which he [O'Brien] makes some very valid points, a lot of which I would agree with and many of which I have made myself,' Varadkar told reporters. O'Brien was not going to resign.

In hindsight, Varadkar's response was politically clever, but it still gave Fianna Fáil leader Micheál Martin plenty of ammunition ahead of the fast-approaching general election. Varadkar went into that election a deeply frustrated Health Minister. He expressed his dissatisfaction with the job and with the HSE in conversations with his inner circle. He resented the agency's practice of sending the minister a list of problems – but with very few solutions.

Varadkar felt that everything was put down in writing so that it could be released under the Freedom of Information Act. 'It's a form of cover-my-ass, buck-passing approach that other agencies rarely do or don't do at all,' says one source. Varadkar also believed the HSE was guilty of passing the buck onto the department, who in turn passed the buck onto the Minister for Public Expenditure. 'It's a vicious, futile cycle, says the source.

Another close adviser goes further, calling health a 'bad place' where Leo was constantly fighting fires:

> He had to deal with the consequences of a patient being left not being fed, not being washed, not being cleaned for twelve hours. That's down to a person not doing their job properly. It's very difficult. Being a minister – yes, you're in charge, but funnily enough, you're not in charge. The HSE is in charge of the staff. The hours were excruciating. The frustrations were really, really difficult. And it became a bad place to be in.

Varadkar points to several personal successes during his time in the department, such as the expansion of the free GP scheme, the introduction of measures to tackle alcohol abuse and the implementation of a first-of-its-kind maternity hospital strategy.

However, Mark Finan is one of a number of close friends who experienced first-hand the negative impact the job had on Varadkar. He says his friend was unhappy, distracted and even somewhat depressed over the state of the health service. 'I think it aged him,' Finan says, recalling how Varadkar would spend much of his time on his phone checking the latest trolley watch figures. Even during social occasions, like a trip to the cinema, Varadkar would be agitated and preoccupied. 'I think what got to him was none of the good news was ever conveyed. And he is quite a positive person. But it doesn't take much to bring him down,' Finan says. 'And if you're in a very negative environment and if you're only asked about negative things, if you're slightly introverted, it would have a deep impact on you and you could see that in him.'

Varadkar's time in the Department of Health represented his greatest political challenge to date, but beyond the horizon was a personal test that would fundamentally shape the rest of his life.

CHAPTER 11

COMING OUT

Leo Varadkar took to his feet in the Dáil chamber to deliver his first speech on the very topic he had agonised over since his teenage years. With his close ally Lucinda Creighton beside him, Leo outlined Fine Gael's qualified support for the Civil Partnership Bill. The bill, which was spearheaded by the Green Party in government, gave legal recognition to same-sex couples in Ireland for the first time.

It was 27 January 2010 – more than five years before the marriage equality referendum – when Leo decided to set out his stall. But if campaigners on marriage equality had been looking to Varadkar to champion their cause, they were left bitterly disappointed. His first speech on the issue was guarded. His contribution was littered with caveats and reservations about the potential impact of the bill in its current form. Civil partnership could have a number of unintended consequences, he warned. But, above all, single people should not have the right to adopt a child. 'Every child has the right to a mother and father and, as much as is possible, the state should vindicate that right,' Varadkar said in his Dáil speech.

That is a much more important right than that of two men or women having a family. That is the principle that should underline our laws regarding children and adoption. I am also uncomfortable about adoption by single people regardless of their sexual orientation. I do not believe I as a single man should adopt a child. The child should go to parents, a mother and father, to replace what the child had before.

Varadkar's deeply conservative address ensured his sexuality would, for now at least, remain a secret.

In Fine Gael headquarters, officials who had got to know Varadkar since his entry to national politics in 2007 were puzzled to say the least. 'Here was our youngest TD coming out with the sort of stuff you would expect from the likes of senator Rónán Mullen,' one strategist noted, referring to one of the country's most conservative politicians. The official in question recalls his bewilderment when, just months earlier, Varadkar invited Mullen to attend as a guest speaker at a constituency event on the issue of civil partnership. At the meeting, Mullen expressed his own concerns about the impact the legislation would have on children – remarks mirrored by Varadkar's contribution in the Dáil. The Independent senator also recalls how Varadkar told his constituents how proud he was to be able to call himself a Christian democrat.

Up until this point, Varadkar had been barely visible in a debate that he was having internally on a daily basis. But that was all about to change. As Varadkar's profile grew, so did his desire to keep aspects of his personal life private. His friends tell of a shy and sometimes socially awkward individual who is at his most comfortable when talking about politics and work. In fact, while most people use a summer holiday to relax with a good book, Varadkar would be seen sifting through White Papers on different areas of government policy while lounging beside the pool. Varadkar comes across as patronising, too, his friends say, which can put people off him during social occasions. But upon getting to know Leo, they add, you are faced with someone who is inherently decent and good company.

Varadkar's close circle of friends had for several years suspected he was gay. He had never had a proper girlfriend or even gone on many dates. Suspicions both inside and outside politics began to heighten. While all the clues pointed to him being gay, his friends say they always believed it was his business to decide when to address the issue of his sexuality.

Varadkar's determination to put work ahead of everything else is reflected in media interviews in which he was quizzed about his love life. In February 2011, Varadkar was described by the *Irish Independent* as one of Fine Gael's most eligible bachelors, alongside his party colleague and friend John Paul Phelan. The paper reported how Varadkar bit his nails awkwardly when asked to describe his ideal woman. 'I'd need someone chatty who wouldn't mind talking to people at events, because sometimes I find that hard to do. She could escort me to these things and look good beside me on camera,' Varadkar said. 'I'd need somebody tolerant. I can be a pain in the ass. I get stressed and can be very cranky.'

The following year, the same publication carried another personal interview. It was reported that Varadkar would not answer when asked to name an actress he fancied. He also gave insights into his concerns over being a high-profile public figure. 'I find it scary when people talk about me as a future leader. It's like putting a big target on your back,' Varadkar said. 'I love what I'm doing and I intend staying in politics, seeing where it can take me, but I wouldn't want to be tied to it. I won't necessarily stay in politics for ever.'

At this stage, supporters of Varadkar in both Dublin West and the Fine Gael parliamentary party were privately speculating that he was gay. Tom Curran, the party's General Secretary, had heard the chit-chat about Varadkar in Fine Gael circles. He took note of the rumours about Varadkar's sexuality in a personal black notepad in which he compiles profiles of all Fine Gael politicians.

Politically, momentum was building rapidly behind a referendum due to be held on marriage equality. A Red C opinion poll showed more than 70 per cent of the public wanted same-sex marriages to be permitted under the constitution and put to a referendum. But many Fine Gael politicians were still deeply unsure as to the outcome of such a vote. Fine Gael was in a coalition arrangement with Labour, whose party leader Eamon Gilmore and other senior figures were vocal about their desire for a change in the law. Gilmore would soon go on to describe marriage equality as 'the civil rights issue of this generation'.

After Justice Minister Alan Shatter publicly backed Labour's position, the pressure quickly mounted on Taoiseach Enda Kenny. Kenny had spent several months sidestepping the issue, having previously been on record as opposed to same-sex marriage. In a notorious moment outside the National Library of Ireland in July 2012, Kenny almost tripped over a flower pot when asked to give his views by TV3's political editor, Ursula Halligan. The embarrassing episode for Kenny was later labelled 'flower-pot gate'. In the Dáil chamber, Kenny was pressed for his views once more by Fianna Fáil leader Micheál Martin. 'Deputy Martin will not pressurise me as a citizen, or as leader of the government, into a box-ticking exercise,' Kenny responded.

But one week after 'flower-pot gate', Varadkar made his own

intervention and became the second Fine Gael Cabinet minister to lend his support to a public vote. However, in a move watched closely within Fine Gael, Varadkar once again showed restraint. 'I suppose, depending on the proposition, if there was a referendum on it, I would probably vote Yes,' Varadkar told *Today with Pat Kenny* on RTÉ Radio 1.

> I do think there is a difference when it comes to raising children. I do think that, by and large, children are best raised in a household with a mother and father but that isn't always possible, for different reasons. But I don't see why a same-sex couple shouldn't be allowed to be married if they wish to. I don't think it would damage society, I don't necessarily think it would damage the family.

After causing serious strain in the Fine Gael–Labour coalition, a referendum on marriage equality moved a step closer. A decision was taken to refer the matter to a forum known as the Citizens' Assembly, which was made up of ninety-nine members of the public.

Interventions by the likes of Varadkar and Shatter were significant factors in developing Fine Gael's position. But these advances also meant Varadkar's ability to keep his own sexuality under wraps was slipping away.

* * *

For Sonia Varadkar, it was very much a waiting game. Having already asked her little brother about his love life in college, she knew deep down he wasn't ready to open up. She decided to park the issue in the knowledge that one day, probably in the near future, Leo would broach the sensitive subject of his sexuality. For Sonia, it didn't matter in the slightest that her brother – the star politician – was harbouring a deep secret. All she cared about was ensuring Leo would never be lonely, that he would be able to get married and have a family, if he so wished. Her only hope was that her brother would be happy. 'I'm his sister. I want it for myself – the husband and the 2.4 kids and the white picket fence. I would always want more for him,' Sonia says. 'I always want more for everybody, but that would be me. We were always brought up that way.'

Sonia says that, upon looking back, Leo dropped a number of hints in his twenties that he was gay. But for a period, the penny just didn't drop. And so, when she learned that Leo had spoken to his other sister Sophie, Sonia felt somewhat hurt.

> That was a bit of a bone of contention for me. He said he tried to tell me a few times, but I didn't pick it up because he was probably trying to be not as direct as I am or as direct as he normally is. I think he was ready then and then he told Sophie and I think he presumed she would tell me so then we went out to dinner and I said it to him.

But why did Leo wait so long to tell the sister he was closest to that he was gay? 'Don't they say it's safer when someone is further away?' says Sonia.

After telling his two siblings, Leo had many more hurdles to cross. The most immediate one was telling his parents, Ashok and Miriam. How would Ashok respond when his only son muttered the words 'Dad, I'm gay'? 'He told them. I think it went fine,' Sonia says. 'It wasn't a big thing. As long as he's happy, as long as there's going to be someone there, because that's always been our worry – that he goes home to an apartment with nobody there.'

*   *   *

Around eighteen months before Ireland would go to the polls on marriage equality, Tiernan Brady received a phone call from a friend. Brady is a political activist and a leading campaigner for LGBT rights. The friend told him that a Member of Parliament was considering coming out and asked whether he would provide counsel. Brady agreed and awaited details of a meeting. But it didn't happen.

Brady knew that his friend had Fine Gael connections, but he had no idea of the identity of the politician in question. Six months later, the same friend phoned again and a meeting with Varadkar was finally arranged. 'We talked about what it would be like to come out in public office, because there are not a lot of people who have done it,' Brady says of the meeting. At this point, there were just three openly gay TDs in Leinster House: Fine Gael's Jerry Buttimer and Labour's John Lyons and Dominic Hannigan.

According to Brady, Varadkar's position as Minister for Health and his membership of a conservative party like Fine Gael made the decision even more difficult. 'There is a profile to the party he was a member of at that time. Your normal instinct is that this could be a negative, high-profile experience, that it could backfire on somebody.'

Brady's advice to Varadkar was both positive and meaningful. He told him that the Irish people would support him wholeheartedly. 'There is a decency in Irish people that we sometimes forget, a real decency,' Brady recalls of the conversation. He told Varadkar, 'They will see this for what it is: somebody taking a really brave step, and isn't it sad that we have to live in a country where people feel that was a really brave step?'

Over the weeks that followed, Brady attended further secret

meetings with Varadkar. A discussion took place over the forum that Leo would eventually use to come out. A decision was taken that it should be done during a radio interview. Brady says:

> He was coming out to a country. How would that make any one of us feel? How difficult would it be that the very first conversation you have on this is to an entire nation on the radio, to say, 'By the way, I'm gay'? That's horrendous. No one should have to do it. But he was a Cabinet minister and this was a big deal.

Privately, Brady knew that the stakes could not be higher for the LGBT community. How Leo handled this interview would have a major impact on others struggling with their sexuality. 'One wrong word and people listening to that say, "I don't know if I can come out any more. Maybe I shouldn't."'

* * *

Nollaig Crowley has known Leo since their twenties, having met while dropping leaflets for Fine Gael in Dublin West. Kate Cullen is a long-term friend and at one point had been rumoured to be dating Leo. Mark Finan is a barrister and former member of the Fine Gael national executive. All three regularly socialise and travel abroad with Leo. They are among his closest confidants. In February 2015, each received the same text message from Leo. He requested they meet him at Peter's Pub, an old-fashioned bar on Dublin's South William Street. 'None of us openly guessed he was going to say he was gay. We thought it might have been he was going into a different job or something else,' Finan remembers.

Over pints, Leo told his friends he was in fact gay. 'He just came straight out. It was blunt. We were like, "Grand. Get a drink in now,"' says Finan. The three friends barely batted an eyelid. The conversation switched back to politics – Leo's default and most comfortable space.

*　*　*

In the months that followed, Varadkar held discussions with his inner circle, notably Brian Murphy and Nick Miller, on the mechanics of coming out when you are a high-profile figure. A decision was taken to avoid any such interview in the autumn, amid fears it would distract from key political events such as the budget. This was particularly important given that Varadkar was engaged in another private battle: to secure more money for his department. As the year neared its end, it was decided once again to delay the interview, given that the health service was suffering from its annual trolley crisis.

But it soon became obvious to Varadkar's inner circle that the ability to manage the decision was being eroded. Nick Miller, Varadkar's press adviser, became nervous as the number of phone calls from journalists enquiring about his sexuality began to increase. The enquiries mostly came in from red-tops, but to Miller's surprise, even some established political correspondents began digging into Varadkar's private affairs. The calls were cryptic, sources say, with some reporters suggesting to Miller that they had been put up to the job by their news editors. Miller had a particularly good relationship with most political journalists and was able to perform his role as Leo's spin doctor effectively. But, at Christmas, one publication published a suggestive piece about how Leo had been seen out socialising with a male friend. The article, albeit akin to a gossip column, only heightened concern in the Varadkar camp. Would a publication go one step further and out Varadkar as being gay?

In December, Varadkar met a number of friends for dinner in Dublin City, where he informed them that the interview was due to take place in the New Year. As Mark Finan explains, Leo was determined to avoid any scenario whereby he was accused of not being up front about his sexuality. 'He likes the fact he has a reputation for being up front. So I think that was the primary concern, people might think he was not being honest.' Plans to stage the interview in January were abandoned after it emerged that a new party was due to be announced, led by none other than Lucinda Creighton. While the timing of the proposed interview kept changing, Varadkar had finally reached a point where he was ready to come out to the nation.

* * *

It was Friday evening in the Department of Health when Leo Varadkar summoned his closest advisers to a crucial team meeting. For those in attendance, this was the briefing they had been preparing for over many months. Varadkar's inner circle are meticulously tuned in to the chatter of Leinster House. They knew their boss was gay – and that the window for keeping it secret was quickly closing. Nick Miller had already been told by Varadkar at a meeting held months previously in Ballsbridge. Nick was surprised at how comfortable his boss was at divulging that he was gay. But telling one of your closest advisers is a far cry from announcing the news to the world.

Hawkins House, the home of the Department of Health, is one of the most outdated buildings in Dublin's south inner city. But on this July evening, the building's sixth floor played host to a discussion that would pave the way for a more modern and inclusive Ireland. Varadkar and his advisers spent over an hour brainstorming, as they regularly do at team meetings. However, this time was different. The discussion centred not on health policy, but on how best to tell the nation that their Minister for Health was gay. The meeting was attended by Leo's chief of staff, Brian Murphy; his parliamentary assistant, Philip O'Callaghan; and, of course, Nick Miller.

At no point in the meeting did Varadkar directly tell those present he was gay. He knew Miller already knew, but he also suspected that so did Murphy and O'Callaghan. The main objective of the meeting was to discuss the potential fallout from the most personal interview that would be given by a politician in years. 'It's funny. He never said he was going to come out,' says O'Callaghan, the youngest member of Leo's inner circle.

> But we knew what the meeting was about and we knew what the interview was about. So it was how he was going to frame it and how he was going to talk about it and how the interview would go and what sort of style it would be. But we never discussed him saying, 'I'm a gay man.'

That discussion did take place, a day earlier, albeit on an impromptu and unexpected basis. The setting was the television studios in RTÉ, Ireland's national broadcaster. Presenter Miriam O'Callaghan had already been contacted by Miller through her producer, Alan Torney, about facilitating a 'personal interview' with Leo on her radio programme that coming Sunday. O'Callaghan had heard the rumours that Varadkar was gay and decided to broach the issue with him during an ad break on the *Prime Time* current affairs show, of which she is a presenter.

Varadkar had agreed to appear on the programme to discuss what he was doing to reduce the significant number of people lying on trolleys in the country's hospitals. But O'Callaghan felt she needed to establish the exact nature of the 'personal interview' he intended to give in the nearby radio studios on Sunday. With the programme off air for a short ad break, O'Callaghan approached Varadkar. 'Minister, might I ask you something? Are you coming on my radio show on Sunday to say that you are gay?' 'Yes, I am,' Varadkar replied. 'OK, see you Sunday,' she responded. 'It was a bit of a risk for me,' O'Callaghan explains. 'What if he had said, "No, I'm not gay"? I texted my producer straight away. It was a wow moment.'

Prior to O'Callaghan's approach to Varadkar in the RTÉ studios, both her producer and Varadkar's team had been engaging in a back-and-forth. But at no point was the nature of what Varadkar was about to say discussed. 'We would kind of double-speak,' says a source in the Varadkar camp. 'They would say, "How deep do you want this interview to go?" We would say, "No holds barred. He's happy to talk about his personal life."'

The night prior to the interview, Miller was anxious. There was concern that a Sunday newspaper had got wind of the plan and was prepared to blow their cover. It didn't happen.

On Sunday 18 January 2015, Leo awoke to birthday messages from family and friends. The country's youngest member of Cabinet had just turned thirty-six years old. But the time for celebrations would have to wait.

As he arrived at the RTÉ complex in Donnybrook, nerves began to set in. Shortly after 9.30 a.m., a casually dressed Varadkar and his advisers Nick Miller and Brian Murphy climbed the cobbled steps of the radio studios, where they were greeted by O'Callaghan and her producer. Varadkar and his team noticed the presence of RTÉ's political correspondent, David Davin-Power. Few words were exchanged, but the presence of the reporter made it clear that word had spread about his intended plans that day.

After some innocuous small talk, O'Callaghan cut to the chase. It was ten minutes before the programme went live on air and still no party was clear about the game plan. 'How are we going to do this?' O'Callaghan asked. Varadkar and Miller looked at each and shrugged. O'Callaghan continued, conscious that her interviewee was feeling nervous. 'How about twenty minutes into the interview, I mention how it's your birthday and yet you're a very eligible bachelor but you've never settled down. That's your cue. Tell me you're gay.'

Just minutes before the interview, Varadkar sent a text message to Tiernan Brady, who was in New York. He told his confidant that he was in the green room ready to have the conversation that had been the subject of secret talks for months. 'The Irish people are thoroughly decent,' Tiernan replied. 'This will be a great experience, don't worry.'

But when *Miriam Meets…* went live on air just after the ten o'clock news, it quickly became apparent that Varadkar was getting cold feet. After a short discussion about his father Ashok's Indian roots, his studies at Trinity College and his experience in the Department of Health, Miriam stuck to the strategy agreed prior to going on air. 'You're thirty-six today, you are by all accounts very eligible, but you haven't settled down yet, have you?' 'No, not at all,' Varadkar replied. 'I suppose I've always put the career, the job and politics, all of that first,' Leo said, before explaining that many of his friends were now getting married or having kids. Varadkar rambled on, prompting his interviewer to look towards the production booth.

Both Miller and Torney had their heads in their hands, wondering if Varadkar was now veering away from the most difficult public discussion he would ever have. Suddenly, the conversation was brought back on track. 'I always thought I'd be alone for whatever reason,' Leo said poignantly. 'I was kind of happy with that. It's only in the last year or two I've sort of re-thought that and made time for relationships and other people,' he added. 'What kind of relationship would you be looking for?' asked O'Callaghan. 'Well, you know I'm a very private person and I still am,' Leo replied.

I keep my private life to myself and that's going to continue. I always think that friends and family are off-bounds. I went into politics, they didn't. But I am a gay man – it's not a secret, but not something everyone would necessarily know, but it isn't something I've spoken publicly about before now.

It was a monumental – indeed, unforgettable – moment. Although slightly awkward, the delivery of the announcement struck a note of both sincerity and innocence. Social media lit up with delight as news of Varadkar's decision instantly travelled around the world. Ireland's first openly gay minister had bared all on national radio.

The interview continued, with Leo speaking about how he came out to his father, Ashok, his mother, Miriam, and his two sisters, Sonia and Sophie. He said his dad came from a conservative background and that his family in India were traditional. As for his mother, Varadkar said she had expressed concern because gay friends of hers in England had suffered a hard time. But overall, he said, his family were extremely supportive.

I know that's not the case for everyone. I do know people who have been rejected by their families and treated badly in the workplace and things like that. I guess I'm lucky it's been OK for me and I'm fortunate as well to be in a country where we can have this conversation in a studio. That wouldn't be the case in Russia, for example, or other countries.

Over the course of an hour, Varadkar explained how he hoped him being a gay man wouldn't prove to be a big deal for anybody listening. He added that as Minister for Health, he had to oversee the introduction of legislation in the area of surrogacy. And he also had to decide whether to enact measures that would see a relaxation of the ban on gay and bisexual men donating blood.

During the interview, Varadkar recalled a phone call he made to Enda Kenny to let him know about his plans to speak about his sexuality. Kenny asked Varadkar whether he had ever been to Panti Bar, one of Dublin's best-known gay bars. 'He said it was my private life, and it's a private issue, and said it was none of his concern, that he wouldn't be commenting on it, nothing would be different and nothing would change,' Varadkar said. 'He asked me if I'd ever been to the Panti Bar … and I said actually no I haven't, and he said, "There you go, Varadkar, I'm ahead of you already."'

But Leo said his overriding motivation was the marriage equality referendum – one that, if passed, would see Ireland becoming the first country in the world to legislate for gay marriage by way of a popular vote. 'What I really want to say is that I'd like the referendum to pass because I'd like to be an equal citizen in my own country, that country [where] I happen to be a member of government, and at the moment I'm not,' he said.

> I don't want anyone to think I've a hidden agenda or that I'm not being fully honest with them and I wasn't going to dwell too much on the referendum – I know this is not a political programme – but that's obviously coming up in May and I was thinking of the arguments I might make.

After the interview, Varadkar and his two advisers went for lunch in a café in south inner-city Dublin. People who had listened to the interview approached Varadkar to congratulate him on his decision.

Among the 250,000 listeners that morning were Leo's family, friends and colleagues. Leo's parents Ashok and Miriam were visiting their daughter Sophie in London. The family were desperately trying to log onto the internet to listen to the programme live but were encountering technical problems. In her Dublin home, Sonia Varadkar was relaying the gist of the interview to the family. Leo visited Sonia for dinner later that day. The brother and sister emotionally embraced. Sonia told Leo how proud she was of him.

Politically, Leo's decision was seen as seismic. By coming out, he became the country's first openly gay minister and one of just four openly gay members of the Oireachtas. It also prompted the Yes side in the pending marriage equality referendum to bring forward their launch date in order to tap into the positive effect of Leo's decision.

One close friend explains that Leo could not legitimately campaign for a Yes vote while allowing the rumour mill to continue in overdrive. 'It was coming down the road. How could he champion it and not say he was gay? He'd lose all credibility otherwise,' the friend notes.

Former Health Minister and leader of the Progressive Democrats Mary Harney, a confidante of Varadkar's, says the magnitude of his decision cannot be downplayed. She says that, 'despite what people tell you', being gay in Irish politics is a handicap. 'You know, if you're not part of the mainstream of Irish society, it's always a disadvantage no matter what people say,' Harney says.

Within the Fine Gael party, some TDs say they suspected

Varadkar was gay months and even years before he came out. Colleagues had often invited him to social gatherings such as weddings and birthdays and noted that he always turned up alone. But others who are close to Varadkar said they were surprised. One of these is Eoghan Murphy. Months before he publicly came out, Murphy met Leo for a drink in the Shelbourne Hotel, during which the issue of his sexuality was raised. Murphy was surprised to learn Varadkar was gay. Varadkar was surprised his friend had not known. Varadkar told Murphy he wanted to come out publicly but he was afraid he would be accused of using the announcement to distract from his work in the Department of Health.

Others closest to Varadkar chose not to listen to the interview with Miriam O'Callaghan. To this day, Varadkar himself has never listened back.

His friends had known for many months that he was about to take this significant step. But they were angry, and indeed upset, that it was a step that he had to take under the harsh glare of the public eye. 'I was upset for him in that it's nobody's business but your own, but you have to go through this interview with Miriam,' one close friend says.

One of the most positive elements of Varadkar's coming-out story was the fact that he did so predominantly on his own terms. His team and indeed his friends are appreciative of the fact that the media refrained from outing him. Mark Finan recalls how members of the media were asking questions about his close friend. He says, however, that he has always been surprised that no newspaper took the chance: 'While it would be public titillation, it's not a public interest story. I don't think we are that type of nation.' The dreaded story that Nick Miller constantly feared was never published. Varadkar and his team still aren't sure why.

Instead, they woke on the Monday morning after the interview to headlines that made bold predictions about Varadkar's future. 'Varadkar on track to be first gay Taoiseach' read the front page of the *Irish Independent*.

But before that could happen, Varadkar had to join others in convincing the nation to make history. The marriage equality referendum was about to begin.

CHAPTER 12

MARRIAGE EQUALITY

The GPO on Dublin's O'Connell Street is one of Ireland's most cherished and historically significant buildings. It is the headquarters of the men and women who took part in the 1916 Easter Rising – a home-grown rebellion against British rule in Ireland. Above any other landmark, the GPO is a symbol of the fight for Irish nationalism and identity. But on 16 May 2015, three men led a fight of a very different kind: the fight for their sons to be able to marry the people they love.

Over 400 people were present outside the GPO as the Yes Equality campaign staged its national canvass. Leo Varadkar wasn't there that day, but his father Ashok was there to proudly take part in the Fathers for Yes event. Ashok had just recently been told that his only son was gay. It was a particularly difficult conversation for both father and son. However, despite his traditional Indian background, Ashok showed no hesitation when asked to take part in the event outside the GPO.

On this glorious Saturday morning, Leo's father became part of a piece of defining imagery; one that leading Yes campaigners say carried extraordinary significance. Standing next to Ashok were fathers who, like him, had strong links to politics. The first was Dr Martin McAleese, the ex-senator and husband to the former President Mary McAleese. Just days before the GPO event, McAleese's son Justin had penned an article in the *Irish Independent* about growing up as a gay man. Justin, a former assistant to Ryanair boss Michael O'Leary, had refrained from coming out after some of his friends joked about the prospect of two men getting married. 'So I stayed in the closet for another eighteen months,' McAleese wrote. 'Language matters, words matter, marriage matters.'

Standing next to McAleese was Tom Curran, the General Secretary of Fine Gael. A week prior to the Fathers for Yes event, Curran had picked up the phone to the editor of the *Irish Independent*, Fionnán Sheahan. He told Sheahan that his son Finnian had recently come out and he wanted to tell his family's experience. Curran, a practising Catholic, wanted his son and other gay people to know that they had nothing to be ashamed of. After consulting Taoiseach Enda Kenny, Curran had penned his own piece for the newspaper in which he spoke of the journey he had been on as a regular mass-goer. 'I've come on a journey, in terms of my belief, and I feel comfortable in urging all people of faith to consider the equal marriage referendum seriously and to vote yes. In my view, it's the right thing – the moral thing – to do,' Curran wrote. Reflecting on the Fathers for Yes event, Curran says it was particularly significant for Ashok to turn up, given his conservative roots. 'Here were three fathers of sons who had come out. It was a proud day. For Ashok, I think it was even greater because his son was in such a public profile,' Curran says.

The public show of support from the fathers of three gay sons was hugely important, as leading campaign figure Tiernan Brady recalls:

It wasn't just about gay people saying, 'I want to get married.'

That's not a big enough picture. It's when your mums and
dads and brothers and sisters stand up for you. When people
say, 'I get that, I would stand up for my brother. I would stand
up for my daughter.'

The images of the three fathers ran prominently in the next
day's newspapers. For Brady, the photographs sent a powerful
message to all four corners of Ireland that marriage equality
was as much about the gay person as it was about their loved
ones. 'Sometimes people will never understand what it's like
to be gay. But what they will understand is what it's like to be
a parent, a brother or sister. And the protective emotions you
feel and the love you feel for them,' Brady says. '[Leo] understood that brilliantly. His family interventions in the campaign
became really important.'

It wasn't just Leo's father who decided to waive his privacy
and make a meaningful contribution during the campaign. On
10 May, Leo's older sister Sonia Varadkar made a poignant plea
for voters to support the upcoming referendum. In an article
published in the *Sunday Independent*, Sonia said she was voting
yes not simply for her brother, but so that future generations
of children could be treated with dignity. In her article, she
recalled the emotion she felt while listening to Leo's interview
with Miriam O'Callaghan, during which he revealed he was
gay. And, like many of Leo's friends, Sonia was angry that her
brother had to announce his sexuality under the public glare.
'Why should he have to tell anyone about his sexual orientation? He's my little brother,' Sonia wrote. 'I'm his big sister. And
I didn't want him having to bare his soul to the nation.' Leo's
interview with Miriam O'Callaghan was cited repeatedly as a
major moment ahead of polling day.

Former government Chief Whip Pat Carey also came out

during the campaign. He told Newstalk broadcaster Pat Kenny that he had 'great admiration' for Varadkar and that he didn't possess the same 'courage and confidence' when he was in office. 'People like him are important role models. He is a different generation, he's a good thirty-something years younger than me. He's able to do this for his generation; maybe I can do something for my generation too,' Carey said.

Another public figure influenced by Varadkar's decision was the respected political journalist Ursula Halligan. Explaining her own reasons for coming out, Ms Halligan wrote in the *Irish Times*: 'Homophobia was so deeply embedded in my soul, I resisted facing the truth about myself, preferring to live in the safety of my prison.' And in a subsequent interview on Today FM, Ms Halligan added, 'I never thought I'd see the day that a government minister would come out as gay and encounter almost nothing but praise.'

But while personal and deeply emotive stories flowed from Leo's own interview, the result was not a foregone conclusion. Differences within political circles and clashes between the Yes and No sides would throw the result into doubt ahead of the poll.

* * *

History has shown that referendums in Ireland don't pass easily. Politicians, particularly on the government side, dread these votes for a myriad of reasons. The campaigns themselves consume a vast amount of energy and are a drain on party finances. Above all, they are difficult to win, and defeat can prove damaging. Take 2001, when voters rejected the Treaty of Nice. Seven years later, the first Lisbon Treaty referendum was also rejected by the electorate – prompting the government to put the question to the people again months later. In January 2012,

Varadkar went as far as saying he did not believe in the referendum system. 'I don't think referendums are very democratic. By and large, referendum campaigns are never about what they are supposed to be about,' he told RTÉ Radio 1.

A relatively little-known fact about referendums in Ireland is that they only pass if the question put to the people is backed by the lead opposition party. Apart from the passing in 1937 of the Irish constitution, Bunreacht na hÉireann, there has never been a referendum passed if the opposition disagreed. Cross-party support is vital. For Sinn Féin, support for marriage equality was absolute across the parliamentary party. However, Varadkar was conscious of divisions within Fianna Fáil – the lead opposition party – which could affect the Yes campaign. While their leader, Micheál Martin, was a staunch advocate of a Yes vote, other senior TDs had no intention of being seen at any Yes rallies. In Fine Gael, meanwhile, there were also a handful of conservative TDs and senators who were privately opposed to marriage equality.

As the campaign entered full flow, one of Varadkar's friends and fellow Trinity graduate, Fianna Fáil senator Averil Power, began to consider her future. Power was not only among those leading her party's support for a Yes vote; she was also one of the main political figures nationally campaigning for marriage equality. However, unbeknown to Varadkar at the time, Power was preparing to leave her party. She was deeply frustrated with her colleagues' ambivalence towards the referendum campaign. But Power kept these frustrations private. She was conscious that highlighting the split in Fianna Fáil over marriage equality could jeopardise the Yes campaign.

With the Yes side becoming concerned about the prospect of a defeat, Varadkar's initial plan to limit his role during the campaign was about to change.

* * *

With just a month until polling day, leading members of the Yes side met Agriculture Minister Simon Coveney, who had just been appointed director of elections of Fine Gael's own Yes campaign. Coveney had contacted Enda Kenny to request the job, an approach he would adopt for other positions in the future. Coveney felt strongly that as a married father he could appeal to some of the more conservative and rural voters in Fine Gael. The move suited Varadkar, who was anxious not to take on such a role for a number of reasons. Above all, he was preparing legislation that would lift the ban on blood donations for gay men and did not want to be accused of allowing his sexuality to influence an important change in policy. Tiernan Brady, who was part of the delegation that met Coveney in late April, says he believed the Agriculture Minister was the ideal candidate to take a leading political role. 'What you wanted was a straight dad and that's what Simon was,' Brady explains.

Justice Minister Frances Fitzgerald would also be appointed as a leading figure in the Fine Gael campaign, along with Children's Minister Dr James Reilly and openly gay TD Jerry Buttimer. But at Fine Gael's referendum launch in Dublin city centre in April 2015, it was Varadkar who made a deeply personal appeal to voters. He said that, given the choice, he would rather lose his own Dáil seat than see the Irish electorate reject marriage equality. 'Initially, a few months ago, I didn't feel as passionate about this as I do now,' he told reporters.

> That's probably because, as somebody who is not involved in a long-term relationship, it's not something that affects me personally or directly, or at least not yet. But I do know that if the referendum is defeated when the votes are counted on 23

May, I'll be absolutely devastated. It will be worse than losing an election, or even losing my seat.

Without doubt, one of the central ingredients for the success of the marriage equality campaign was the ability of the Yes side to adopt a respectful tone at all times. Campaigners such as Brady, Gráinne Healy, Brian Sheehan and Averil Power ensured the debate was at all stages about one simple thing: one person's love for another. The decision to focus on personal, poignant stories of courage and struggle appealed to the hearts of voters.

In contrast, the No campaign was both fragmented and, at times, divisive. However, there were certain moments during the campaign in which they managed to muddy the waters – prompting Varadkar to make an intervention. The best example related to the issue of surrogacy. Towns were flooded with posters depicting a young girl and her mother accompanied by the phrase 'She needs her mother for life, not just nine months.' The issue of adoption was also being raised by the No side. The tactics led to last-minute jitters.

And, just four days out from polling, Varadkar made a number of media interventions. This time, it was his knowledge and experience as a doctor that would come to the fore. Varadkar compared the arguments of the No campaign in the same-sex marriage referendum to issues raised in the vote on divorce in the '90s. 'The number of people who avail of surrogacy every year is absolutely tiny – and almost all of them are straight couples,' Varadkar said. 'It's already the case that under our laws on surrogacy and adoption, we don't discriminate against single people, unmarried couples or gay people.' Varadkar's assured performance comfortably defeated the final argument of the No campaign.

Having initially intended to play a low-key role in the

campaign, Ireland's only gay minister spent the final days canvassing in his constituency with Fine Gael members and colleagues from other political parties. On the eve of polling, Varadkar was part of a group that canvassed in the relatively new suburb of Hollystown in his Dublin West constituency. It was past 9 p.m. but the group had no intention of calling it a night. Ronan Melvin, one of Leo's key supporters and a seasoned canvasser, says he was concerned people would react badly to being disturbed at such a late hour. 'I said, "Come on, lads, it's ten past nine. We are going to be ate,"' Melvin says. 'Nobody ate us. It was a campaign like no other, it was unbelievably positive.'

Eight separate opinion polls since March had predicted that Irish people were ready to legalise same-sex marriage. Efforts by members of the clergy to prevent a Yes vote failed to make any real impact. On the eve of the vote, it was left to Taoiseach Enda Kenny – a devout Catholic – to make a final appeal to voters to say Yes to same-sex marriage. 'The Yes will obliterate, publicly, the remaining barriers of prejudice or the irrational fear of the "them" and "us" in this regard,' Kenny said. It was a message that had permeated throughout the entire campaign.

Polling day saw an extremely strong turnout, which gave the Yes side reason to be confident. And, on 22 May 2015, Ireland made history.

* * *

From mid-morning, crowds of thousands of people streamed into Dublin Castle in anticipation of the official referendum result. Some of those present had been involved in the campaign to decriminalise homosexuality some twenty-two years previous. Others were there just for the occasion.

What was most apparent on that morning was the hordes of young people who had flown into Dublin, Cork and Shannon airports in the preceding hours. The vast number of Irish emigrants drawn home was fuelled by the social media campaign #Cominghometovote. It was a major success of the Yes campaign.

Across the country, voters gathered in polling centres to celebrate as the results rolled in. But it was the sun-kissed courtyard of Dublin Castle where the final national result was announced around teatime.

At 9.29 a.m., an emotional Leo Varadkar pulled his mobile phone from his pocket and sent a tweet that he will never forget. 'So far Dublin West is 76pc yes with 5pc of boxes open. Predict national Yes over 60pc History in the making #MarRef #YesEquality'. His tweet was followed by a declaration of defeat from leading No campaigner David Quinn of the Iona Institute. Just minutes later, Varadkar tweeted again: 'Question now is will any constituency vote No? #MarRef'.

He would shortly tell RTÉ broadcaster Bryan Dobson that the result represented a decisive day for Ireland. 'If there are going to be any constituencies that vote No, it'll only be a handful,' Varadkar said, adding:

> It makes it a really historic day for Ireland. We are the first country in the world to enshrine marriage equality in the constitution by a popular mandate. That makes us a beacon, a light for the rest of the world for liberty and equality. It's a very proud day to be Irish.

As the results trickled through, Varadkar's early projections were proven right. In the end, just one constituency – Roscommon–South Leitrim – voted to reject marriage equality, by a small margin. His home, Dublin West – like many other constituencies – voted overwhelmingly in favour. The final tally confirmed that 1,201,607 people voted in favour compared to just 734,300 people who voted against.

The result prompted deeply emotional scenes at Dublin Castle. Varadkar looked out at the jubilant crowds as he celebrated with other leading campaigners such as Averil Power, Colm O'Gorman and senator David Norris. Varadkar turned to his party colleague Simon Coveney and shared a rare embrace. 'It's for days like this we do politics,' Varadkar said.

He would go on to describe the result as being much more than just a referendum. For him, and for many other gay people, it was a social revolution, one that marked a new chapter for the Irish Republic. 'Something has been awakened in the Irish people in this referendum and it will be very good for Ireland,' he continued.

I think this referendum for so many people was personal – not just gay men and lesbians but their friends, family and co-workers. People in the LGBT community are a minority but with their friends we're a majority. [It] became a catalyst for a national conversation about this issue. It's been really important.

For Tom Curran, the decision by Varadkar to come out prior to the referendum cannot be overstated. 'Politicians often are not authentic,' Curran says. 'Here Leo was, being authentic, saying, "Well, this is who I am."' Curran likens the decision by Varadkar to come out to Enda Kenny's emotional Dáil speech in February 2013, in which he apologised to the women who were treated like slaves in the Magdalene laundries.

People could see this party, that was supposed to be representing X class and Y class and Z class, had actually a heart.

And it was as significant for me as Enda Kenny's Magdalene laundry speech and so on that equally showed the party had a heart. We need to speak to people in that kind of language, that's what politicians need to do.

The referendum result made headlines around the world and piled pressure on other countries to follow suit. Ironically, just hours after the Irish people voted to legalise sex-sex marriage, the then Prime Minister of Australia Tony Abbott ruled out the prospect of a similar poll happening there. As history has proven, he was wrong.

Tiernan Brady travelled to Australia to work on the successful marriage equality postal survey in November 2017. The challenges facing Brady and other campaigners were different from those present during the Irish campaign, but Varadkar's experience of coming out was often raised by Brady as he and his colleagues built up their campaign. While there, he met similar senior politicians who, like Varadkar, were worried about being branded 'the gay politician'. His message to these politicians was simple: 'You can look at Leo's experience and see you don't get branded.' Brady says, 'It's hard to impress on people the value of having a role model in life, and having a Prime Minister who is gay sends a phenomenal message to young people in Ireland. There are no barriers. And if you don't believe us, look at the Taoiseach.'

*   *   *

Even prior to the referendum result, friends of Leo say they noticed a marked change in his behaviour. With the weight of keeping his sexuality secret now off his shoulders, Leo felt more comfortable socialising in gay bars and in settings that he previously would have avoided. At times, friends and colleagues say, Leo's socialising was a cause for concern. However, others close to Varadkar insist he was always conscious of acting responsibly as a minister. Early on in his ministerial career, he was given a stark reminder of his responsibilities when his late-night antics ended up in the pages of a Sunday newspaper. 'In his first year as minister, a Sunday newspaper ran a tiny story about Leo having a couple of drinks in a nightclub and bumping into people,' an adviser says. 'It was a really harmless throwaway thing, but it was in his first year of being in government and it really brought home to everybody about how careful he needed to be, so he was always very careful after that,' the source adds. Before and after Varadkar came out, he was conscious of how he acted in public, according to one adviser. 'He always minded that there was a responsibility when you're a minister as to where you go and how you are.'

One evening, while socialising in the well-known bar 4 Dame Lane, Leo met Dr Matthew Barrett. Matt, a cardiologist, was introduced to Leo through a mutual friend. The pair immediately hit it off and began dating. Very soon, the same friends who harboured concerns about Leo noticed a huge shift in both his mood and his behaviour. 'Matt is a good match. He really is,' remarks one friend. 'Before Matt was on the scene, Leo was different. Like totally different. Matt comes in, grounds him, tells him how it is. Quite direct.'

A fluent Irish speaker from the tiny village of Geesala in Co. Mayo, Matt is a son of two teachers. In Dublin, he worked as a junior doctor in St Vincent's Hospital, where he was held in high esteem. The pair quickly gelled over their shared interests of fitness, medicine, music and occasional nights at the theatre. But they are also competitive as a couple, with Leo at times rueing the fact that his other half can read faster. But as word of Matt spread through political circles, Leo expressed concern about the sort of pressures his public profile could place on the relationship. 'Matt has a super career ahead of him, he is super intelligent. He has his own life. He doesn't want to be defined by his relationship [with Leo],' one friend close to the couple says.

As their relationship grew stronger, Leo began to bring Matt to more Fine Gael events. Matt agreed to teach Leo Irish, which he would need if his leadership ambitions were to be fulfilled. During social occasions, if Leo spoke out of turn, Matt would mark out a star on his partner's hand. It was an affectionate way of telling him to shut up.

For the Varadkar family, Matt became like a second son. Leo had finally dispelled his sister Sonia's long-held fears that her little brother would always be alone. 'They are good as a couple, they both gel and they have very similar interests and they are well able to learn and teach each other,' Sonia says.

In July 2017, Leo and Matt's relationship became a long-distance one. After completing his specialist cardiology studies in Ireland, Matt wanted to gain some international experience and travelled to Chicago to take up a fellowship. How would being thousands of miles apart affect the couple? 'I think Leo does struggle,' one friend says, adding, 'Then you would wonder, would it be even stranger if Matt was in Dublin and not able to see him because he is so busy as Taoiseach? Maybe it's a case of because Matt is away, it makes it easier for him not to get frustrated.'

Leo has visited Matt in the US on a number of occasions and the pair keep in touch via Facetime. As Sonia points out, living apart is a challenge that many couples face. 'No, I think they are making things work. I think like any modern couple there are going to be times when you are apart and times when you are together. I think they are doing well.'

With a newfound stability in his personal life, Varadkar was able to put more focus on his political career. Fine Gael was riding high in the opinion polls following the marriage equality referendum, but a divisive general election campaign was just around the corner.

CHAPTER 13

GENERAL ELECTION 2016

——

J oan Burton just wouldn't let it go. Every time the Tánaiste managed to get Kenny on his own, she would pester him about the date of the general election. The Labour Party leader was on edge following leaks to the media suggesting the Taoiseach was planning to cut and run and call a snap election for November 2015. Burton was deeply opposed to the idea of an early polling date. She would sit in his office and talk at length about the various reasons for holding off until the spring. The days would be brighter, Burton argued. Voters would not be receptive to politicians calling on them during the dark and wet winter evenings, she told Kenny. A November election would particularly affect politicians living in urban areas, where most of Burton's Labour colleagues were based. Labour also wanted voters to feel the financial benefits of the budget in their pockets before they went to the polls. But the main factor underpinning Burton's desperation was her party's dismal poll ratings.

Labour was feeling the brunt of public anger for the years of austerity. One opinion poll released in the autumn placed the party's support at a mere 6 per cent. Despite the appearance of the green shoots of recovery, all the indications pointed to an electoral drubbing for Burton and her colleagues. Labour supporters were angry, too. They had endorsed the decision to enter office with Fine Gael on the basis that their party would rein in their conservative partners and reverse the cuts introduced by Fianna Fáil. But with the country still wounded by the financial crash, Labour was on course to be punished. There was an impression, perhaps unfairly, that Fine Gael had run rings around Labour in government and claimed the credit for the measures that had led to a modest improvement in people's lives. Now, Enda Kenny was poised to add further insult to injury by pulling the plug early on the coalition arrangement – before Labour felt prepared to face the electorate once again.

Fine Gael's opinion poll ratings were solid, and the economy was slowly but surely improving. Some political commentators expected Fine Gael to be rewarded at the ballot box for making the necessary tough decisions that had put the country's finances onto a more sustainable footing. Leo Varadkar, who shared the Dublin West constituency with Burton, strongly favoured a November election. He knew, as Minister for Health, that the annual trolley crisis in the country's hospitals was on the horizon. And, if the crisis was anywhere near as bad as the one that had struck the previous winter, Fine Gael's support was sure to suffer. If they cut loose early, the health service would not be the main political issue during the campaign.

Varadkar used any influence he had with the Taoiseach to convince him to pull the plug on the coalition. He wasn't the only senior Cabinet figure to push Kenny towards a November poll. Michael Noonan, the wise old owl of Fine Gael, had the ear of the Taoiseach above any other minister. Those backing a November vote told Kenny that the weather in late January or early February is generally cold and miserable. Voters are financially broke and in a slump after the Christmas and New Year festivities. Going early would also put the other main parties and the growing number of Independent candidates on the back foot. The lobbying by Varadkar, Noonan and others appeared to be working. Kenny seemed to have been convinced of the merits of an early poll and Fine Gael began secretly preparing for such a scenario.

With an election on the cards, the stakes could not be higher when it came to announcing Budget 2015. The coalition was finally in a position to spend again after years of austerity. In stark contrast to the recession years, there was now an air of positivity among Fine Gael and Labour ministers. The talk in Leinster House switched from austerity measures to tax cuts and increases in social welfare payments. The budget was touted as a pre-election giveaway, designed to win over voters who had borne the brunt of the country's bailout programme. In reality, most of the tax cuts and welfare increases would end up being paltry at best.

However, Labour was eager for people to feel these benefits in their pockets before polling day arrived. A source in the Varadkar camp insisted Labour were 'total fools' for believing their electoral chances would improve once the budget measures came into effect. Varadkar's team were of the belief that tax cuts and spending increases sound much better when they are announced. When they actually materialise, the public soon realise that the increases equate to the price of a pint. 'Opinion only shifts when the public get back what was taken from them in the first place. Not when they see the first sliver of it,' remarks one Leo strategist.

As the budget loomed, all the main political parties were at advanced stages of election planning, putting in place their strategies in the event that Kenny succumbed to pressure from within Fine Gael. Committees had been established and parts of manifestos were being regularly leaked to the media. The budget itself was carefully crafted with the aim of attracting votes from the so-called squeezed middle or Middle Ireland. These were the people who had been hit the hardest by the recession. These were the families who had been let down by politicians and indeed the banks. Their homes were in negative equity. Paying the mortgage was a monthly struggle that caused couples to lie awake anxiously at night. Rising childcare costs meant, in many cases, that one parent had to forego full employment. In many other cases, parents were forced to wave goodbye to their emigrating children at airports, wondering if they would ever return home permanently. It was a period Irish people pray will never be repeated. Fine Gael and Labour knew that to be returned to power, they needed the endorsement from Middle Ireland. The coalition was also determined to attract the 'grey vote': pensioners who had seen their incomes drop dramatically during the economic downturn and who were guaranteed to show up on polling day. The time for Kenny to decide when that day would be had arrived.

Kenny revelled in teasing the media about an early election. The more he was asked about the date, the more he refused to kill off the speculation. Newstalk radio show host Ivan Yates, who was a former Fine Gael minister, was responsible for starting the election speculation frenzy. In late September, he told listeners he'd received a tip-off from a well-informed source who had confirmed to him that the election would be on 20 November 2015. Michael Noonan ramped up the speculation in the same week by telling reporters that, as he saw it, there were 'two windows for an election'. Noonan said, 'It's either between now and Christmas or it's after Christmas and the Taoiseach will call it in due course, taking all the relevant factors into account, and he's a very good political judge.'

Kenny continued to fuel speculation and Labour kept panicking. During an interview on his local radio station, the Taoiseach once again refused to rule out a November vote. At a jobs announcement the following day, he joked that the constitution allowed him to remain in power for seven years and that he might hold the election in 2018. At the same event, Burton revealed that she had a 'long conversation' with the Taoiseach and insisted she 'wouldn't bet on an early election'.

On Thursday 8 October 2015, as election talk reached fever pitch in Leinster House, the *Irish Times* ran a front-page story that stated Kenny was 'leaning strongly towards' a November poll. The prominence of the story and the fact that it was authored by the paper's political editor, Stephen Collins, suggested it was a done deal. Collins had been spotted speaking directly with Kenny outside the Dáil canteen the day before and it was widely thought within political circles that the Taoiseach was the source of the story. Kenny had made his decision.

* * *

The *Irish Times* story sparked anger and panic within the coalition. Fine Gael and Labour ministers were now openly briefing against each other. Labour figures felt betrayed and went as far as to threaten to pull out of the coalition if an early election was called. Further meetings between Burton and Kenny took place. Burton, for a final time, urged the Taoiseach to hold off until the New Year.

As the parties prepared for an imminent election announcement, Kenny appeared on RTÉ's *The Week in Politics* on the Sunday after the *Irish Times* story ran. Before the show, his advisers were actively briefing that he would continue to leave the door open for a November vote. But once the cameras were rolling, Kenny appeared to go off script. He firmly stated that it was his intention to hold the election in 2016. This was always his plan, he said, adding that he saw no reason to change his mind.

The panic in Labour eased. But Fine Gael ministers were both surprised and disappointed with their leader's decision. In the aftermath of the interview, Kenny was accused of capitulating to Burton and failing to listen to his own party. None were more disappointed than Leo Varadkar. He would now face another winter of discontent in the health service, which his own friends and family believed was taking a toll on his well-being.

*   *   *

Despite resisting Varadkar's urging to go to the country early, Kenny had already appointed the Health Minister to the party's national election strategy committee. That appointment took place at a secret meeting in the Shelbourne Hotel in Dublin city centre in November 2014. Varadkar was asked to oversee communications. Simon Coveney would be in charge of policy and James Reilly would head up party membership. All three would report to Frances Fitzgerald. Also in the room that afternoon was Mark Mortell, a director of Fleishman Hillard consultancy firm and a long-standing adviser and friend of Kenny's. The meeting was also attended by the Taoiseach's chief of staff, Mark Kennelly; his economic adviser, Andrew McDowell; Fine Gael's General Secretary, Tom Curran; and head of research Terry Murphy. Fine Gael MEP Brian Hayes wasn't at that particular meeting but was later appointed director of elections.

A long-running criticism of Kenny had been that he was

too insular in his decision-making process and overly reliant on a small cohort of paid advisers rather than his TDs. The appointments were therefore initially viewed as a positive step. Varadkar and other senior party figures would, on the face of it, be given a leading role in campaign strategy. Or so Kenny had led them to believe. But Varadkar and his colleagues quickly realised that the committees were nothing more than talking shops. In the crucial months before the election, Kenny reverted to type and began to rely on his backroom strategists rather than his ministers. 'One of Enda's strategies was to set up committees and put people on to them to keep them busy and keep things moving,' one senior minister observes. 'But all the decisions were made at the centre by Mortell, Kennelly, Curran and McDowell.'

At irregular meetings in Fine Gael headquarters, the national committee would discuss campaign messaging, policies and strategies. The overarching political message they planned for the campaign centred on the economy. Research conducted by Fine Gael suggested large chunks of voters still felt they had yet to feel any benefits of the recovery. The party believed it had built up a reputation for being responsible when it came to job creation and the economy.

It was now clear that its message needed to go further and convince families that their lives would see improvements under a Fine Gael-led government. And so, the campaign slogan 'Keep the Recovery Going' was born. Its exact origins and the level of consultation around the message continue to sharply divide opinion within the party fold. But Varadkar admits that he had little objection to the slogan when it was first communicated: 'Definitely when I saw the slogan, I didn't baulk, I didn't go, "Oh, that's terrible," you know, or, "That will jar."'

Kenny's advisers worked off research that showed voters

responded well to the slogan. It struck a chord with the type of people they wanted to target in the election. It resonated with Middle Ireland, Kenny was told. Other slogans, such as 'Keep the Recovery Real', were considered. But Kenny's inner circle was convinced of their approach. '"Keep the Recovery Going" was about appealing to those in mortgage arrears, while tightening up on areas of public expenditure and driving job creation,' one strategist says of the slogan. 'The thought process was utterly consistent and completely sympathetic to where people were at in their lives.'

Another key election promise was to completely abolish the universal social charge (USC), an emergency tax introduced at the height of the recession. Sinn Féin and Fianna Fáil proposed reducing but not abolishing the USC in their election manifestos. Fine Gael, however, was determined to completely eliminate the tax, which had been introduced by Fianna Fáil. Varadkar now admits the election pledge on USC was misguided. 'I'll accept my share of the responsibility. I did think abolishing USC was a good policy. In retrospect, it wasn't a good idea,' he says.

In May 2015, Fine Gael had a chance to road-test their campaign messaging during the Carlow–Kilkenny by-election. Fine Gael's David Fitzgerald lost to Fianna Fáil's Bobby Aylward by almost 5,000 votes. An internal Fine Gael report compiled after the by-election flagged problems with Fine Gael's message. It put party strategists 'on notice' that voters' appetite was very much for 'better services and a fairer Ireland'. But no one seemed to heed the warnings.

In the weeks that followed, Kenny's inner circle once again took a decision that the party would soon regret. In June, Mortell, Kennelly and Curran flew over to London to meet the Conservative Party's political advisers to discuss their recent election success. The Tories had just secured a surprise majority in Westminster with a tightly controlled campaign that centred on Prime Minister David Cameron. The Fine Gael team was impressed and decided to delve further into the Tory handbook for guidance. Details of the secret rendezvous were kept under wraps, even from Fine Gael ministers. The last thing the party hierarchy wanted was the opposition finding out their election strategy was based on Cameron's success.

The meeting in London gave the Fine Gael delegation more confidence that their strategy to focus heavily on the economy was the correct option. 'Keep the Recovery Going' was eerily similar to the Conservatives 'Let's Keep Going' slogan, which had underpinned Cameron's campaign. It seemed each and every hallmark of the Tories' strategy was being used to build Fine Gael's campaign. Tom Curran said one aspect of the Tory campaign that appealed to Fine Gael was the manner in which the party had controlled Cameron's public appearances. There were fears within Fine Gael that Kenny would be targeted by protesters, particularly those leading the anti-water charges movement. Fine Gael liked the Tories' idea of placing a major focus on a leader's tour. 'If you remember at the time a lot of the places where the Taoiseach went there were a lot of demonstrations and we knew that it was going to be difficult for him to be out on the street,' Curran explains. 'So we were looking at a different type of campaign and the Tories seemed to be pretty successful. There was a close enough link between some in the Taoiseach's office and the Tory Party in Ireland,' he adds.

As the starting pistol sounded on the campaign itself, Fine Gael was nervous to say the least. Privately, senior party strategists knew they would be coming back with fewer seats than they had in 2011. The number of Dáil seats had been reduced from 166 to 158 and most of the constituency boundary changes directly affected Fine Gael TDs. Five Fine Gael TDs had also been expelled from the party in 2013 over a vote on abortion legislation, and a sixth, Denis Naughten, lost the party whip after voting against a decision to close down an Accident and Emergency department in his local hospital. There was no question this time round of the party securing seventy-six seats, like it did when it made history in 2011. Internal analysis instead predicted Fine Gael would come home with between fifty-eight and sixty-two seats. One senior source says the party purposely hid these calculations from TDs because the grim reality of the campaign would 'frighten the shite out of them'. 'Everyone in their heart of hearts knew a whole lot of people in this parliamentary party were under threat,' the source adds.

While the party knew it would face challenges, particularly stemming from Kenny's media appearances, senior strategists believed their plan, modelled on the Tories' campaign, was the best option. The party also felt it had a star-studded line-up of ministers, with Varadkar, Coveney, Fitzgerald, Paschal Donohoe and Simon Harris leading the charge. When it came to the cut and thrust of live TV debates, Varadkar and his colleagues were expected to outperform their rivals. But politics is unpredictable, as Fine Gael learned from day one of the campaign.

At around 9.30 a.m. on Wednesday 3 February 2016, Enda Kenny sauntered into the Dáil chamber and calmly announced his plans to dissolve Parliament. Before the opposition could respond, Kenny upped and left. Moments later, his official Twitter account announced the date of the general election: Friday 26 February.

At 2.30 p.m., Fine Gael held their official campaign launch in the Alexander Hotel, just a short walk from Leinster House on Dublin's Fenian Street. Running about fifteen minutes late, Kenny was bundled in through the side door of the conference room, surrounded by his handlers, before joining his ministerial team on the stage. The event went from bad to worse. Kenny arrogantly dismissed questions about the costings of his party's manifesto, saying he did not want to talk about 'economic jargon which the vast majority of people don't understand'.

The Fine Gael leader then turned to Minister for Finance Michael Noonan for support. Noonan was seen as Fine Gael's best performer on the economy and was viewed by party strategists as their secret weapon for the campaign. But, like Kenny, Noonan was having an off day. Pressed on the costings behind the party's election promises, Noonan rambled on about 'fiscal space', a term that still gives Fine Gael TDs nightmares. The phrase itself refers to the amount of money available in the economy to spend. But its technical nature immediately categorised Fine Gael as being out of touch with the ordinary voter. 'Noonan started off very badly and that did not help us,' one senior adviser notes. 'Sometimes someone has a bad day, but then we got into that whole fiscal space fucking thing.' Tom Curran also admits the party 'got off on the wrong foot' at the campaign launch. 'It was all about fiscal space and that was the wrong space for us to be in,' he says. 'It was only in the last couple of days when it really turned, but the beginning of the campaign was a nightmare.'

Fine Gael TDs across the country soon realised that the man who had steered the country out of the recession had become a major liability. Kenny appeared flustered and distracted at campaign events and never recovered from his faux pas on day one. The Taoiseach's uninspiring speeches relied heavily on campaign slogans and were being ridiculed by the opposition and the media. 'Keep the Recovery Going' and 'Make Work Pay' were the hallmarks of a flat and one-dimensional campaign for Fine Gael.

As the campaign passed its first week, concern heightened among Fine Gael candidates. But as director of communications, was Varadkar not responsible for changing campaign messaging? Noel Rock, a first-time candidate who was running in Dublin North West, lays the blame for the messaging at the feet of Brian Hayes. 'I hear now and then, "Ah, Leo was director of communications, he let people down,"' Rock says, adding, 'That's not true. He stepped down from that role if I can remember at least a month before the election. He had no real hand, act or part in the slogan that everyone focuses on.'

The complaints about the slogan continued to increase. 'I and others texted Brian to complain: "After day one on the doors, this slogan isn't landing properly at all,"' Rock says. In response to the complaints, Fine Gael bosses adopted what became their default mode for the duration of the campaign: candidates were told to stay calm and ignore the mid-campaign criticism, as it would all come good in the final days, just like it had for the Tories.

Over in Dublin West, Varadkar's campaign team, led by director of elections Henry Minogue, noticed early on that the campaign themes were not working on the doorsteps. Even in the more affluent, Fine Gael-friendly parts of the constituency, voters were not buying the message. Varadkar was repeatedly confronted by voters during canvasses and told that the recovery hadn't come to their door. 'The campaign started and we were ringing the door bells and it was very clear that "Keep the Recovery Going" was not working for people,' a senior Varadkar campaigner says. From Varadkar's perspective, it was time to change tack.

Varadkar took the decision to alter his campaign literature and abandon the Fine Gael approach. The 'Keep the Recovery Going' slogan had to go and was replaced with 'Bring the

Recovery to Every Home'. The change was subtle but effective. It was more human and more digestible for voters who had not yet felt the impact of the economy improving. 'Leo made a conscious decision to change it,' says an adviser. 'He felt, if it wasn't going to change nationally, it had to change locally.' A local campaigner explains that the messaging had to change to appeal to the middle-ground voters who were so key to Fine Gael's success. 'Most people's economy is between their front door and their back door,' the source says. 'It's putting shoes on kids going out to school, putting a jacket on their back for the winter – that's their economy. National recoveries don't mean anything to these people. It's about how much money comes in and out of their house on a given week.'

Hayes, however, denies the suggestion that Varadkar ran a significantly different campaign from other Fine Gael candidates. He also rejects any suggestion that Varadkar and other ministers had raised a flag about how the campaign was being run. Frances Fitzgerald was the only exception, Hayes recalls. 'If they are arguing now that they tried to change things, that's a load of bullshit and I don't believe it,' he says. '[Varadkar] thought it would come right, like Mortell and Kennelly. "Stick with the Tory brand and it will come right,"' he adds.

Fine Gael had initially planned to utilise its full Cabinet line-up in media interviews, rather than simply fielding its leader. This strategy was demonstrated on the day the election was called, when Varadkar represented Fine Gael on the RTÉ's *Six One News*. Every other party put forward their leader. Fine Gael felt the approach would demonstrate to the voters a diverse team of politicians ready to take the country forward. Varadkar looked out of place beside the other party leaders, but Kenny's handlers were adamant that they would not allow broadcasters to dictate their campaign. In the end, though, the media demanded Kenny and the party's communication strategy had to be ripped up.

Fine Gael rented an ultra-modern underground campaign headquarters in the Custom House Quay building close to the river Liffey in Dublin. The crypt-like office space was the hub for the party's morning meetings and conference calls. Varadkar was asked to show up only a handful of times. Now dropped from his strategy post, he was initially content at having more time to concentrate on topping the poll in Dublin West. But as the campaign progressed, he became both concerned and frustrated with Kenny's performance and the poor reaction on the doorsteps to Fine Gael's message.

With polling just days away, the worrying direction of the Fine Gael campaign was finally raised at a press event in the Dublin's docklands. The press conference was unremarkable. Varadkar and other ministers, including Frances Fitzgerald and James Reilly, felt deflated. Finally, a flag was raised. 'There were definitely a number of us who were worried about the campaign; it wasn't going well,' Varadkar remembers. 'The feedback from the ground was the slogan was sort of jarring with people.'

But, once again, the ministers were urged to keep calm and carry on. 'Relax – this will come good in the end,' Varadkar recalls one strategist saying. Varadkar adds:

> Somebody said the Tories told us this would happen – that the politicians would get windy in the middle of the campaign. Of course, that is what happened in Cameron's election. The politicians did get windy halfway and, in the end, in the last week, they bounced back and won a majority.

During the campaign, Joan Burton recalls meeting Varadkar at a constituency event. She said he was not at all happy with the way the campaign was going. 'He indicated to me he wasn't very happy with the election and, in fact, I remember at one stage him indicating that it was the worst election experience he'd had over and beyond the election Michael Noonan was leader when Fine Gael did very badly,' Burton says.

Fine Gael and Labour had agreed a vote pact going into the election itself. The agreement meant that in places like Dublin West, Varadkar would ask his supporters to give their third-preference votes to Burton, and vice versa. But during the second week of the campaign, the *Irish Independent* published a specially commissioned opinion poll of the constituency. It spelled potential danger for Burton. She was polling at just 10 per cent, the survey showed, and was on course to lose her seat to Sinn Féin's Paul Donnelly.

With Varadkar set to comfortably top the poll with over 20 per cent, his commitment to the vote pact between Fine Gael and Labour was essential for Burton. Burton made an appeal to Varadkar's voters, telling reporters on the campaign trail that she was 'very transfer-friendly'. A subsequent letter sent to voters throughout the constituency pleaded for their support and implied that while her seat was under threat, Varadkar's was safe. 'Local surveys suggested the election for the final seat in Dublin West may go down to the wire,' Burton wrote. 'So on Friday the choice will be between myself and either Ruth Coppinger [local socialist TD] or Sinn Féin. It's quite a stark choice. Do you want to swap me for one or other of those candidates?' the letter added. She signed off by saying voters could 'beat the opinion polls' by giving her a no. 1 vote. The aim of the letter was clear: Burton wanted to convince supporters of the government to give her a no. 1 and Varadkar a no. 2 to prevent Sinn Féin getting a foothold in the constituency.

Team Varadkar was furious at the approach and in the dying

days of the campaign drafted its own letter to supporters. The letter, which arrived the day before polling, hit back at suggestions that his seat was safe. 'No seat is safe, including mine,' Varadkar wrote. 'Opinion polls and pundits are often wrong. I have never topped a poll in a general election, never had a quota and have always relied on transfers to get elected,' he said. The letter asked voters to give Leo their no. 1, his Fine Gael running mate Catherine Noone a no. 2 and their third preference to Burton. Significantly, the leaflet made no mention of 'Keep the Recovery Going'. Instead, it said Fine Gael wanted 'to spend the next few years bringing the recovery to every home in Ireland by increasing income and investing in public services needed by you and your family'.

Elsewhere in the Dublin West constituency, Varadkar's running mate Catherine Noone was having difficulties making an impact in the run-up to polling day. Noone was nominated to run alongside Varadkar so Fine Gael could meet its gender quota obligations. But she was parachuted into a constituency with which she had little connection and she didn't really stand a chance. Before the campaign officially kicked off, Varadkar ensured he was delegated the 'Fine Gael-friendly' areas of the constituency, while Noone was given housing estates that had been newly added to the area. Varadkar was never going to let a blow-in steal his thunder and despite her hard work Noone ultimately failed to gain a foothold in the constituency.

While the battle continued in Dublin West, senior Fine Gael figures began to fear that the change of tide they had promised candidates would not materialise. A series of campaign opinion polls also dispelled hopes of Fine Gael and Labour reclaiming power. Labour's support had all but bottomed out and Fine Gael was hovering around the 28 per cent mark. Much of the talk throughout the campaign was about who would make up the next government. Kenny and Fianna Fáil leader Micheál Martin had refused to do business with each other, while Sinn Féin President Gerry Adams said he would not prop up either of the 'establishment' parties. Meanwhile, support for candidates unaligned to any political party rocketed. A stalemate was on the cards. It became increasingly likely that the next government, whichever party led it, would have to rely on the support of Independent TDs.

Fine Gael handlers did their best to avoid putting Kenny on the front line wherever possible. In the leadership debates, he was consistently outperformed by a fresher and more energetic Micheál Martin. Varadkar's inner circle were growing more concerned by the day. The minister's press adviser, Nick Miller, had been told by Fine Gael headquarters that Varadkar was not pencilled in for any major media events for the latter half of the campaign. Varadkar's senior team could not understand why one of the party's most able performers was not being utilised by Fine Gael election chiefs. Miller decide to take matters into his own hands and began organising media appearances for his boss. 'There were no events involving Leo for a week and a half, which was when the penny dropped with us that we are going to have put him out there ourselves, which is what we ended up doing,' a senior campaign source says.

One of those events was on RTÉ's *Prime Time*, which was broadcast towards the end of the campaign. Varadkar was due to take on Fianna Fáil's finance spokesman Michael McGrath in a live television debate. Fine Gael had a trick up their sleeve. Excited party strategists believed they had found a hole in Fianna Fáil's manifesto figures and were confident that Varadkar was best placed to land the knockout blow. Ministers convinced themselves this would be the turning point in the campaign, and it would be executed by one of their biggest stars and best debaters. On live television, McGrath would have nowhere to hide, Fine Gael figures believed. 'In our head we were pitching this as the big moment,' a minister recalls. 'The view here was that we need a game-changer and Varadkar was the game-changer. He was clearly the best and most polished. We needed him to fucking expose this and drive a horse and cart through Fianna Fáil's arguments. And of course he didn't,' the minister adds. Varadkar admits that his punches didn't land that night or on another occasion when he tried to target Micheál Martin during a radio interview. 'I tried it twice, once on *Prime Time* and another time on *Morning Ireland* when I had a go at Micheál Martin. It wasn't that they were disastrous performances or car crashes – it just didn't work,' he says.

While Varadkar was failing to damage Fianna Fáil, Kenny was inadvertently landing self-inflicted wounds on Fine Gael. The campaign was filled with awkward moments involving Kenny as he travelled the country seeking a mandate to return to power. However, his biggest gaffe happened in what should have been the safe surroundings of his home town of Castlebar in Mayo. Speaking at a campaign rally five days out from polling day, Kenny launched a bizarre attack on people who criticised the lack of investment in his constituency. 'God knows we have some All-Ireland champions here in Castlebar. I don't mean Castlebar Mitchels [the local GAA club], I mean the whingers that I hear every week saying there's nothing happening,' he said. The footage of the 'whinger' comments went viral and caused huge damage for Fine Gael. The gaffe came at a critical moment and scuppered any chances of a change in fortunes. But Kenny made matters worse the next day when asked about his remarks. The Taoiseach told reporters that the whingers he was referring to 'wouldn't know sunshine if they saw it'.

Varadkar was incensed and called Mark Mortell, demanding

that the Taoiseach publicly apologise for the comment. 'I understood where he was coming from, but the public heard it differently. They heard it as someone saying, "How can you not realise all I've done for you and why are you so ungrateful?"' he says now. 'I said to Mortell, "Look, I understand where he is coming from and why he said it but it's being interpreted in this way. It's hurting in Castleknock, not just in Castlebar, and he has to take it back straight away."' Kenny did eventually take it back but, it was too late. The damage was done.

The pressure was clearly getting to Kenny. At a rally in Dublin the day after the whingers comment, he tried to re-energise his team by launching an emotional attack on their opponents. He shouted, roared and called out his rivals, but, again, it didn't work. 'The shouting round the place – that was very strange,' Varadkar recalls. Fine Gael was despondent. The entire campaign had been a disaster. The strategy had failed miserably and losing a raft of seats was now a strong possibility.

Just after 10 p.m. on election day, those fears were compounded. An exit poll by the *Irish Times* showed Fine Gael's support had dropped ten points. Varadkar was in his constituency office in Ongar with some of his campaign team. The news hit them hard. 'It was as if there had been a death in the family. Everybody was totally deflated. Nobody believed the exit poll was going to be that bad,' Varadkar says. 'And you're really thinking of who is going to lose their seat and I was thinking, Paschal [Donohoe] is going to lose his seat on those figures.'

The next morning, an RTÉ exit poll was even worse for Fine Gael. Varadkar's election ritual generally involves him travelling to his local count centre in Coolmine, West Dublin. There, he would spend the day peering over the shoulder of vote counters. But that Saturday morning, he got up, put on his trainers and went for a long run in the Phoenix Park to clear his head with

LGBT running club the Dublin Front Runners. Throughout the day, his director of elections Henry Minogue texted him results as they came out. It was clear he would be re-elected, but his thoughts were with his colleagues who would not be re-joining him in the Dáil.

The final results showed Fine Gael down a massive twenty-six seats on the previous general election. Labour was all but obliterated, down thirty seats, and would be returning to the Dáil with just seven TDs. Emotions were running high. It was a day that no Fine Gael or Labour TD will ever forget.

Election day brought completely different fortunes for Fianna Fáil and Sinn Féin. Fianna Fáil had bounced back from its 2011 election wipeout and increased their seat count to forty-four. Sinn Féin was up from fourteen seats to twenty-three. As expected, Independents and smaller parties would now hold a record number of seats in Parliament. The makeup of the next Dáil was anyone's guess and assembling it would be a huge challenge for whoever the next Taoiseach might be. As a depleted and devastated Fine Gael considered its next move, Varadkar wondered whether it was time to return to opposition.

CHAPTER 14

GOVERNMENT
FORMATION TALKS

It was a dark day for Fine Gael. The party had been punished by the public despite steering the country back from the brink of the economic abyss. As far as most Fine Gael TDs were concerned, one man was to blame. 'Enda Kenny loyalists like me expected him to resign by dinner time. I genuinely thought if you lost twenty seats you'd be gone,' one senior Cabinet minister says of the sense of despair that gripped Fine Gael. The haemorrhaging of seats was catastrophic for the party. Even ministers and TDs who clung onto their seats were physically shaken and upset over the days that followed. The bruising experience of the 2016 general election forced them to re-evaluate their political futures.

There was no hiding from the fact Fine Gael had lost the election. But, more importantly, its leader had lost his mandate to serve as Taoiseach. To see that mandate restored, Kenny had to overcome the most difficult challenge he would face during more than forty years as a member of Dáil Éireann.

Only Kenny and his wife Fionnuala could predict his next

move in the hours that followed results day. Ministers speculated via phone call and text message about Kenny's future, but
no senior figure – including Leo Varadkar – was prepared to
call on him to resign. 'There was such a feeling of disappoint-
ment in the party. There was also a feeling that if we were to
change leader at that point, it would make things even worse,'
recalls Finance Minister Paschal Donohoe, who had secured
the second of three seats in Dublin Central.

Fine Gael may have returned with the most seats, but the
choices facing the party were stark: coalition government
again, a return to opposition or another election. While the
first option was the preferred one, finding a suitable coalition
partner seemed virtually impossible. Labour had suffered its
worst election in its 104-year history. The party had returned
with a mere seven seats and was resigned to going into opposition. Sinn Féin had increased its seats by nine but the party had
already ruled itself out as a potential coalition partner. From
Fine Gael's perspective, the prospect of doing a deal with its
arch-rivals Fianna Fáil – the big winners of the election – appeared to be a long shot to say the least.

But there was a fourth option. It was one the Irish people and
indeed their political system are not accustomed to: minority
government. Varadkar himself believed a minority government
propped up by Fianna Fáil, now the country's second largest
party, was fraught with danger. In the period that followed the
election result, Varadkar told some of his closest friends in Fine
Gael that returning to opposition should be actively considered
ahead of the minority option. 'I remember Leo saying to me,
"Sure, if we're back in opposition, we're back in opposition.
It's not the end of the world,"' recalls party MEP and election
strategist Brian Hayes. 'He didn't mind the prospect of opposition because we'd be back as the biggest party. He was very,

very relaxed about opposition.' A key Varadkar adviser adds, 'When it came to it, would he have been prepared to go into opposition? Yes.'

While Varadkar refrained from mooting the idea of opposition publicly at the time, he now admits that it was something he was personally leaning towards. 'I was really worried about a minority government of us and Independents at the mercy of Fianna Fáil,' he says. 'I would have been one of those who was most reluctant about – ironically – being in the scenario we are in now, which hasn't worked out that badly.'

Enda Kenny's credibility was decimated and his authority in Fine Gael had hit rock bottom. But he was still the leader and responsibility for determining the party's next move rested with him. 'Around that time it was all so unclear because the result of the election had come through and it wasn't clear we were going to be in government at all,' Varadkar says. 'Obviously if we weren't going to be in government in those scenarios, he would have resigned as leader. I'm sure he would have had to.'

Ministers at the time recall how Kenny was both exhausted and emotional during the government talks. He knew his personal performance in the campaign had contributed strongly to Fine Gael's electoral drubbing. As per tradition, he travelled to Washington for the annual St Patrick's Day visit, which was scaled back given the political instability at home. Kenny handed over the bowl of shamrock to President Barack Obama in the knowledge that he was now merely Ireland's caretaker Prime Minister. It was Obama's last St Patrick's Day in the White House. Many people believed it would be Kenny's too.

But as Kenny agonised over his own future, he allowed some of his most trusted senior colleagues to get the ball rolling in terms of cobbling together an administration. Up stepped Simon Coveney, who was the first political figure of any party to grab the initiative and begin government formation talks. Coveney met a number of rural-based Independent TDs in the Midlands town of Athlone. The group included Kevin 'Boxer' Moran and Denis Naughten – two deputies Fine Gael believed could be persuaded to support a minority government. 'Coveney was the man with the plan to form the government, there's no doubt about that,' says one senior source involved in the meetings. 'Enda Kenny was not in the head space to be able to. He was absolutely devastated. He needed a haircut. He needed a shave. He was beaten. Coveney took it by the scruff of the neck.'

That evening, following the meetings in Athlone, Coveney sat down with Simon Harris and a number of others and began to do the maths. The goal was to reach the magic number of seventy-eight TDs required to form a government. 'The more I think about it, it is more and more fucking mad,' remarks one source at the meeting.

> Simon had a way that would form a majority. It wasn't a rainbow government, it was a patch-quilt government [made up of] Social Democrats, Greens, all the Independents, Labour. You name it, everyone was joining this government. This was magical. But he could get you to seventy-eight on this scrunched-up piece of paper he was bringing around.

Coveney's ambitious attempt to form a government was in stark contrast to the do-nothing approach being adopted by Varadkar. In fact, Varadkar fuelled suspicion about his own level of commitment to forming a government when he said that the onus on doing so did not necessarily rest with Fine Gael. 'It is clear that the public decided not to re-elect this government,' Varadkar says. 'I don't think the obligation to form a new government necessarily falls on us at all.'

Varadkar also became the first Fine Gael minister to address the prospect of striking a deal with Fianna Fáil. 'I don't favour it. I don't think it's a good idea for either party. I don't think it would last. I don't trust them and I think it would open the door to Sinn Féin as the lead opposition.'

Varadkar cancelled a planned St Patrick's Day visit to Dubai as the talks moved from the Midlands to Government Buildings. At this point, both Fine Gael and Fianna Fáil had put together teams of negotiators who began trying to woo Independents and smaller parties. The vicinity of Parliament was like a circus at times, as all sides involved invited a host of colourful characters into the talks. Michael Noonan joked that he wandered into what he believed was a negotiation before realising after twenty minutes that he was in fact in discussions with two American tourists and a nun who were on a tour of Leinster House. Independent TDs from rural Ireland enjoyed the limelight. Relatively unknown deputies were now regularly featured on the evening news and quoted at length in the daily newspapers. 'It was like the Model UN. It was like the world and their mother. The Independents would bring supporters with them, like contestants on *Winning Streak* would bring people to the audience. They were only short of holding up banners saying, "Would you spin the wheel, Mattie?",' remarks one Fine Gael negotiator, referring to Independent TD Mattie McGrath. 'I remember parking my car and meeting Independent TD Michael Collins getting out of his car with half of his family. He said, "We're up for the talks." "Up for the talks"? – like "Up for the match." This was a day out.'

Eoghan Murphy phoned Varadkar and warned him to be careful. Murphy could see that this was turning into a charade and believed his friend would soon be targeted if the talks ran into trouble. Murphy's warning soon materialised.

* * *

The five-man Independent Alliance, seen as potential king-makers, fell afoul of Fine Gael following comments made by its de facto leader Shane Ross in his newspaper column in the *Sunday Independent*. Ross likened Kenny to a 'political corpse' just days before the first vote for Taoiseach. It was a remark he would later withdraw, although it was shared by many others involved in the increasingly frustrating process. With Kenny and Fianna Fáil leader Micheál Martin the only realistic candidates, TDs made their way into the Dáil chamber and cast their votes. The result was a stalemate, forcing all sides to take stock.

Varadkar was still attracting the ire of the Independents during the talks. Several TDs criticised him publicly and privately for his apparent lack of engagement. He was accused of spending too much time engrossed in his mobile phone during the talks and showing a blatant disregard for the process. It's a charge Varadkar strongly rejects. '"Uninterested" was very unfair. I was no more on my phone than anyone else was. I was Minister for Health. I was busy even when there wasn't an election on,' he says. 'Michael Healy-Rae was taking phone calls at the table, never mind sending a few texts or checking an email.' Paschal Donohoe, who sat alongside Varadkar during those talks, admits that his colleague ran out of patience at times. 'But by God, if he did run out of patience at any point, it was only because he is ultimately human. It was very tough,' Donohoe says.

Amid the clashes with the Independents and smaller parties, Fine Gael figures like Donohoe and Varadkar were aware that far more substantive talks were taking place at a different location in Government Buildings. The Labour Party was being courted once again by Enda Kenny and Michael Noonan in a bid to cobble together a coalition. 'This thing happening with Independents may not have gone anywhere if Labour had agreed to stay in government. It wouldn't have needed any Independents,' Varadkar says. 'So we were just left in there with these chaotic talks with Independents. Meanwhile, we knew full well there were other conversations happening with Labour.'

Varadkar was under fire from a number of angles. It wasn't just the Independents. He was also suspicious that his own Fine Gael colleagues were spinning against him.

I definitely think there was a bit of briefing going on against me by some of my own people. In fact, some of the Independents told me this. That there was some Fine Gael people making out, which was half true but not fully true, that I wasn't up for this. That I didn't want there to be a Fine Gael–Independents coalition, so that made them suspicious of me.

Varadkar all but confirmed those suspicions when he tweeted a picture of his election posters accompanied by the caption 'My posters cleaned, counted, stored and ready to be deployed.' Senior Fine Gael figures were incensed at what they saw as an attempt by Varadkar to push the party into opposition, where he could take over as leader.

During private talks off-site, Varadkar continued to insist that Fine Gael should not choose 'government at all costs'. But his suggestion of opposition was met with hostility and anger from Kenny, Noonan and Frances Fitzgerald – none of whom were prepared to hand over the keys to Government Buildings. 'Noonan, Frances and Kenny were apoplectic at this suggestion,' says a senior negotiator. 'This young buck Varadkar who has the rest of his life ahead of him, and here's three people in their sixties and seventies, it's their last chance to be in government, and he's saying, "Ah, sure, we'll go back to opposition and rebuild." They went ballistic.'

Leo himself admits that the Fine Gael negotiating team was divided on whether opposition was a realistic option. But he insists he wasn't on a solo run. 'I was up for opposition as an option. A good few of us were. [Michael] Creed certainly was. Paschal [Donohoe], again, thought it should be an option we should consider,' he says. 'But obviously for Kenny and Noonan, for them, opposition would have been the end of their careers. So they were very much for getting into government. I think Frances was in that space as well.'

Inside the Dáil chamber, TDs gathered for a second and third vote for Taoiseach. Once again, neither Kenny nor Martin secured the necessary votes. The third consecutive defeat appeared to focus the minds of both leaders. Privately, Kenny told his senior ministers that if he failed to be elected on the fourth occasion, he would seek permission from the President to hold another election. The stakes couldn't be higher.

On 6 April, following a dramatic day at Leinster House, Kenny played his ultimate trump card. In a small room just off the ministerial corridor, Kenny offered Martin a 50:50 partnership arrangement. Fianna Fáil would have an equal number of ministers, despite holding six fewer seats. And a rotating Taoiseach was on the table – meaning Martin would take over from Kenny halfway through a five-year term. It was a major gamble and it stunned TDs in Fine Gael and Fianna Fáil.

Martin rejected the offer of a role in a partnership government. However, he was open to discussing a minority government arrangement that would see Fianna Fáil facilitate a Fine Gael led-government.

Three days later, the parties' two negotiating teams met for what would be the first set of real talks aimed at striking a confidence and supply agreement. Fine Gael was confident they would have enough support from the Independents to pass the new magic figure of fifty-eight TDs in the event of Fianna Fáil abstaining from the vote. The talks shifted from Government Buildings to Trinity College. Here, in Varadkar's alma mater, Fine Gael and Fianna Fáil negotiators would square off for days. Despite the criticism of Varadkar in the talks with the Independents, Kenny opted to keep him on as a senior negotiator.

It wasn't long before trouble kicked off – once again heightening the prospect of fresh elections. Fianna Fáil demanded that water charges be scrapped and that the public utility known as Irish Water be replaced with a slimmed-down agency. A number of Fine Gael ministers were prepared to barter and agreed to suspend water charges. But Varadkar was incensed by his party's capitulation to the demands. He publicly criticised Fianna Fáil and accused the party of holding the country to ransom. Senior Fianna Fáil figures, including Michael McGrath and Barry Cowen, rounded on Varadkar in a move that brought the talks to the brink of collapse.

For Cowen, Varadkar was one of the most difficult politicians he has ever negotiated with. 'You could shout and argue with Coveney but ultimately do a deal with him,' Cowen says. 'But with the other fellah [Varadkar], you didn't know what he was thinking or where he was going. He is very difficult to read or understand.' Cowen says he and others believed it was in Varadkar's interests for the talks to collapse, given his leadership ambitions:

I don't think he'd be too perturbed or too annoyed if it did break down. The impression I got was he was surprised to say the least Kenny was going to fulfil his ambition of getting a second term

on the back of such a poor result. And your man [Varadkar] was
flabbergasted but resigned to it at the same time.

During one interval in the talks, Varadkar appeared to extend
an olive branch to Cowen and the rest of the Fianna Fáil delegation, suggesting the teams should pop across the road for
a glass of wine in the luxury Marker Hotel, where he and his
partner Matthew Barrett had met for their first date. The offer
was not well received, as Cowen explains:

> He was looking across at the Marker Hotel and said to us,
> 'I'd much rather be out there on the rooftop drinking a glass
> of wine.' I said, 'I'd rather be downstairs in that bar over the
> street having a pint.' Two different characters, two different
> approaches, two personalities, two different parties.

Varadkar still feels a sense of bitterness over Fianna Fáil's refusal to negotiate on retaining water charges. 'It was deliberate
ritual humiliation,' he says. 'I thought it was really irresponsible
for them to pursue this policy. It wasn't like Fianna Fáil were
really against water charges: they were going to bring them in
themselves. So I thought it was irresponsible from what was
right for the country's point of view.'

Varadkar's close friends who spoke with him throughout the
talks process believe he was standing up for Fine Gael values.
'I think he had a different view than a lot of senior Cabinet
ministers at that time. Senior ministers wanted to stay in government at all costs. Leo saw the potential downside. He was
right too,' according to Dublin North West TD Noel Rock.

Brian Hayes says Leo's approach went down well with the
party faithful. 'You get the sense with Varadkar, it is never at all
costs. He won't throw the towel in on things that are important.

He is very good at articulating what the average Fine Gael member wants in politics,' Hayes says. 'Saying the hard thing, drawing the hard yard. He articulates that "brand Fine Gael" that a lot of people believe in.'

Eventually, Fine Gael negotiated the support of Fianna Fáil under a confidence and supply deal that was due to last three budgets. The deal was done – but Enda Kenny still had to convince a substantial number of Independent TDs to vote for him as Taoiseach.

* * *

Irish politics is not used to the type of protracted political impasse that followed the 2016 general election. For the civil servants working across government departments, it was a particularly strange period. Ministers were in place but only in a caretaker capacity. Proposed legislation sat on shelves as those who had drafted it wondered when it would finally be progressed. Politically, the country was on a standstill.

One civil servant who was watching from the sidelines with a sense of concern was HSE Director General Tony O'Brien. Despite the impasse, the health service still had to continue operating. Leo Varadkar was still Minister for Health, but O'Brien wondered whether he would remain in the post once the new government was formed. In the run-up to the election, the HSE boss had been convinced Varadkar was looking for a way out of the troublesome portfolio. But O'Brien changed his mind during the government formation talks, when Varadkar gave him the distinct impression he wanted to be reappointed to health. O'Brien remembers:

It was very clear, from the very outset during his time in

health, that he was a politician with good political instincts who was really committed to what could reasonably be done in the short time he had to improve the health service in Ireland. He was good to work with.

With Fine Gael edging closer and closer to power, Enda Kenny asked to meet Varadkar privately to discuss his future in the Cabinet. Varadkar was conscious of the miserable time he had endured in health and decided to hatch a strategy with his close confidants Brian Murphy and Philip O'Callaghan. For him to remain in health, he needed to be given a large bag of cash and a mandate for sweeping change. Varadkar was not prepared to stick with the status quo. The prospect of returning to the department ahead of another trolley crisis that winter was unpalatable. It was a particularly dreaded scenario given that Varadkar knew Kenny's days as Taoiseach and Fine Gael leader were numbered. He couldn't devote the necessary time and attention to a leadership contest while at the same time tackling the myriad of crises that health throws up. One close Cabinet ally of Varadkar's believes the leadership was firmly on his mind when he attended that meeting with Kenny:

I think at that point, Leo had been through the mill for nearly two years on it. And was beginning to think, if he was going to have a go at party leader at some point in the future, it would be beneficial to have another ministry under his belt.

During the meeting itself, Varadkar told Kenny that for the past eighteen months he had felt he was an apologist for the health service. He said he didn't want to continue putting on a brave face when very little progress was being made. But Varadkar's next move was a gamble. He laid down a set of demands for Kenny that he suggested were preconditions for him remaining in the job. The first was about money. Varadkar wanted health to be made a special case in terms of spending. He said the €500 million black hole in the health budget should be dealt with in the first half of the year instead of the usual approach of announcing a supplementary budget in the winter. To put it simply, he wanted an early pay day.

The Health Minister's second ask was equally ambitious. He wanted to be able to bypass the rules surrounding recruitment, which were laid down by the Department of Public Expenditure and Reform. Making health a special case in terms of hiring staff would represent a major policy shift for the government. And it would surely lead to demands by other departments to be treated in such a manner. But Varadkar was frustrated with the restrictions around staffing and told Kenny the change was necessary.

The conditions didn't end there. Varadkar told Kenny that health needed far more support from his own Department of An Taoiseach. A veteran politician like Kenny would not have enjoyed being lectured by one of his youngest Cabinet ministers. But Varadkar felt the current set-up left the minister of the day isolated and maintained that the Taoiseach should take a far more proactive role. 'When there was a crisis in health, Kenny would shy away from it. He didn't want to know,' a Varadkar aide claims.

Varadkar set out his demands face to face with a politician he privately believed was on his last legs. He also suspected Kenny and his advisers had been actively briefing against him during the government formation talks. Kenny listened but said very little and promised nothing during the meeting. He asked Varadkar if he wanted another portfolio. Varadkar insisted he was not pitching for another job. Kenny then proposed the appointment of a number of junior health ministers who would have specific roles covering various facets of the health service. Varadkar pushed back and said this approach would solve nothing.

The meeting ended with no resolution. Varadkar expected a follow-up meeting to be called, but it didn't materialise. As one source in the Varadkar camp observes, 'Kenny was a master at avoiding you when he wanted to.'

Nonetheless, the Taoiseach had a huge call to make. The last thing he needed was a minister in the Department of Health who didn't want to be there. Equally, he did not want to sack a minister for laying down a series of demands that appeared reasonable on face value. Phil Hogan believes Kenny was never in a position to agree to the Varadkar wishlist. 'The Taoiseach would not make any commitment in relation to the future financing of the Department of Health when he is doing a Cabinet reshuffle,' Hogan says. 'This wasn't the occasion where he could give any commitments on the future financing of the Department of Health to anyone he wanted to put in the job.' Other senior figures within the party believed Varadkar was trying to force Kenny to sack him entirely from the Cabinet. However, another well-placed source said Varadkar knew he couldn't be sacked because doing so would very quickly result in a leadership contest.

It was widely believed in Leinster House that Varadkar effectively ran away from the health ministry so that he could carve out his leadership campaign. 'Health was one of the trickiest issues we had in the country and we had our best and most gifted politician in there who had street cred and streaks of political ability and could have helped the party and helped the health service with getting it fixed,' one Cabinet source notes.

The fact he walked away from it after such a short time, I think if you ask most of the parliamentary party, even some of his biggest supporters, they were disappointed with that. It was obviously done with a view to the leadership election. There was obviously a calculation made that you cannot go from health to the Taoiseach's office. Certainly not in a contested election when you have to go around canvassing.

But Kenny knew he was facing a dilemma: move Varadkar into a different department or sack him from the Cabinet altogether.

* * *

Following an impasse that lasted seventy days, Enda Kenny awoke on Friday 6 May preparing for a Dáil vote that would either return him to high office or end his political career. By lunch time, TDs were, for the fourth time, making their way into the chamber to listen to speeches from Kenny's proposer and seconder, Noel Rock and Catherine Byrne. Rock invoked the words of Michael Collins, telling the country that Ireland was for ten weeks 'a ship without a captain'.

Kenny had sewn up the support of non-aligned Independents Denis Naughten and Katherine Zappone. He also had the backing of Clare TD Michael Harty and Tipperary deputy Michael Lowry. However, to reach the magic number of fifty-eight votes, he also needed the support of the six-member Independent Alliance. This group of disparate TDs was a central voting bloc during the government formation talks and key to ensuring Kenny's victory.

However, just before the vote, news broke that all was not well in the Independent Alliance. The Alliance was thrashing out last-minute changes to the Programme for Government with Fine Gael negotiators Michael Noonan and Simon Coveney. With the vote just minutes away, Fine Gael suddenly did not have the numbers to ensure Kenny's election. Opposition spokespeople remarked how Kenny did not appear to be a man who was just about to be handed back the keys of Government Buildings for a second consecutive time.

Just before lunchtime, five of the six members of the Independent Alliance arrived in the chamber – much to the relief of Kenny and his Fine Gael colleagues. Roscommon–Galway TD Michael Fitzmaurice decided not to support the government and quit the Alliance.

However, Kenny secured fifty-nine votes – one more than necessary – and made history, becoming the first Fine Gael leader to serve two consecutive terms as Taoiseach. He would now head up a minority government. He announced that the Dáil would rise for three hours and, upon resumption, he would reveal the makeup of his new Cabinet. Kenny made his way out onto the plinth, where he was met by rapturous applause from his party supporters. But as he made his way back to his office, Kenny began to agonise over his ministerial selection. Central to his dilemma was Leo Varadkar.

* * *

The previous evening, a number of members of the Fine Gael negotiating team had gathered for a drink in the Cellar Bar of the Merrion Hotel. Among those having a drink were Frances Fitzgerald, Michael Noonan and Simon Harris. Harris was receiving strong signals from his colleagues that he was about to make the leap from the post of junior finance minister to Cabinet. The job of government Chief Whip or perhaps Minister for Social Protection were being mooted. Promoting Harris was a no-brainer from a Fine Gael perspective. He was a very capable junior minister.

As is tradition, the Taoiseach requested the attendance in his office of members of his Cabinet to offer them their new roles. At his request, he handed the job of Minister for Housing to Simon Coveney, who, like Varadkar, was being widely tipped to contest the leadership when it arose. Paschal Donohoe was handed the influential ministry of public expenditure, while Frances Fitzgerald was appointed Tánaiste and Minister for Justice. One by one, ministers made their way up the corridor to Kenny's office to learn their fate. But there was one exception.

Instead of meeting Varadkar face to face, Kenny decided to contact him by phone. It was a peculiar decision and one that disappointed members of Varadkar's inner circle. Kenny asked Varadkar whether he had given more thought to his health demands. It was, in essence, an offer to remain in the post. He told Varadkar that the government was only going to last a year or so. It was a forecast Kenny made in conversations with other ministers during the government formation talks. Varadkar said his views remained the same. For him to remain in health, he required the commitments surrounding spending, support and recruitment. Kenny had heard enough. He offered Varadkar a move to social protection. Varadkar accepted the new job and the phone call ended.

Shortly afterwards, Kenny summoned Simon Harris to his office. To his complete shock, Kenny asked Harris if he was up for the challenge of health. Harris duly accepted. Back in the Dáil chamber, Varadkar received a tap on the shoulder from his constituency colleague Joan Burton. She asked him what job he had been handed. Moments later, Burton clasped her hand over her mouth and leant back into her seat in near hysterics.

The Varadkar camp began frantically spinning that the

position was in no way a demotion. Publicly, Varadkar said it represented a sideways step and that it was a move to a portfolio he had always had an interest in. But as the media obsessed on Varadkar's apparent demotion, privately his team were delighted. 'Enda decided to get him out of the way but ironically it gave us more time to do what we wanted to do,' says one key figure.

Varadkar was now out of the department referred to as 'Angola'. The focus could now turn to the main prize: the Fine Gael leadership and the position of An Taoiseach.

CHAPTER 15

LEADERSHIP SEEDS
ARE SOWN

On a mild Saturday afternoon in July 2014, John Paul Phelan found himself at a loose end. The Fine Gael TD had just finished up some business in Dublin city centre and was contemplating staying the night rather than returning home to Kilkenny. Like a lot of his colleagues, Phelan was in a bit of a slump over the party's disastrous local election results. In May, Fine Gael had lost more than 100 council seats and been removed as the largest party in local government. Labour had fared even worse. Fine Gael's coalition partners had lost almost two thirds of their councillors in a result that devastated the party.

The experience of the 2014 local elections became even more sobering for the government due to the revival of Fianna Fáil. Five years after being obliterated, Fianna Fáil was now the largest party in local government. Coalition figures were aghast at how Fianna Fáil was making an extraordinary comeback at council level so soon after being shown the two fingers by a betrayed and angry electorate.

Within Fine Gael, the blame for their own electoral drubbing was assigned to the botched handling of the introduction of water charges and the medical card fiasco. But for John Paul Phelan, a close ally of Leo Varadkar, the election failure was a consequence of a more fundamental problem with the party's leadership. He had never been a fan of Enda Kenny and was among the conspirators who had unsuccessfully tried to oust him during the notorious 2010 heave. Phelan was completely unconvinced by Kenny's qualities and was worried that his inability to listen to members would bring Fine Gael's time in power to an abrupt end. The local election results merely reinforced Phelan's view that the party needed to prepare for life after Kenny. And, in his opinion, there was only one heir to the throne.

Phelan had been impressed by Varadkar since they had first got to know each other almost ten years earlier through Young Fine Gael. While the pair weren't particularly close at the time, Phelan believed Varadkar had a star quality that was being underused by party chiefs. For some time, Phelan had planned to approach Varadkar directly and tell him that he – and he alone – was the right man to lead the party into the future. Varadkar could be painfully shy, Phelan knew, and a narrative was developing in the media about his aloof attitude to certain colleagues. It was clear some factions in the party were also spinning against him. But Phelan wanted him to know he had a strong enough support base that was prepared to back him to become leader, whenever that moment arrived.

That afternoon in Dublin, Phelan phoned Varadkar and asked him if he was around for a few beers and a chat. Varadkar was immediately on board. He invited Phelan to his home in West Dublin, where, over a few bottles of Heineken and a pack of Benson & Hedges cigarettes, the pair mused over the state of Irish politics. 'The discussion was actually very one-sided because Leo didn't say much at all – he was very coy,' Phelan says of the conversation. 'We were at a low enough ebb because the locals had gone the way they had gone, and I was at a personal low ebb I suppose as well. But I wanted him to feel there was a group of people who would back him.'

As the two party colleagues sank a few more beers, the conversation became more serious. Little did Varadkar know at the time, his leadership bid was being mapped out in front of him over alcohol and cigarettes. 'I'd bitten my lip on so many things over the years and I'd got so many kicks,' Phelan says. 'I didn't want to let the moment pass without saying to this fellah, who was always a bit shy as a person, "You have what it takes."' Phelan told his friend he would fully support him should he decide to run for the leadership. But Varadkar didn't bite. He was flattered by the suggestion but said his focus was still on his ministerial career.

In fairness to Varadkar, there was – at this point in time – no vacancy at the top of Fine Gael. But Phelan's intervention certainly gave him food for thought. Shortly afterwards, Phelan became part of Leo's inner circle and would regularly dine out with his closest advisers: Brian Murphy, John Carroll, Nick Miller and Philip O'Callaghan. The Fine Gael leadership would sporadically be discussed at these social gatherings. But it was not at the top of the team's agenda. At this point in time, there was no plotting, no appetite to replicate the sort of scenes that had ripped Fine Gael apart in 2010. There was no covert campaign or sense of scheming. But the prospect of Varadkar launching a leadership bid was in the background.

Phelan, who was the first person to push Varadkar towards the leadership, believes the issue was constantly on his mind. 'He put his best foot forward when he was made a minister with the people he appointed,' Phelan explains. 'Whether you can say in hindsight that was because he was planning right from the get-go, sure he probably was – that's politics,' Phelan says.

* * *

Questions about Varadkar's leadership ambitions dogged him from the moment he was elected to Parliament. His star potential and ambition were obvious to everyone within politics. But Varadkar's advisers constantly warned him against straying into the leadership sphere. Nick Miller, Varadkar's trusted press adviser, would tell him over and over again that he had to 'be seen to focus on the day job'. Miller warned Varadkar that voters would respond badly if he was perceived as taking his responsibilities as a minister for granted.

However, in an interview for this book, Varadkar admitted for the first time that he began weighing up his leadership bid during his tenure as Minister for Transport. 'I didn't just wake up one day and decide, "Wouldn't it be great to become leader of Fine Gael?"' Varadkar said. 'It was something that was always a possibility from the time I became Minister for Transport, Tourism and Sport. Except we never knew if and when, under what scenario, it would arise,' he added.

Indeed, the difficulty for leadership hopefuls like Varadkar was the fact that nobody in the party knew exactly how, or when, Enda Kenny would step aside. 'The most likely scenario, up to 2016, would have been we got re-elected,' Varadkar says, adding:

I thought we were going to get re-elected. Maybe Fine Gael and Labour, plus some Independents. That's what most people thought. I thought Enda would probably not serve a full second term. I had an idea in my mind – or plan or projectory – [that the leadership issue] was something that would arise in 2019 or 2020 or something.

From John Paul Phelan to Nick Miller and others, Varadkar decided to take his supporters' advice on board. But he also knew he had to carve out his own identity. He needed to be different. From early on in his ministerial career, Varadkar pointedly tried to stand out. He was often slow to back the government line and was not afraid to speak up when he felt it was the right thing to do. Varadkar would go against the grain in the knowledge that it would generate publicity, which he constantly craved. This played out well with voters but not so well with his Fine Gael Cabinet colleagues. 'He was very quick to take advantage of anybody at any point if he saw it to his advantage. It's just his nature,' says one ministerial colleague. Varadkar's advisers played up the image of their minister as a straight talker. He had integrity, they insisted, and vocalised the opinion of the man on the street.

Varadkar's first ministry was ideal for a politician who harboured leadership ambitions. The Department of Transport, Sport and Tourism is considered a 'good news' portfolio. Ministers are generally announcing new initiatives rather than dealing with controversy. The job also gave Varadkar the opportunity to tour the country, attending sport and tourism events in between turning the sod on new stretches of motorway. Before each gig, his staff made sure to invite all local Fine Gael representatives from the area they were visiting. Time was always scheduled in his diary to meet and greet the local TD, senator or councillor. It was important to hear their views, Varadkar would say, in the knowledge that most other ministers paid scant regard to the views of the party membership.

Within Fine Gael, Varadkar's practice of love-bombing colleagues was perceived as the genesis of his leadership bid. But for Varadkar it was an approach all ministers should adopt. 'I know some people will say, "From day one you were calculating your future plans." I just thought it was good practice, good politics, because when you get into trouble as a minister you need TDs who will back you up,' he says, adding:

> I had been a councillor and came up through the party. I think it was Enda who asked us to make a point any time you visit a constituency to meet the councillors and very few did it. We just made it part of our standard programme and they appreciated it.

While Varadkar spent much of his time visiting constituencies, he had a separate strategy when it came to building his national profile. Varadkar's stance on the garda whistleblower scandal gave him an edge over his two main leadership rivals: Justice Minister Frances Fitzgerald and Housing Minister Simon Coveney. But it soon became clear to the Varadkar camp that there was still a large group of TDs who were relatively unconvinced by his style. This section of the party, who were seen as being extremely loyal to Enda Kenny, viewed Varadkar with suspicion. They considered him untrustworthy. He had put the knife through Kenny's back before and was surely capable of doing so again. This cohort of middle-ground TDs were sceptical of Varadkar's outspoken nature and the ease with which he challenged the Taoiseach's authority. They valued loyalty above all else in politics and perceived Varadkar as being a young minister in too much of a hurry.

Kenny was never hugely popular with the public, but within some factions of Fine Gael he was deeply respected. Varadkar knew if he was to become the next leader he would have to win over these TDs by showing deference to Kenny. But he also had to remain tight with the growing number of dissidents who were desperate for a regime change. The Varadkar team threaded this line very carefully – and indeed secretly – for almost three years.

*   *   *

Varadkar's appointment as Minister for Health was a make-or-break moment of his career. Some viewed Kenny's decision to hand him the dreaded portfolio as an attempt to put the brakes on Varadkar's ambitions. But the reality is Varadkar was a highly capable minister and the Department of Health was the government's Achilles' heel. It was in Kenny's interest to see Varadkar succeed and, above all, for the problems in healthcare to finally be tackled.

The ministry, however, did not lend itself to travelling the country and meeting party colleagues in the same way that Transport did. Varadkar found himself stuck in meetings in Hawkins House for hours on end as crisis after crisis hit. Parliamentary questions and Oireachtas committee meetings also dominated Varadkar's work schedule in Leinster House. It was a ministry of constant fire-fighting.

Varadkar's bid to become leader was being inhibited – and he knew it, too. But a conscious effort was made by the minister's team to ensure TDs and senators had full access to his office. Health is one of the main areas that prompt queries from TDs and senators, working at the behest of their constituents. Varadkar was aware that backbenchers regularly complained about ministers being difficult to contact. An open and accessible Health Minister would, without doubt, build relationships with deputies in Fine Gael.

Philip O'Callaghan, Varadkar's parliamentary assistant, was the main point of contact for Fine Gael politicians. Polite and mild-mannered, O'Callaghan was given a chance by Varadkar – and he was determined to repay the favour. Any queries relating to medical cards or hospital appointments were now treated with a sense of urgency by the minister's office through O'Callaghan. Even simple courtesies, such as personally responding to a TD's text message or email, became the norm for the Varadkar team. 'That sort of work with the parliamentary party lent itself to what happened subsequently in the leadership campaign because they knew the type of service they were getting if he was Taoiseach,' a Varadkar adviser says. As a result of his availability to colleagues, Varadkar was quickly setting himself ahead of his rival Simon Coveney. Coveney, unlike Varadkar, had become a source of frustration for many backbenchers. He was often impossible to get on the phone and TDs' queries would regularly go unanswered for days.

The Fine Gael leadership question was not up for debate throughout the latter half of the coalition's tenure in office. It was taken for granted that Kenny would lead Fine Gael into the next general election. But what would happen after that was anyone's guess. Any time Varadkar was asked if he harboured leadership ambitions, he would dance around the subject, giving the stock answer that all politicians would like to lead their own party one day. Varadkar's local branch members would also pester him with questions about his intentions every time they read media speculation linking him with the job. 'There's a time for that, we have a leader at the moment,' Varadkar would reply. 'It would come up at constituency meetings on a regular basis,' a local party source observes. 'If a member would raise an issue about the leadership of the party, Leo would always say, "I'd prefer not to discuss that at this particular point."' But his supporters – who had canvassed side by side with Varadkar throughout several elections – knew he would eventually step forward.

* * *

An interview with the government's Chief Whip Paul Kehoe, published in the *Irish Examiner* on a quiet weekday in August – caused a sudden shift in the leadership debate. The election was about six months out and Kehoe was asked if he believed Kenny would serve a full five-year term should he be re-elected as Taoiseach. The Wexford TD, who was extremely close to Kenny, gave what he thought was an on-message response: 'I believe Enda Kenny, if he is returned as Taoiseach after the next general election, will serve another five years and more.'

Unbeknown to Kehoe, and indeed his leader, the comments soon caused panic in Fine Gael. The notion of Kenny serving three terms was inconceivable to most party members, not to mention the public. Kenny's personal popularity was plummeting in the polls and the suggestion that he could lead the party for three terms went down like a tonne of bricks.

Kehoe's comments immediately created the impression that he as Chief Whip had been sent out to float the prospect of 'Endless Enda', as it soon became known. In reality, this wasn't the case. But Kenny was livid. He publicly slapped down his Chief Whip and accused him of using 'a lot of poetic licence' during the interview.

Kenny then insisted he did not intend to remain Taoiseach beyond his second term in government, should he be re-elected. 'It would be very arrogant and presumptuous of any public representative to assume that they can be elected to anything, myself included, until the people vote,' he said.

Kenny's comments were intended to bring an end to political rumblings in the summer months before a general election. But, unbeknown to Kenny, he had effectively put a timeline on his leadership. He now found himself in a serious quandary. If Fine Gael was to go on to win the election under his leadership, the focus would immediately shift to when he was prepared to step down. He would have to give the next leader enough time to settle into the role before the next election came around. Did this mean he would stand down one or two years out from the vote itself?

Fine Gael was in a state of confusion. Varadkar, now known for being unpredictable, decided to intervene. He weighed into the debate by giving his full backing to the Taoiseach serving another five years. 'Enda's done a phenomenal job as Taoiseach for the last couple of years. We've turned the economy around, we're in a much better place than we were four years ago,' he said. 'There'll be an election next spring. I really hope in the interest of the country that the people re-elect the government and re-elect Enda Kenny as Taoiseach and that he serves a full second term,' he added.

Varadkar's move calmed the nerves within an ever restless party. But the list of rebels seeking to see the back of Enda was only growing.

* * *

As mentioned in an earlier chapter, the 2016 general election was a disaster for Fine Gael and was followed by seventy days of gruelling Programme for Government negotiations. Kenny's leadership came into sharp focus as soon as the votes were counted. His most trusted Cabinet ministers expected him to resign on the day of the election results. But Kenny was determined to lead the next government and negotiated a confidence and supply agreement which would see Fianna Fáil prop up a Fine Gael-led minority administration for three years. Even his most outspoken detractors praised Kenny's chairmanship of the talks.

Towards the end of the negotiations, Fine Gael believed they had been double-crossed by Fianna Fáil after Varadkar and Jim O'Callaghan, Fianna Fáil justice spokesman, reached agreement on a minority government. As part of the deal, Fianna Fáil had agreed to allow Fine Gael to attempt to secure the numbers for an administration. But Fine Gael discovered subsequently that Micheál Martin's party was still courting the support of In-dependent TDs. Ministers anxiously discussed whether Kenny should go to Áras an Uachtaráin, the President's residence, and request President Michael D. Higgins to approve a snap second election. One minister told a colleague, 'Holy shit, he is actually going to the park.'

But above any other party, a second election posed serious challenges for Fine Gael. The first problem was Kenny himself. The Taoiseach had said publicly that the recent election – which had produced a stalemate – would be his last as leader of Fine Gael. His parliamentary party were eager, to put it mildly, for Kenny to honour that commitment. The second problem was the Fine Gael rule book. It was party policy that every member was entitled to vote in a leadership contest. The campaign itself would take the guts of three weeks to run. The one member, one vote policy was proposed by Leo Varadkar when he was a member of Young Fine Gael. Ironically, it now looked like the rule change was coming back to haunt him.

Fine Gael had two choices in the event of another election being called. The party could either face the electorate again under Kenny's deeply unpopular leadership – running the risk of being outflanked this time round by a re-energised Fianna Fáil – or they could stage an internal contest, which may have to be run in tandem with an election campaign. Neither option was a runner from the perspective of Varadkar or his team. One of his senior advisers said there was a deep fear within the party over what would happen if the government talks collapsed. During the negotiations, the close aide told ministers, 'Look, we need to find a way of sorting this out and actually have an agreed candidate.' The aide felt the party was hamstrung because of the rules surrounding electing a new leader. 'We clearly couldn't go into a leadership-type contest. We could have shortened the contest, but even that wasn't going to work.'

With the talks making little progress, a concerned Tom Curran decided to act. He began ringing the leadership contenders to seek their counsel on what the party should do. Curran contacted the three front runners: Varadkar, Coveney and Fitzgerald. 'There wasn't a meeting about it but Tom Curran as General Secretary rang me, rang Frances and rang Simon to have a conversation about what would happen if we were heading into a second election and how we would avoid a leadership election,' Varadkar says. 'Because of the rules … it wouldn't have been possible to run that election,' he adds.

A plan was hatched that would see the parliamentary party decide on a single candidate, whose name would then be put before the membership. Such an approach would eliminate the need for weeks of campaigning and a series of hustings, as there would be only one candidate on the ballot paper. It was a high-risk strategy by Curran, who devised the fallback plan in secret.

However, Kenny finally did cobble a government together and the strategy was parked. The Mayo man returned as Taoiseach, but his authority in Fine Gael was now seriously undermined. Throughout the negotiations, Kenny regularly pulled ministers aside for a quiet word. He asked for their support in forming a government and assured them he did not plan to remain in post as Fine Gael leader in the long run. 'He had a conversation with a number of us, one to one, where he said he basically wants to get this government up and running and then after, he didn't put a timeframe on it now, but after that, "I'll leave it to you guys" or whatever,' Varadkar says.

> I think he meant it at the time. He was very down after the election. [He] felt responsible for people losing their seats. I think he genuinely meant it at the time but then at a certain point, to use his own phrase, he got his mojo back. So it was quite possible at that time he meant it and subsequently changed his mind.

A second minister confirmed the conversations instigated by Kenny and believes it made Varadkar's job of replacing him even more difficult. 'Enda was at pains to say to me and others, "I just want to get this sorted for you guys. To leave you well set up and I'll be gone,"' the minister says. 'Leo had to operate on the assumption he can't touch him.'

Varadkar didn't trust Kenny. He thought his talk of stepping down soon after a government was formed was just a ploy to get buy-in from his senior ministers for the deal he was organising with Fianna Fáil and the Independents. But with Fine Gael now leading the most unstable government in years, any sign of dissent could topple the entire house of cards.

* * *

Junior finance minister Eoghan Murphy had developed a good working relationship with Leo Varadkar. They were not close friends, but they did socialise in similar circles. Eoghan – or 'Murph', as his friends call him – often invited Varadkar to join him and his pals for a few pints to watch the rugby. Murphy's friends didn't really take to Varadkar and would ask, 'What's wrong with your man?' when he was out of earshot. But Murphy thought his friend's aloofness gave him an almost statesmanlike aura. Varadkar didn't pander to people and didn't engage in small talk when he didn't have to. Like others in the party, Murphy noticed Varadkar's potential but felt at times his shyness was holding him back. He pushed him to socialise more with the Leinster House crowd, having a few pints in the Dáil bar, where he could engage with the other TDs and senators, particularly the Five-A-Side-Club. The pair had not spoken directly about the leadership or replacing Kenny, but Murphy had decided he would back Varadkar once it was clear a contest would be called.

By late 2014, public trust in the coalition was fast evaporating and morale in Fine Gael was plummeting. The local elections, the garda whistleblower scandals, the introduction of water charges and the party's calamitous attempt to win a Seanad by-election all fed into a sense of disquiet and despair. Murphy decided it was time to take the bull by the horns. One Saturday evening in the run-up to Christmas, he phoned Varadkar and asked to meet him in the city centre for a pint and a chat. Varadkar had been out socialising with friends earlier that evening and by the time Murphy arrived he was not interested in a heavy political discussion. Murphy let it be and the moment passed.

It would be more than a year before Murphy approached the subject again with his colleague. Despite not being in Cabinet, Murphy was drafted in to assist with the government formation talks after the 2016 general election. The Taoiseach was impressed by his work on the Public Accounts Committee and was aware of his ambition to move up the ranks. Murphy put his shoulder to the wheel during the talks but was as frustrated as anyone by the lack of progress. One Saturday afternoon in the middle of the negotiations, Varadkar called over to Murphy's southside apartment for a few beers before going to a Six Nations rugby match in the Aviva Stadium. From the moment he arrived, Murphy knew Varadkar had something on his mind. He was edgier than usual. After a few drinks, Varadkar eventually loosened up. He turned to his friend and asked if he would have Murphy's support if he put his name forward for the Fine Gael leadership.

Murphy was taken aback. He asked Varadkar if he was ready for the challenge. Varadkar had clearly given a lot of thought to the matter and listed the reasons he believed he was the man for the job. He said the election campaign was the catalyst for his decision. Kenny's handling of the campaign had been a mess from day one, Leo said, before explaining the strategies he would have deployed if he had been leader.

Murphy was on board, but he had one question: 'What about Paschal?' Minister for Transport Paschal Donohoe was the only other member of the Cabinet whom Murphy considered capable of leading Fine Gael. Murphy wanted to know if Donohoe was prepared to back Varadkar or if he planned to throw his own hat into the ring. Leo responded cryptically. He didn't say outright that Donohoe was in his corner, but Murphy was left with the clear impression that he would be part of his team.

After a Kenny government was formed, Donohoe was promoted to the powerful Department of Public Expenditure and Reform, where he worked closely with Murphy. Their offices were in the same building on Merrion Street and they would regularly bump into one another. Donohoe would often ask

Murphy the same pointed question: 'How are things going?' He never said explicitly what those 'things' were, but Murphy understood it to mean Varadkar's leadership bid.

Varadkar says he did not have any in-depth conversations about the leadership with Donohoe after the government formation talks but he knew he could count on Donohoe's support. 'I knew he was for me ... a lot of people pledge support and you never know if it's true or not and I didn't necessarily know it was true, but he certainly indicated [he would support me],' Varadkar recalls.

Varadkar's ministerial career also changed dramatically after the Programme for Government was agreed with the Independent Alliance. As already shown, he was stripped of the health ministry and appointed as Minister for Social Protection. It was viewed as a demotion within political circles, but the 'good news' ministry once again freed up Varadkar's time and allowed him to focus on shoring up support for his leadership bid.

Spanning the country is a network of welfare offices known as Intreos, which fell under Leo's new department. The offices were situated in every constituency – providing Leo with an ideal reason to travel the length and breadth of the country meeting councillors, all of whom now had access to the minister through Philip O'Callaghan. This was important because councillors held 10 per cent of the overall vote in the leadership contest, once it arose. 'Social protection was great for us,' says an adviser. 'We travelled everywhere. We went to every parish hall. Every councillor we got to meet. The campaign indirectly started when we were meeting councillors.'

The election had reduced the size of the Fine Gael party in the Dáil but there were still new faces who had to be approached for their support. There was also work to be done on the Cabinet, especially with the cohort of Kenny loyalists who were always coy about their future voting intentions. Then there were the TDs and senators who were always keen to give Leo the impression that he had their support. But he didn't trust any of them. They are politicians, after all, he thought, and will vote for the candidate most likely to serve their own interests.

*   *   *

Fine Gael TD for Cork South West Jim Daly and his adviser Darren Hourihane call it the 'Mars bar night'. It was the summer of 2016 and not long after the government formation talks had concluded. They wanted to know Varadkar's thinking in terms of the leadership and they arranged to meet him in Reilly's Bar, just around the corner from Government Buildings, one Wednesday evening. The pair had read all the speculation and gossip in the newspapers about a potential leadership bid, but neither had actually spoken to Varadkar about his ambitions. Both believed he was the politician best placed to replace Kenny, but backing him could prove awkward in Daly's constituency, as the other main contender, Simon Coveney, was a fellow Cork TD. Throwing everything behind the 'Dublin candidate' was a high-risk move for Daly and he needed assurances from Varadkar. 'We were kind of saying, "Is he up for it or not?" You'd think he was and then he'd go very quiet and relaxed, so we just wanted to hear it from himself,' Hourihane says.

In Reilly's Bar, the pints and the conversation were in full flow. But not long after they arrived, the trio were joined by another group of Fine Gael TDs, which made it difficult to broach the subject they had come to discuss. Last orders were eventually called, and the pair still hadn't found an opportunity to pull Varadkar to one side. In search of a late pint, the group wandered down to the Mont Clare Hotel on the other side of Merrion Street to see if it was still serving. As the night wore on, Hourihane began to get frustrated. 'Leo, are we going to have this chat or not?' he asked the minister. Varadkar asked where they could speak privately at this hour of the night. Hourihane suggested they go back to the hotel where he and Daly often stayed when they were working in Dublin. 'Will we get in there?' Varadkar asked. Darren assured him they could. 'We went up anyway and we had the place to ourselves and we had a very frank conversation,' Hourihane recalls. 'He said, "I'm very much up for it, we are talking about it, thinking about, planning about it, but I'm doing nothing unless Enda Kenny moves first."' It was one of the first times Varadkar had declared his intentions to anyone outside his close inner circle.

At the time, Varadkar was on a strict diet and fitness regime. Even the few pints he had that night were a rare occurrence. In the early hours of the morning, hunger eventually kicked in and Varadkar asked whether there was any food. The hotel kitchen was long closed and room service had finished for the night. 'They had no crisps or anything like that, so I went up and got three Mars bars,' Hourihane says. Daly wasn't hungry and neither was his adviser. Instead they sat back and watched the man they had just pledged to support as the next Fine Gael leader devour three Mars bars at three in the morning. 'Jim texted him the next day and he wrote back, "Oh shit, I forgot about that,"' Hourihane says.

A couple of months later, Varadkar travelled to Skibbereen in Cork to open Daly's new constituency office. Within Fine Gael, the event was seen as a clear declaration of support for Varadkar and a snub to Simon Coveney. But Daly saw the opening as a chance to see how the locals in West Cork reacted to the leadership challenger. 'We were really blown away – the Leo factor blew up in our face,' Daly says:

> Obviously we'd know the Fine Gaelers and they wanted to come up and say 'hello' and that's fine but there were people I'd never seen before or heard before queuing up to get photographs. It didn't matter what politics they were, what creed they were, what age they were, it didn't matter what orientation they were – they just wanted a photo with Leo.

After a successful canvass of the town, they visited local pub the Horse and Hound. The following morning, as a gesture of gratitude, Hourihane organised a sailing trip so Varadkar could relax and take in the rugged West Cork coastline. They arranged to meet at Baltimore Pier, where they would sail out towards the stunning Cape Clear. Daly, Hourihane and two of their friends, who owned the yacht, met Varadkar's adviser Philip O'Callaghan on the pier at 10 a.m. But there was no sign of Varadkar. They rang his mobile. No answer. They rang his hotel room. No answer. After an hour or so, Varadkar eventually called and apologised for sleeping in. They set sail later in the afternoon and Varadkar travelled back to Dublin that evening safe in the knowledge that he had secured one key vote at least.

In the weeks and months that followed, Varadkar would take part in several versions of 'Mars bar night'. He was now on a charm offensive with the parliamentary party. The leadership contest was well under way.

* * *

The summer months were tough for Enda Kenny. Within weeks of forming his second consecutive government, the

Mayo politician's leadership soon came under threat. Before the Dáil broke for the summer recess, Kenny found himself facing down angry TDs over his decision to reappoint James Reilly as deputy leader of Fine Gael. A few weeks earlier, Kenny had announced at a press conference that Reilly had been sacked after failing to win his seat in the general election. But now he had reappointed Reilly to the Seanad, as well as reinstalling him to the no. 2 position in the party. TDs were puzzled by the move, which they put down to loyalty. But the dissidents raised major questions about the leader's judgement and warned that the reappointment showed the party was stuck in the past.

A group of rebel deputies discussed putting down a motion of no confidence in Kenny before the summer as a result of the Reilly appointment. Varadkar refused to engage. He knew every move he made was now under the microscope of the leader's office. Moving against Kenny when he was weak and wounded would be the wrong decision, Varadkar told supporters. He insisted the Taoiseach should be given the space to decide when and how he would step down.

Instead of plotting against Kenny, Varadkar continued his charm offensive. Near the end of the summer, he organised a night at the races for new TDs. Dinner and drinks by the track in Leopardstown in south County Dublin. It was pitched as a casual summer get-together, but news of the event quickly filtered through the party. Suspicion grew in the Kenny camp. Other TDs and senators were brought out for dinner or drinks in Dublin city centre. Varadkar even went for dinner and drinks with a number of political correspondents he knew would be at the forefront of writing about the campaign. Varadkar actively avoided meetings in Leinster House. During working hours, he invited colleagues for lunch in the Royal Hibernian Academy or the Alliance Française headquarters. They would shoot the breeze for a while before, inevitably, the leadership question came up. 'I would have been meeting people all the time and I would have made the point of trying to meet every TD and senator one to one. What was funny was I never had to bring it up. Almost always they would bring it up,' he remembers. Overall, the feedback was positive. There was certainly a decent rump of parliamentarians saying they would back him when the time arrived. But, as per his suspicious nature, Varadkar refused to believe them all. 'Huge numbers of people were pledging me their support, but I didn't really know. This is politics,' he says.

Two conversations took place in the run-up to the leadership bid that would prove pivotal for Varadkar. The first happened on Sunday 10 July 2016. Varadkar was attending a National Day of Commemoration event in the Royal Hospital Kilmainham in Dublin. Most of the Cabinet were there, as was the President. But it was Minister for Defence Paul Kehoe who sought Varadkar out. He asked the Social Protection Minister if he wanted to grab a bite to eat after the event. Varadkar suggested the Hole in the Wall pub near the Phoenix Park. Kehoe didn't waste any time. After they ordered, the minister said, 'I will support you 100 per cent and I will bring a cohort with me and I will do whatever I have to do to get you over the line, but on one condition – there's no heave against Enda Kenny and he's allowed go of his own accord.'

Varadkar was slightly taken aback. Firstly, he hadn't realised the lunch meeting would be about the leadership and, secondly, Kehoe was a devout Kenny loyalist. He was an integral part of the team who fought tooth and nail for Kenny during the ill-fated heave in 2010. Now he was offering himself up to Varadkar. Varadkar had no intention of moving on Kenny. His inner circle continuously warned of the perils involved in trying to oust the sitting leader. Kehoe could play a crucial role in convincing other Kenny loyalists to back his candidacy, he thought. He could assure them that Fine Gael's young prince would not move on the king and would patiently wait for his time to come. Kenny would go of his own accord, Varadkar thought, and, for now, he would have to be content with picking off his lieutenants. After the meal, Varadkar and Kehoe shook hands and agreed to keep in touch in the coming months.

The encounter was followed by an even more significant conversation two months later. Phil Hogan was another long-time Enda Kenny ally. Hogan is credited with masterminding Kenny's defence during the heave and has an encyclopaedia-like knowledge of Fine Gael's inner workings. He served as national organiser for two general elections and was appointed national director of elections for the successful 2011 national vote. In coalition with Labour, he was appointed Minister for the Environment, Community and Local Government, which allowed him to work closely with councillors. Hogan later went on to become EU Commissioner for Agriculture and Rural Development. He is Fine Gael royalty.

Varadkar knew he needed Hogan's backing if he was to have any chance of winning the leadership campaign. He decided to call Hogan and set out his leadership pitch. 'He rang me in September 2016; this was the first conversation I had with him where he wanted to meet me to discuss if I would support him,' Hogan says.

> He asked if I thought it would be a good idea for him to become the leader of Fine Gael and subsequently Taoiseach. I asked him a considerable number of questions: why he wanted the job as Taoiseach, why he wanted the job as leader of Fine Gael, what he was going to do for the country, and what he was going to do for the Fine Gael party. So I didn't make it easy for him.

Hogan was impressed. He agreed to assist Varadkar but, once again, on the proviso that Kenny would be able to choose his own time to step down. Varadkar agreed but told him that he was coming under pressure to move on the Taoiseach. People were pushing him to make a public pronouncement on the future of the party to let Kenny know his time was up.

Hogan told him it was important to dismiss the pleas of the plotters and urged him to show Kenny the respect he deserved. 'I think that was a good calculation and a well-informed calculation that the vital twelve or fourteen members of the parliamentary party that were strong supporters of Enda Kenny would never forgive the leadership candidate that was going to contribute to the removal of Enda Kenny from office,' Hogan says.

Not long after the conversation, Varadkar let Eoghan Murphy know that Hogan had signed up to the campaign. Murphy travelled to Brussels, where Hogan was based. There, the pair thrashed out strategies and drew up lists of potential supporters.

* * *

Winning the Fine Gael leadership was not just about votes. The practicalities of running a successful campaign also had to be considered. Varadkar needed to set out his vision and give disillusioned party members something to believe in again. He needed new policies, original ideas and party reforms to convince members to back him. He also needed a campaign team of battle-hardened politicians and advisers he could trust.

To date, he had kept any preparations for the road ahead water-tight. But the time had come to get serious. In late October 2016, a new entry began appearing in the Minister for Social Protection's weekly diary. Varadkar was suddenly scheduled to attend regular meetings with the mysteriously named Ongar Group.

Ongar is a recently developed commuter community on the Dublin–Meath border. Varadkar's constituency office is tucked away just off the main street in the growing suburban town. It's a difficult spot to find, as some of those who attended the early meetings attested to. But it was here, surrounded by constituency maps and dusty election posters in a backroom office, that Varadkar and his most trusted lieutenants gathered to plot his rise to power. On quiet days, they would meet in Varadkar's ministerial office in Government Buildings, but it was more discreet to gather in the outer reaches of West Dublin. 'The reason it was called the Ongar Group for diary purposes was you couldn't put in "Election Strategy Group" or anything like that,' one source says.

The central players were often present: Brian Murphy, Nick Miller, Philip O'Callaghan, John Carroll and John Paul Phelan. Trinity College history professor Patrick Geoghegan also attended some of the early meetings. Everyone in attendance was sworn to secrecy. The brainstorming sessions were chaired by Murphy and minuted by O'Callaghan. The discussion focused on campaign themes and messaging – who exactly is Leo Varadkar and what does he stand for? How could they tap into the post-election discontent within the party and sell the idea of a rejuvenated Fine Gael under Leo Varadkar? 'It was all about what the pitch should be and who it should be to. A lot of it was about the parliamentary party, without getting into names, just what they want after fifteen years of Kenny. What do they want the next leader to be?' a source says.

Basic campaign logistics also had to be considered – election literature, posters, office space and, most importantly, volunteers. But all of that planning was secondary to the biggest dilemma facing Leo Varadkar: how – and, more importantly, when – was he prepared to say, 'Enough is enough. The time for a leadership change has arrived'?

CHAPTER 16

LEADERSHIP PART 2

It was a sweltering afternoon in Bogotá, Colombia, in February 2017. Varadkar was two days into an official state visit to South America with President Michael D. Higgins. But he couldn't concentrate. Back home, the government was on the verge of collapse following yet another garda scandal. A frustrated Varadkar phoned and texted supporters to find out what was happening, but none of them were responding. Finally, Noel Rock called. 'You need to come home, this thing could go down at any minute,' Rock said.

Varadkar felt helpless. The state visit had been organised months in advance, but it could not have come at a worse time. The cause of the political instability once again centred on garda whistleblower Sergeant Maurice McCabe. This time, it was the emergence of an alleged plot to smear him with child sex abuse allegations. Accountability was at the heart of the latest crisis. Who in power knew about the sordid allegations levelled at the crusading police officer and who had started the malicious claim, the opposition wanted to know. But no one in government seemed to have the answer.

The treatment of Sergeant McCabe by the state was severely

damaging Fine Gael. Sinn Féin tabled a no confidence motion in Taoiseach Enda Kenny which was due to be debated in the coming days. But the situation quickly became worse. Just before Rock spoke to Varadkar, an opinion poll was published that showed Fine Gael trailing Fianna Fáil by a staggering 11 per cent. The poll result caused panic within sections of the party, as Rock explains. '[Varadkar] rang me from a weird number. The signal was bad and I rang him back, it cost me like 32 quid because I was ringing fucking Colombia,' Rock says. 'I was telling him to come home and he was saying he didn't really think it was worthy of coming home.'

Varadkar decided to call Enda Kenny and ask him if he should return. The Taoiseach said, 'Hold off for now.' But the situation was eating away at Varadkar. He would find himself on the back foot if a leadership contest was called while he was on the other side of the world. 'I checked with Eoghan [Murphy] and Paschal [Donohoe] and they were of the view it was OK and I didn't need to rush back, but I took the decision that I would,' Varadkar says.

In an attempt to allay fears, Varadkar sent a message to a private Fine Gael WhatsApp group, made up of TDs and senators. The group included Enda Kenny. 'Worrying poll and trend. Important not to panic or to be seen to panic. Need to stay together now so we can beat Sinn Féin confidence motion,' he wrote. Rock responded, 'Are you coming home?' Another Fine Gael TD, Alan Farrell, wrote, 'Agree with Leo. Let's stick together. We have been through worse and come out stronger.' Varadkar replied, 'Yes. Just asked the President for permission to leave early. He was very gracious and understood fully. Looking for flights. Will be back before the Sinn Féin motion.' Junior minister Sean Kyne added, 'Will need everyone to be present for Sinn Féin motion.' Senator Jerry Buttimer wrote, 'Our hero returns to the rescue' (followed by happy face emojis). Varadkar took exception to this. 'None of that now, Jerry,' he said. Buttimer responded with more smiley faces. Alan Farrell chipped in again: 'We must be united on this. Our very future depends upon it. None of us want a general election but if we don't come out unified we will falter.' Senator Maria Byrne added, 'I agree with Leo, we all need to stick together. Party unity very important.'

The conversation took a bizarre turn when Minister for Foreign Affairs Charlie Flanagan commented on a news report by RTÉ's political correspondent Micheál Lehane. 'Somebody give Micheál Lehane an oxygen mask, he'll collapse if the government survives,' Flanagan said. The remark was followed by junior finance minister Eoghan Murphy asking Flanagan, 'Charlie, what are you doing about North Korea?' 'I've told Kim Jong-un to be careful, I'm watching him,' the Foreign Affairs Minister joked. It was gallows humour, masking a real fear that the government was sailing dangerously close to the shores of a general election.

Rock was especially spooked by the opinion poll and decided to go public. On Monday 13 February, he told the *Irish Independent* political editor Kevin Doyle that the uncertainty surrounding the Taoiseach's future was damaging the party. By that afternoon, Rock had appeared on RTÉ's *News At One*, where he called for Kenny to set out a timeline for resigning.

Government Chief Whip Regina Doherty sent him a furious text almost immediately after the interview. 'That was spectacularly unhelpful. You've put the government at risk,' she said. Rock knew his views were privately shared by many in the party, but once he went public, pandemonium broke out. It was seen as the ultimate act of betrayal. After all, it was less than a year since Kenny had personally asked Rock to nominate him as Taoiseach. On four separate occasions, Rock had stood up in the Dáil and lavished praise on Kenny before he was eventually elected leader of the country. Now he was calling for the Taoiseach to set out his exit strategy. 'Everything has to come to an end. We were facing a general election. I said to set out a timeline,' Rock says, adding that the party needed clarity from Kenny about his future.

Rock's close allegiance to Varadkar led many to believe he had been dispatched as a stalking horse to take out Kenny. This wasn't true. Anxious to dispel any suggestion that he was behind the attack, Varadkar unleashed Eoghan Murphy to brief the media against Rock. Shortly after Rock's interview, Murphy sent a text message to political journalists distancing the Social Protection Minister from the TD's comments. He told journalists it was nothing to do with Leo, and they could attribute his comments to a minister close to Varadkar. 'I asked Eoghan to administer the slap-down,' Varadkar confirms. 'I was very keen not to be associated with it. First of all, I wasn't behind it, but secondly, I knew full well that people would put two and two together and decide it was me and it wasn't,' he adds.

Rock ignored the briefings against him and doubled down on his attack, but Murphy wasn't far behind him. 'It was like a cartoon. Eoghan Murphy was chasing me, often literally chasing me around the RTÉ campus from interview to interview and would stand behind me; as I would do one interview, he would slot in and do another interview,' Rock says.

Rock was hurt but understood why Varadkar distanced himself from the comments. 'You were never gonna get a scenario where Leo came out immediately after me and said, "You know what, Noel is right. This is bollocks,"' he says.

* * *

Later that evening, Minister for Children Katherine Zappone marched confidently to a waiting gaggle of reporters on the steps of Leinster House. She had flown in from America and wanted to set the record straight about her knowledge of the bogus allegations of sex abuse made against Maurice McCabe. She had been thrown under the bus by the Taoiseach while she was out of the country. Kenny had claimed she failed to tell him about the explosive file containing the false allegations. He said they had met before she spoke to McCabe, but he had heard nothing from her since. This was all completely untrue, according to Zappone. Although their departmental officials had been in contact, she hadn't spoken to the Taoiseach before meeting McCabe and his wife Lorraine. More importantly, the minister revealed she had told Kenny about the fictitious sex abuse allegations a week earlier.

This was a devastating blow for the already damaged Taoiseach. Huge questions arose surrounding his recollection of being told by one of his own Cabinet ministers about a smear campaign against a whistleblower. Kenny eventually admitted his minister's version of events was correct. The under-fire Taoiseach then faced accusations that he had fabricated one meeting and completely forgotten about another.

The future of the government depended on whether Kenny could survive the Sinn Féin motion of no confidence. Fianna Fáil, as per its commitment in the confidence and supply agreement, was prepared to abstain. But Micheál Martin was exasperated with the government's handling of the garda whistleblower crisis. Martin insisted on the establishment of a public tribunal of inquiry to investigate all the matter relating to McCabe. The Taoiseach agreed and the garda scandal was parked – for now.

But relations between Fianna Fáil and Fine Gael were at

rock bottom. The government didn't look like it would survive to mark its first anniversary in office. Kenny knew his authority was now shot. Having already survived one heave, the Fine Gael leader was edging closer towards another leadership crisis.

* * *

A blood-red sunset burned in the distance as Enda Kenny took to his feet in the Fine Gael parliamentary party meeting later that week. Varadkar and Coveney could smell the blood from the swirling red and orange skyscape as they sat watching the Taoiseach speak. It was two days since Zappone's intervention and Kenny was there to seek forgiveness. But he wasn't going to get it. 'I know it's a difficult time for everyone here and I accept my responsibility,' he said, before adding, 'I beg your indulgence.' Behind the closed-doors meeting, Minister for Finance Michael Noonan tried to rally support for Kenny, but his efforts fell on deaf ears.

Varadkar decided to pounce. 'The events of last week have shown how vulnerable this government is,' he said in reference to the whistleblower crisis. 'Fianna Fáil are preparing over the next weeks and months for an election and so should we,' he added. The comments were seen by everyone in the room as a direct challenge to Kenny: an election is coming and we need you gone.

Coveney quickly weighed in behind Varadkar's call to prepare for an election. He said the government's handling of the whistleblower scandal was 'calamitous' and was beginning to 'undermine unity' within the party. It was assumed the two leadership rivals had orchestrated their interventions before the meeting, but Varadkar claims this is not the case. 'I stood up and said we need to plan for the next election. Simon Coveney stood up and said something similar and again people assumed we had pre-planned our comments, but we hadn't,' he says.

Before the meeting, Varadkar had discussed what he would say with his adviser Brian Murphy. Fine Gael's lack of election preparations concerned them both, especially since the government seemed to be perilously close to collapsing. 'Because the leadership question was open, everything else in the party was open,' a source says.

Once the meeting was over, Varadkar called his press adviser Nick Miller to discuss the details of a line to provide to the media. The quickly developing narrative suggested Varadkar was moving against Kenny, but his team were anxious to highlight Coveney's involvement. 'Subsequent to the meeting there was an attempt to characterise it as Leo trying to push Enda out when in fact Leo *and* Simon used those remarks,' an adviser says.

Varadkar invited Coveney to his office in Government Buildings later that evening to chew over what had happened in the parliamentary party room. Neither wanted a heave against Kenny. They still bore the scars from their last attempt to oust him. But they knew the Taoiseach's time was running out. 'We were both of the view that there shouldn't be a heave or a push against Enda but we might have to talk about it again in a few months' time,' Varadkar says. 'There were definitely people at that time who wanted the two of us to go to Enda together and we weren't willing to do that. I wouldn't like to give you names but there was a whole lot of people who wanted us to do that,' he adds.

Coveney confirms that he spoke to his rival on a number of occasions about Kenny's future. He believed Varadkar was under far more pressure than he was to move on Kenny, as his supporters were anxious for change. 'There was a group of about ten TDs who would be strong supporters of Leo and they would have been impatient for Leo to make a move and to push for change,' Coveney says. 'I think he would have felt some pressure from that group who clearly believed in him and wanted him to take control of the situation.' Coveney says the pressure was coming from 'inexperienced' politicians who did not understand the realities and potential divisions that would be caused by an adversarial leadership contest. 'I think Leo to his credit didn't respond to that pressure in the way he could have. I think he showed some maturity in that context and I hope the conversations with me helped him to make those decisions,' Coveney says.

* * *

Officially, Varadkar was not moving against the Taoiseach, but the actions of his supporters suggested otherwise. On the morning before the parliamentary party meeting, John Paul Phelan, one of Varadkar's key lieutenants, told his local radio station that Fine Gael needed a new leader 'within six to eight weeks'. The next day, Phelan's constituency colleague Pat Deering told RTÉ's *Morning Ireland* he would table a motion of no confidence in Enda Kenny if he did not set out a timeline for his departure. This time, there was no negative briefing against either deputy. Both had contacted Varadkar before they went on air and let him know their plans.

On Friday 17 February, Dublin Fingal TD Alan Farrell went a step further and issued a statement saying he had no confidence in Enda Kenny. 'He showed me the statement and I told him I think it's going too far,' Varadkar says. The statement was still issued. Farrell, however, insists he did not show the statement to Varadkar in advance and that he was not asked to issue it. 'That wasn't coordinated, I didn't discuss it with him, I didn't seek his approval, I didn't do anything,' Farrell says.

Either way, Enda Kenny's supporters were furious. Journalists' phones lit up with calls from angry ministers loyal to the Taoiseach. The message was clear: Leo Varadkar would never receive their backing if he moved on Kenny. 'Kenny was treated like shit. Kenny has broad shoulders, but he was treated badly,' one Cabinet minister says. The same minister said Varadkar may not have orchestrated the attacks on Kenny but, at the same time, he did very little to prevent his supporters openly criticising the Taoiseach. 'I don't believe there was any coordination but nor at any stage did he pick up the phone and say stop. Had he, it would have stopped,' the minister says.

On Saturday 18 February, the *Irish Independent* ran a front-page story under the headline 'Varadkar Panics Over FG "Judas" Accusations'. A Cabinet minister was quoted comparing Varadkar to 'Judas Iscariot', the apostle who betrayed Jesus Christ after the Last Supper. Varadkar says Minister for Health Simon Harris 'still gets the blame' for the off-the-record comment, adding, 'I'm not sure if it was him or not.' Harris always insisted it was not him.

Varadkar knew the aggression towards the Taoiseach by his supporters could lose him vital votes from Kenny loyalists. But it was a risk he was willing to take. 'I was very conscious at that time that I was potentially losing ground among the parliamentary party and among the members because of some of this,' he says. 'It was kind of like I was damned if I do and damned if I don't because I was getting the blame for it anyway. At a certain point I thought maybe I should be behind it because I'm going to get the blame anyway,' he adds.

Back-channel talks aimed at preventing a heave were organised by Tom Curran. The long-standing Fine Gael chief had a good relationship with Minister for Public Expenditure Paschal Donohoe, whom he knew to be supporting Varadkar.

Curran also knew Donohoe wanted a bloodless coup. Kenny should be given the respect and time he deserved to make his own decision, Curran would say. Donohoe agreed and relayed the message to Varadkar.

Curran would also urge Brian Murphy to deter Varadkar from moving on the Taoiseach. Varadkar's team insisted a coup was not an option they were considering with any conviction. Pressure would be exerted on Kenny, but he would not be directly challenged. Others in the party were also anxious to avoid a heave. One night in the Dáil bar, Michael Noonan pulled aside the two would-be leaders. Having competed in divisive leadership contests, Noonan wanted to offer some sage advice. 'I remember Michael Noonan in particular saying, "Look, whatever happens here, it is going to be the two of you in this contest." This is long before the contest happened,' Coveney recalls.

> [Noonan] said, 'Whoever loses actually has as big a responsibility as the person who wins it to make sure you don't divide the party in a way that weakens it for many years.' Leo and I did speak before this contest and said we would try to ensure it was very competitive but at the same time respectful and I think I have played my part in that bargain, and, to be fair, Leo has too.

On the Saturday of the 'Judas' headline, Varadkar decided to intervene publicly. He called Nick Miller and asked him to issue a statement, which read: 'Everyone is waiting to hear from the Taoiseach. The current situation is distracting and destabilising for the government, the party and the country. I have full confidence in the Taoiseach to settle it.' The far-from-cryptic statement led the news bulletins and heaped pressure on Kenny to make a move. 'I gave Nick a line and my intention was it was supposed to be a holding line or whatever and then RTÉ led with it on the news, so it turned out to be a bigger statement than I intended it to be,' Varadkar claims.

* * *

Coincidentally, the wedding of former Fine Gael senator Eugene Regan and his wife Janne Storgaard was being celebrated that same Saturday evening. A host of senior Fine Gael dignitaries, including Kenny and Varadkar, were invited to the event in Dublin's InterContinental Hotel. The party's top brass were all photographed in their finery as they got out of their chauffeur-driven cars. But two photographs stood out. The first was of Simon Coveney protectively draping his arm around the shoulder of his wife Ruth as they posed at the entrance of the hotel. The second was of Varadkar smiling uncomfortably with his hand awkwardly by his side as the bulbs flashed on the cameras. He attended the wedding alone.

The Sunday newspapers ran the photographs the following day. They told a vivid story – one that Varadkar was hoping he would not have to address at this very early point in his leadership campaign. Here was a family man – Simon Coveney – with his adoring and beautiful wife, versus a lonely and awkward-looking Varadkar. Varadkar was far from lonely; he was in a loving relationship with his partner, Matthew Barrett, but they were not ready to go public. However, their relationship had been reported on in newspaper gossip columns.

The *Irish Independent* decided to vocalise a debate happening in homes, workplaces and pubs around the country – did Varadkar's marital status matter in the leadership campaign? In an opinion article, well-respected journalist Miriam Donohoe tackled the issues under the headline 'Image matters: why a spouse in the picture is seen as important for political leaders'. Donohoe noted how the photographs showed Coveney and his wife as a 'happy, glamorous, glowing couple' while Leo was pictured on his own. 'Image is very important in politics and it is always assumed that our leaders will fit into a traditional stereotype,' she said. 'In Ireland, we have come to expect our leaders to be settled, married, family men (not women),' she added. She wrote that if Varadkar becomes Taoiseach it would be 'a shift from what we expect of our leaders' private lives'. She concluded that this would be 'another step forward in our maturity as a country'.

The column shocked and infuriated Varadkar's camp. They hadn't seen it coming and were unprepared. The piece hit Varadkar especially hard. 'He was rattled by that in a way that I'd never seen him rattled by anything in his life in the years I've known him,' John Paul Phelan recalls. Varadkar gathered his campaign team to discuss a response. 'We were all very worried about that,' Varadkar admits:

> Like, what is going on here? Why was the *Irish Independent* – and it was the *Irish Independent* rather than the *Sunday Independent* – why is this angle being pushed and why are they backing Coveney essentially? This is the paper that Middle Ireland reads.

One senior adviser was worried that Varadkar's sexuality would 'loom large' over the contest or be seized upon by Coveney's supporters. Phelan and Eoghan Murphy argued that the issue was always going to come up during the campaign. They told Leo it was actually beneficial to have it out in the open at this early stage rather than in the heat of the battle. 'We decided quite early on that we weren't going to let the issue of sexuality become a determining factor in how we fought the campaign anyway,' a senior adviser concludes.

* * *

After months of pressure, Enda Kenny finally succumbed. At a parliamentary party meeting in Leinster House in late February, the Taoiseach committed to setting out his departure timeline. He would do so, Kenny told his colleagues, once he returned from the annual St Patrick's Day state visit to Washington, DC in March. Within Fine Gael, there was a collective sigh of relief. At last, the party could now plan for the future.

Varadkar's campaign was already in full gear. Secret meetings were regularly taking place in Leinster House and other locations around the city. A meeting room in the offices of the Public Relations Institute of Ireland was often used to discuss election strategies and tactics. John Carroll, Varadkar's former parliamentary assistant, was CEO of the institute and allowed the team to gather in his office. Nick Miller, Brian Murphy and Philip O'Callaghan would attend most meetings, as would Eoghan Murphy and John Paul Phelan. Wexford TD Michael D'Arcy and Dublin senator Neale Richmond were also drafted in at this point. Later, Paul Kehoe, Josepha Madigan, Joe McHugh, Olwyn Enright, Frank Feighan and Paddy Burke were brought on board.

The campaign was just weeks away and the team began to focus on where the key votes would come from. A master list was drawn up and protectively guarded by Murphy, who had been appointed as the campaign's official director of elections. The list had five columns, each signalling a certain level of support for Varadkar. As information was gathered on TDs and senators, they were categorised as a 'strong yes' or a 'suspected no' and so on. The other members of the team fed into the list with what D'Arcy termed 'emotional intelligence' on voting intentions. Varadkar asked John Paul Phelan to draw up a so-called spouse list, containing the names of spouses and partners of all parliamentary party members. It allowed Varadkar to seem more knowledgeable about the personal lives of the TDs and senators he was courting.

Varadkar's campaign structures were built within silos and secrecy. Only a select few knew the full extent of his operation. Some key figures didn't even realise that close colleagues were involved in the campaign until after the contest. Varadkar trusted few and feared leaks. The vast majority of Fine Gael backbenchers had no idea there was a well-oiled election team in operation for months. When Phelan, D'Arcy or any of the others sidled up beside them in the Dáil Bar to discuss politics, they didn't even realise they were being canvassed. 'You are almost posing questions as many as you are answering anything,' Phelan recalls.

> What do you want, what are you looking for? Where do you think the party should go? Should it be steady or do we need a little bit of a new direction type of thing? D'Arcy's phrase [was] 'emotional intelligence'. He was spot on, of course. Different emotions affect different people in different ways.

It was all part of a covert campaign. Any information gleaned from party members in Leinster House or elsewhere was reported back to Murphy and added to the master list. Murphy compared and contrasted information he was receiving from each politician. A TD might tell Paul Kehoe they were voting for Varadkar but suggest to John Paul Phelan they were leaning towards Coveney. On receiving this information, Murphy would put the TD's name in an 'undecided' column. If the TD told two or more politicians they were supporting Varadkar, their name would become a 'strong yes'. 'If you wanted to triple-check something that you weren't sure of, you might recruit someone else to take the person for a pint or just have a chat with them,' a campaign source explains. 'You had to have multiple ways into people and no one moved into a "solid yes" unless Murphy was 100 per cent satisfied,' the source adds.

Brian Murphy and Philip O'Callaghan were tasked with sounding out councillors, who made up 10 per cent of the vote. O'Callaghan had built close ties with Fine Gael's local authority members since being appointed as Varadkar's parliamentary assistant. For the past three years, it had been his job to be at the beck and call of councillors who needed the minister's services. Now it was time to call in a few favours.

Neale Richmond and John Paul Phelan also knew the councillor circuit well, having previously sought their support when running for Seanad seats. 'We discussed which is the best route and which councillor in the group should we approach. Generally, in every county council there is a councillor who is very influential and there might be one or two who have no influence,' Phelan says.

Meanwhile, Varadkar focused on his Cabinet colleagues. Locking down votes was easier with some than others. Government Chief Whip Regina Doherty had always been close to Varadkar and did not take much convincing. Varadkar then received a major boost as he secured the support of Minister for Foreign Affairs Charlie Flanagan. 'Charlie came to me and voluntarily committed support to me quite early on. It was one I didn't necessarily think I'd have but he did,' Varadkar says. Paul Kehoe was instrumental in securing the backing of

Minister for Arts and Heritage Heather Humphreys due to their close relationship.

But there were Cabinet members whose leanings were somewhat of a mystery. Minister for Education Richard Bruton was one unknown whose support only came to light late in the campaign. Months earlier, Varadkar had approached Bruton but got a non-committal, albeit polite, response. He suspected the Education Minister was weighing up his own options in terms of the leadership race. A number of media outlets had speculated that Bruton would run.

Tánaiste and Minister for Justice Frances Fitzgerald was long considered to be in the running for the leadership. Fitzgerald had endured a torrid time in the Department of Justice throughout the policing scandals but was still anxious to put her name forward. At the forefront of her mind was the fact that Fine Gael had never had a female leader and a woman had never occupied the office of An Taoiseach. Some months before the campaign began, Fitzgerald met with Varadkar for a coffee in Leinster House. In a frank and honest conversation, she confirmed to her one-time protégé that she was considering a run for the leadership. Varadkar asked how she would come to the decision and Fitzgerald said it would depend on the level of support for her candidacy in the party. However, should she not run, the Tánaiste said she would fully support Varadkar's leadership bid. 'I had that conversation with him and I was very clear that I would support him because I did feel he was an excellent candidate,' she says now.

Minister for Health Simon Harris also harboured leadership ambitions. At just thirty years of age, Harris was keen to have his name mentioned in the debate. It was initially presumed he would support Fitzgerald, but instead he allowed his own name to be circulated as a contender for several weeks.

Intelligence collected by Varadkar's team suggested Harris was not serious about running. But it was unclear whether he would back Varadkar or Coveney. Varadkar approached Harris and asked for his vote. Harris responded that he would give the request consideration. Varadkar's team didn't trust Harris. They felt he was playing games and speaking out of both side of his mouth. They also blamed him for the 'Judas' story that had infuriated Varadkar.

Eventually, Harris decided to endorse Coveney, giving a significant boost for the Minister for Housing. Just before he officially declared his support for Coveney, Harris sent Varadkar the following text message:

> Hi Leo. Tried to call you there. It was unfortunate we couldn't meet last night because I wanted to say this in person. It won't come as any great surprise to you, but I'll declare my support for Simon Coveney. Best wishes with your campaign and I hope our friendship can continue. I respect you and your abilities and will fully support the next leader of Fine Gael. Keep in touch and happy to talk anytime.

Varadkar responded: 'No problem. I appreciate the courtesy of you letting me know. Let's try to keep this clean. Only way we can work together in June and July.'

Harris's supporters say the texts show there was no bad blood between the Cabinet colleagues. But Varadkar remembers it differently. 'Simon and I would have had a strange relationship around that time but now we get on very well as Taoiseach and minister. We have never really discussed the leadership campaign. Maybe we should,' he says.

* * *

One afternoon, parliamentary assistant Darren Hourihane received a phone call. He was told by the person on the other end to wait by the back gate of Leinster House opposite Merrion Square. Hourihane, who was PA to Cork TD Jim Daly, had offered his services to the Varadkar camp and was now being called up for duty. Alan Holmes, a former accountant and one of Eoghan Murphy's supporters, pulled up in a black jeep and told him to get in.

They drove 100 yards and parked outside a building on nearby Mount Street. 'Are we here already?' Hourihane enquired. Holmes said he didn't want to risk being spotted by watchful eyes around Leinster House. He welcomed Hourihane to campaign HQ and told him they would both be spending most of their days in the building over the coming weeks. The office would eventually be filled with Fine Gael staffers who wanted to support Varadkar's campaign. Volunteers were designated workstations and given administrative tasks such as leafleting and preparing for the nationwide leadership hustings. Once the campaign was in full swing, strategy meetings were held in the office boardroom between 6.30 a.m. and 7.30 a.m. Staffers were given strict instructions not to be in the building during this hour.

Michael D'Arcy was the self-appointed campaign bagman. He spotted a weakness early on and took it upon himself to raise funds and source properties for the election team. Along with the Mount Street office, D'Arcy secured access to an apartment on School House Lane. The small property was less than a minute's walk from Leinster House and allowed Varadkar's strategists to nip in and out of the Dáil between votes. TDs and advisers who lived outside of the city regularly spent the night in the apartment when the contest kicked off. When Josepha Madigan joined the campaign, she offered up her law practice on Molesworth Street as a meeting place. 'Certainly, D'Arcy was a great fixer, a great organiser and a great coordinator. Josepha was fantastic in terms of coordinating things through the parliamentary party, representing Leo to people, bringing people on side and making her office available,' a campaign source says.

Back on Mount Street, the campaign's social media strategy was devised. Twitter and Facebook were seen as essential platforms. At one point, Varadkar floated the idea to one TD of creating anonymous accounts to make positive comments under online stories on popular news websites. It's unclear how far the proposal was pushed.

Personalised emails and text messages from Varadkar to Fine Gael members were also directly controlled from the office. The Varadkar campaign machine was now well oiled. But before he could declare, the current leader needed to formally step aside.

* * *

On Wednesday 17 May 2017, an emotional Enda Kenny stood before his parliamentary party as Fine Gael leader for the last time. 'Last year I indicated that I would not lead the Fine Gael party into the next general election,' he said. 'I have decided to implement that decision today. Therefore, I will retire as leader of Fine Gael effective from midnight,' he added.

The announcement had been a long time coming, but it did not make it any easier for the Mayo politician. Kenny was close to tears, as were many members of the party he had led for fifteen years. He beat the leakers to their own game by arranging with Fine Gael head of communications Barry Duggan for his statement to be released publicly while he addressed the private party meeting. When he finished his address, Kenny meekly asked, 'Can I go now?'

The party rose to their feet for a standing ovation and there was an attempt by some TDs to make statements. But the Taoiseach didn't want to hear them. He walked through the sea of once loyal supporters declaring, 'Let the games begin' as he left the room. It was an extraordinary scene.

* * *

Eoghan Murphy was insistent. No one declares until Coveney moves, he told the campaign team. Murphy and John Carroll had meticulously plotted out a grid of times and places for party members to declare support for Varadkar. But nothing was allowed to happen until Coveney made the first move.

Luckily, they didn't have long to wait. At 1 p.m. on Thursday 18 May, the Minister for Housing organised a press launch outside Fine Gael headquarters on Mount Street. Coveney and sixteen supporters marched up to the Georgian building and stood in between two large black and white photos of the minister.

As Coveney was peppered with questions by the press, directly across the street, Varadkar's campaign team peered down from the fourth floor of their rented office space. They were surprised that Coveney had rolled out what they believed to be the vast majority of his supporters at his first press conference. As far as they were concerned, he didn't have many more votes. But the event wasn't the first surprise of the day.

Around half an hour before Coveney's campaign launch, Richard Bruton had announced a press conference outside the Department of Education on the other side of the city. Bruton called Varadkar before he briefed the media, but the phone rang out. He also phoned Coveney to break to the news to him. Outside the department, Bruton officially announced he would not be contesting the leadership election and instead would throw his support behind Varadkar.

During a day of frantic action, Minister for Justice Frances Fitzgerald and Minister for Foreign Affairs Charlie Flanagan also announced they would not be contesting, but would not say how they planned to vote. Minister for Finance Michael Noonan said he would resign once the new Taoiseach was elected and would not contest the next election.

In the apartment on School House Lane, Murphy got word that Coveney's launch had concluded. He was ready to move. Murphy wanted to unleash wave upon wave of supporters. However, he had one final instruction: there was to be no press conference on the plinth outside Leinster House. 'He didn't want echoes of the 2010 heave, with everyone marching out to the plinth saying opposing things. He was very concerned about keeping it collegial throughout, which was the guiding principle of the entire campaign,' a Varadkar source says.

First out was a group of nine senators who had been rounded up by long-time Enda Kenny supporter Paddy Burke. The move quickly dispelled suggestions circulating before the contest that Coveney would win over the majority of the upper house.

Not long afterwards, a group of a dozen TDs met in Buswells Hotel opposite Leinster House. Many were surprised to meet colleagues they assumed were backing Coveney in the foyer of the hotel. 'It was a complete shock to me. I didn't know who was coming or who wasn't coming. It was all kept separately,' says Josepha Madigan, who many thought would declare as a Coveney supporter. Madigan was close to three other rising stars in the party – Kate O'Connell, Hildegarde Naughton and Maria Bailey – and it was presumed she would join them in voting for the Housing Minister. In the end, she was the only female backbencher to endorse Varadkar. 'I imagine they would have liked if I would vote for Simon Coveney, but I had to follow my own decision-making in my own heart and my own head as to what I thought was right regardless of the fact it may lead to a fallout,' Madigan says. 'As a female backbencher, it wasn't an easy decision for me because all the other females went another route and it would have been easier maybe to take the same decision, but I couldn't make my decision on that basis,' she adds.

On the RTÉ *Six One News*, Minister for Arts and Heritage Heather Humphreys declared for Varadkar. The next morning, Friday 19 May, Minister for Public Expenditure and Reform Paschal Donohoe also publicly declared his support for Varadkar. More junior ministers, TDs and senators followed suit. It was less than two days into the campaign and the momentum behind Varadkar looked like it would steamroll his opponent out of the race. Within twenty-four hours, he had the backing of forty parliamentarians, while Coveney had only twenty. And Varadkar had yet to hold his official campaign launch.

Under Fine Gael rules, first proposed by Leo Varadkar, the leadership is decided by an electoral college which gives parliamentary party members (fifty TDs, nineteen senators and four MEPs) 65 per cent of the vote, ordinary members of the party 25 per cent, and local authority representatives 10 per cent. Varadkar's decision to focus heavily on the parliamentary party put him miles ahead.

Coveney was hurt. He felt let down by several key party figures he believed would support him. 'A week before, we were running our numbers and talking to people honestly and we felt that we were pretty close,' Coveney says.

We were within about five [votes]. We felt there was a large group of undecided people and we felt we would take half of them at least and that would have allowed me to win in terms of the vote I got with the membership. That isn't what happened and once people in the parliamentary party saw Leo was ahead – as is always the case in politics and sport – people who are neutral will row in behind the person who they think will be the likely winner, out of their own interests.

Over the course of the first two days of the campaign, Coveney says he received a number of apologetic calls from supporters who felt they had to back Varadkar. 'I understood that, and I think you would struggle to find anyone in the party who would say I held any grudges,' he adds.

On Friday evening, Coveney was embarrassed further when he posed for an interview beside Clare TDs Pat Breen and Joe Carey ahead of a leadership rally in their constituency. With Coveney standing beside them, neither Carey nor Breen would say who they were supporting. Before the meeting was even over, newsrooms had received embargoed press statements from both politicians announcing they were voting for Leo Varadkar.

Other Coveney supporters, such as Kate O'Connell, were not for turning. On the way to a Clare campaign rally, O'Connell and her sister Theresa Newman discussed the onslaught from the Varadkar camp. Coveney had been adamant that he wanted a clean campaign: no dirty tricks or smears of their opponents. But the two sisters agreed they needed to put some energy into the Coveney campaign. O'Connell had committed to making an address at the rally, so Newman started jotting down a few talking points during the car journey. On stage at the private meeting, O'Connell lashed out at the TDs who had come out in support of Varadkar as 'boys that are singing for their supper'. She told the meeting, 'I am very disappointed at the last few days. At the choreographed, coordinated choirboys that came out. Boys that are singing for their supper. You want to be heard as members. The process, the way it is turning at the minute, your voices will not be heard.' O'Connell also personally attacked her constituency colleague Eoghan Murphy, with whom she shared a well-publicised rivalry.

An audio tape of the speech was leaked to the *Irish Independent* not long afterwards. Murphy immediately texted his campaign team and insisted they should not respond to the 'choirboy' taunt. He then called Damien English, who was Coveney's campaign manager. Before the contest, both candidates had signed a 'fair play' charter and Murphy believed O'Connell's comments represented a breach. Fine Gael General Secretary Tom Curran was particularly furious. He phoned Kate O'Connell and gave her what one source describes as a 'bollocking'. The source adds, 'Curran saw this as a veiled reference to sexuality. Choirboys are seen in a particular way, Church of England and so on. And this was a reference to these gay young men or whatever.' He thought it was below the belt and unacceptable. Curran told O'Connell to 'keep it clean' for the duration of the campaign. But the 'choirboy' jibe had gone viral and would stick for the remainder of the contest.

Choirboys aside, Coveney had bigger problems. Saturday was Varadkar's big reveal, where he would unveil the true extent of his parliamentary party support at an event in Dublin. There were still several TDs who had yet to declare and Coveney's campaign team were deeply anxious. At the event, Tánaiste Frances Fitzgerald and influential Minister of State for Regional Economic Development Michael Ring – along with a host of other TDs – weighed in behind Varadkar. Coveney looked on in despair. He had his own rally in Cork later that evening. But some of his key backers were getting flaky. By Saturday morning, they knew winning the contest was now impossible.

Varadkar had it in the bag. The numbers just didn't add up. They dreaded the prospect of enduring a three-week campaign that they knew from day two would end in failure.

Coveney was sitting in his family home in Carrigaline, Cork, when the calls started. As Coveney's only supporter in Cabinet, Simon Harris felt duty-bound to set out the grim reality of the campaign to his friend. When he called, Harris said, 'Look, I don't see how there's a roadmap to win this and I need to know how serious you are.' Harris was never going to tell him to quit the race, but he wanted to be sure Coveney was not oblivious to the insurmountable challenges before him. 'I'm sticking with it,' Coveney told Harris. 'I'd like your support, but I absolutely understand if you can't play any further role in the campaign,' he added. Harris wanted to quit but he was never going to leave Coveney in the trenches after he had decided to battle on.

There were other calls, too. Senator Tim Lombard, one of Coveney's closest allies, received a call from a key member of Varadkar's team who advised him to 'get Coveney off the pitch'. The junior minister told Lombard that Coveney would be 'damaged' within the party if he went ahead with the campaign. Lombard ignored the plea, but he did feel the race was over and told Coveney as much that afternoon.

Coveney admits he was under pressure to pull out but insists he was never going to give up. 'To be honest, I never really thought about or wanted to quit the contest at that point, but others did ring me to say should we think about it,' he says. 'When I spent a little bit of time thinking about it, I said, "No, we have started this. We are going to finish it and let's get on and have this rally this evening," which was that night in Cork,' he adds.

Coveney was determined to put on a brave face but still needed validation for his decision to fight on. He put a call into

Michael Noonan, whose judgement he trusted on all matters. Noonan, as a former Fine Gael leader, had vowed not to publicly declare for either candidate, but Coveney's camp were almost certain they had his vote. 'Michael is someone I am close to and I trust his judgement,' Coveney says. 'I rang him to say, "I'm going to see this through" and I wanted to get his view on that and he said, "I think you're right and the party needs this contest." He was right, the party did need the contest and for me I wasn't going to quit,' he adds.

* * *

Not unlike the 2010 leadership heave, another bizarre rumour circulated that Saturday afternoon. At around 5 p.m., speculation emerged that Simon Harris had made enquiries about entering the contest at the last minute. The *Sunday Independent* heard the rumour and contacted Harris, who outright denied he had done any such thing.

Leo Varadkar was told about the rumour by his chief of staff, Brian Murphy. 'I was told, or Brian was told, that Simon Harris had been on to find out what the procedure was to get nominations, that he was willing to run. I've never asked Simon about that. I really should,' Varadkar says. 'It's just as possible that it could be a story that someone put out to harm him, but it was given to me as if it was true that he had sought nominations,' he adds.

* * *

Varadkar had the parliamentary party sewn up, but he was still facing a gruelling three-week election campaign. He was almost certain of victory, but he could not take anything for granted. Not a single vote had been cast and how councillors or grassroots members would vote was anyone's guess. Much could depend on how he performed in the four scheduled leadership debates scattered across the campaign.

When the team prepared for the debates, Paschal Donohoe played the role of Simon Coveney, while former Fine Gael TD Olwyn Enright acted as the moderator. Enright peppered Varadkar with questions and allowed Donohoe in with his rebuttals. 'Paschal was superb, he was scarily good,' says a source who attended the meetings.

Varadkar was clearly the front runner going into the debates and knew there was no need to go for the jugular. He was so far in front, why jeopardise his chances by taking unnecessary risks? The team had not rated Coveney as a strong debater before the contest. They felt his reserved and honest approach to politics would restrain him from going on the attack. But they were soon proven wrong. At the first debate in the Red Cow Hotel in Dublin, Coveney came out all guns blazing. He delivered a powerful opening speech about transforming Fine Gael into a party for all sections of society. 'We suspected that Simon had had work in terms of public speaking and in terms of posture, body language and delivery,' a Varadkar source says. 'I could be wrong but there was quite a marked change between the Simon everyone knew and the Simon that was up there on stage,' the source adds.

Coveney dismissed the suggestion that he received professional training for the debates. He explained that he took the stage that night in Dublin as a man with 'nothing to lose' who was determined to fight until the last round. 'I was on the offensive to a certain extent. It was never personalised, I don't think, but I needed to make a mark when we started those debates in Dublin,' he says.

Coveney had a vision for the party that was inspired by the 1960s blueprint 'Just Society' policy document, produced by Declan Costello. The document emphasises the need for the party to live up to its social responsibilities. He wanted the members to know he had substance. He wasn't going to be an also-ran. 'I want this party to be a party that reaches out to everybody, and that was the theme of the debates for me,' Coveney recalls. 'This isn't a party that has a niche support base that we should look after. It is a catch-all party that is a friendly home for everybody,' he adds.

Varadkar admits he was caught off guard by his opponent's aggressive approach to the debates. He hoped the events would be almost boring; policy-heavy debates rather than emotional mudslinging fights. They were not being aired on television, so there was no obligation to play up for a national audience. 'I was hoping it wouldn't get dirty at all and I only realised it could get nasty enough at the first hustings in Dublin,' he says. 'Coveney was very good. He definitely did way better than I expected or we expected, but he also went negative and I didn't think that would happen and that caused me to recalibrate strategy a bit. It was quite negative.'

Varadkar took the punches for the first three debates but decided to swing back at the final contest in Coveney's home city of Cork. He didn't want to fight back but was bruised from the other debates and believed he had to take a more aggressive stance. Coveney spotted Varadkar's tactics. 'For the first three debates, the perception and coverage of them was that I had won them, and I think he wanted to put a marker down particularly in Cork that he wasn't going to be pushed around, so he came out in a more aggressive style, which suits Leo anyway,' Coveney says.

* * *

In many ways, Coveney's decision to remain in the race was the right one. He secured 65 per cent of the membership's vote, clearly illustrating his appeal to voters outside of Dublin. But Varadkar's ability to sew up the support of the parliamentary party meant the result was never in doubt. On 2 June 2017, he was declared the new leader of Fine Gael at the count centre in Dublin's Mansion House. Just days later, he was sworn in as the country's fourteenth Taoiseach.

It was speculated that, in a bid to heal the divisions within the party, the new leader would offer the position of Tánaiste to Coveney. But Varadkar had promised Frances Fitzgerald she would remain as Tánaiste should she support his campaign. Coveney, however, could have anything else he wanted, including the deputy leader position. 'One of the first things I had to do as leader was bring Simon totally in. We met in [the] Department of the Taoiseach a day or two after the result and it was really going to be a case of he can have any ministry he wanted,' Varadkar says.

The Taoiseach says the only 'significant decision' he had to make when appointing his first Cabinet centred on Simon Harris. Harris was the only senior minister who hadn't supported his leadership campaign and he was very unpopular among Varadkar's supporters. Varadkar was under intense pressure to sideline the minister. 'A lot of my supporters wanted me to sack him and that would have freed up a seat around the table. I decided not to. Frances certainly spoke up for him and he is a capable guy,' he says.

Varadkar regularly turned to Fitzgerald for political advice and trusted her judgement. She was not only a loyal political supporter but also a close family friend whom he was happy to have as his Tánaiste. But very soon, just weeks into his tenure as Taoiseach, that loyalty would be put to the ultimate test.

CHAPTER 17

LEO'S FIRST CRISIS

The most difficult conversation of Leo Varadkar's tenure as Taoiseach took place in his office in Government Buildings on the morning of 28 November 2017. Sitting opposite his large oak desk was a woman for whom he cared deeply. Tánaiste and Minister for Enterprise Frances Fitzgerald had helped mould Varadkar and had given him his first start in Leinster House as a work experience student. They had served in Cabinet together and she offered one of his most important endorsements for the leadership campaign. Now they were discussing her own political future and whether or not another justice controversy would result in a snap general election.

The reason behind the political turmoil was textbook modern-day Irish politics. The never-ending controversy surrounding the treatment of garda whistleblower Sergeant Maurice McCabe had once again reared its head. Over a period lasting almost five years, the government had struggled to handle a debacle that led to the removal of two Garda Commissioners, a Minister for Justice and a Secretary General. Fitzgerald had been parachuted into the Department of Justice following the shock resignation of her predecessor, Alan Shatter. The garda whistleblower controversy had brought about Shatter's demise. Now, Fianna Fáil were demanding Fitzgerald's head due to her alleged inaction over the treatment of Sergeant McCabe.

Labour Party TD Alan Kelly, a former minister in the previous government, had spent weeks doggedly probing the Department of Justice over the garda force's handling of the whistleblower affair. Kelly wanted to know what correspondence the department had received from garda headquarters prior to and during the hearings of the O'Higgins Commission of Investigation, which was set up to probe Sergeant McCabe's allegations of garda malpractice. These allegations included claims that gardaí failed to properly investigate both physical and sexual assaults, as well as claims that a dangerous criminal went on to carry out a murder after gardaí mistakenly released him on bail.

The commission, led by Mr Justice Kevin O'Higgins, was also asked to examine a botched investigation into a clerical sex abuse case, as well as an attempt by gardaí to blame Sergeant McCabe for the loss of a laptop owned by a priest jailed for child abuse. McCabe was completely exonerated of having any links to the missing laptop, but was forced to endure a lengthy disciplinary process before this fact was established.

Overall, the commission vindicated the garda whistleblower, who had struggled for years to get anybody to listen to his claims. Mr Justice O'Higgins did, however, find that some of Sergeant McCabe's claims were either inaccurate or exaggerated. After the O'Higgins Report was published, allegations emerged that Garda Commissioner Nóirín O'Sullivan had instructed her legal team to question McCabe's credibility, motivation and integrity during the commission's hearings. The legal strategy adopted by O'Sullivan's lawyers seemed to fly in the face of public comments she had made previously, in which she commended the whistleblower for exposing garda misconduct. Leaked transcripts from the hearings detailed the legal strategy to go after Sergeant McCabe.

It was alleged by O'Sullivan's legal team that McCabe's campaign to expose garda misconduct was driven by a grudge he held against senior officers who had previously investigated him over the spurious child sex abuse allegations. His complaints, the legal team claimed, were fuelled by a desire for revenge motivated by the ordeal he and his family had been put through. The false set of accusations had been made against him by the daughter of another garda with whom he had fallen out.

The controversy played out behind closed doors at the O'Higgins Commission over many months. In May 2016, when details of the legal strategy emerged, O'Sullivan was forced to issue a statement insisting she had not questioned Sergeant McCabe's integrity and did not believe he was motivated by malice. But it was too late.

McCabe, battered by the experience of appearing in front of the commission, took stress-related sick leave. The story of the Garda Commissioner's alleged bid to target McCabe shone a spotlight on her position. As Minister for Justice at the time the strategy had been adopted, Fitzgerald also came under pressure and was repeatedly asked to express confidence in O'Sullivan. Fitzgerald's responses were, time and time again, far from emphatic. She batted away questions about the garda legal strategy to discredit McCabe by insisting it would be against the law to discuss the leaked commission transcripts. But her response simply did not cut it. The opposition piled in on Fitzgerald and demanded answers that she claimed she was not in a position to give. Fitzgerald's relationship with the Garda Commissioner had reached a point of strain – but publicly she was not prepared to call for her head.

Fitzgerald would leave justice for her new role as Minister of Enterprise in June 2017, upon Varadkar's election as Fine Gael leader. But if Fitzgerald thought she was closing the door on a garda controversy, she was seriously mistaken.

All of this formed the backdrop of intense grilling of the Justice Department by Alan Kelly months later. It was suspected in political circles that Kelly was in touch with informed justice or garda sources who were feeding him insider information. The Labour TD wanted to know if Fitzgerald and her officials were kept abreast of developments surrounding the O'Higgins Commission and the garda legal strategy. Was there a paper trail, even calls? What information was passed to who and when? Kelly specifically wanted to know if O'Sullivan had contacted the Secretary General of the Department of Justice, Noel Waters, about the allegations. Unbeknown to Kelly, his relentless probing was causing consternation within justice circles. And it would soon lead to a breakthrough that would have devastating political consequences.

On Tuesday 14 November, Kelly's investigation gathered steam. Fianna Fáil leader Micheál Martin weighed in as he grilled Varadkar in the Dáil about the Department of Justice's knowledge of the alleged plot to discredit McCabe. Martin asked if the department had been informed by the Garda Commissioner or any of her senior officers of the legal strategy used during the commission hearings. Varadkar could not definitively answer the question. But he insisted Fitzgerald had had 'no hand, act or part' in the controversial strategy and only found out after it became public knowledge.

The next day, Labour Party leader Brendan Howlin demanded more answers from the Taoiseach. Howlin demanded to be told precisely what Fitzgerald and her officials knew about the garda legal strategy while she was Justice Minister. The

Taoiseach again told the Dáil he believed his Tánaiste had no role in the legal strategy and insisted she first became aware of the matter in May 2016 when the leaked transcripts were published. For the second day in a row, Varadkar told the country there was nothing to see here. During tense exchanges, he said he had been told by the Department of Justice that officials were not aware of the strategy. But his answer was littered with doubt. 'It is a body with hundreds of staff. Can I put my hand on my heart here and say that there is not one person somewhere who might have been told something by someone? I cannot give the House that answer,' Varadkar said.

Minister for Justice Charlie Flanagan, who had replaced Fitzgerald, then made a surprise intervention. During a Dáil debate, a clearly under-pressure Flanagan accused Kelly of running a smear campaign against him. 'I will not have my good name and my professional reputation traduced by Deputy Kelly inside or outside the House,' Flanagan angrily declared.

Over a number of days, the story looked like it was about to die down. There was no smoking gun and no indication that any senior political figure had been informed of the garda legal strategy. Then, all hell broke loose.

On the evening of Monday 20 November, a Department of Justice spokesman confirmed to RTÉ that Fitzgerald and her officials had been made aware of the clash between McCabe's legal team and the Garda Commissioner's lawyers in May 2015. The email correspondence was between the Department of Justice's assistant secretary Michael Flahive and Fitzgerald's private secretary Christopher Quattrociocchi. It had been sent at 4.57 p.m. on 15 May. Mr Flahive said he had taken a call from Richard Barrett, a senior official in the Attorney General's office. Barrett told Flahive the Commissioner's legal team was seeking to introduce evidence into the O'Higgins Commission relating to the false sex abuse allegation made against McCabe. 'Presumably the Garda Síochána are raising the matter on the basis, they could argue (and Sergeant McCabe would deny), that it is potentially relevant to motivation,' Flahive wrote in his email to Quattrociocchi following the call. 'Richard advised me that counsel for Sergeant McCabe objected to this issue being raised and asked whether the Garda Commissioner had authorised this approach. Richard also told me that the Garda Commissioner's authorisation had been confirmed (although I understand separately that this may be subject to any further legal advice).' Crucially, the letter ended by stating that it had been agreed that the Attorney General and, most importantly, the minister could not get involved. 'Richard and I agreed that this is a matter for the Garda Commissioner, who is being legally advised, and that neither the Attorney nor the Minister has a function relating to the evidence a party to a Commission of Investigation may adduce,' Flahive stated. Nonetheless, Fitzgerald had been told of the email and her position would soon come under intense pressure.

The email was disclosed on RTÉ's *Prime Time* late on the Monday evening while the Tánaiste was still on board a passenger plane flying back from the United Arab Emirates. The Taoiseach only learned about the email at around eleven o'clock that evening. When her plane eventually did touch down, the Tánaiste switched on her phone to see a number of text messages from political correspondents. She was taken to her home in West Dublin, where she gathered her thoughts for little more than an hour. Then, without any sleep, she was driven to Government Buildings for an early morning meeting on Tuesday 21 November with the Taoiseach and Minister for Justice Charlie Flanagan.

The 2015 email was damning. It completely contradicted

the Taoiseach's previous Dáil statement, as well as Fitzgerald's claims that she had no knowledge of the strategy to discredit Sergeant McCabe. Everything fell apart at the seams. Just months into his tenure, Varadkar had a huge crisis on his hands. He was furious. He demanded answers from his two ministers and insisted Fitzgerald urgently address the matter in the Dáil.

Fitzgerald had been informed by Justice Secretary General Noel Waters about the existence of the email the previous Thursday while she was on state business. She had requested an update as soon as more information became available. Varadkar found himself dealing with a crisis that not only exposed his two ministers, but also threatened the stability of his new government. He had to get a handle on the situation fast.

At 7 p.m., an hour before Fitzgerald endured a lengthy Dáil debate on the controversy, the Taoiseach picked up the phone and called Maurice McCabe. It had been three years since the pair had spoken. Their previous conversation had been in the Department of Transport when Varadkar was minister and McCabe was embarking on his campaign for justice. Now, the Taoiseach asked McCabe for his thoughts on the email, which had been published earlier that day. They shared a frank conversation, during which the officer pointed out that there were inaccuracies in the correspondence. For one thing, the O'Higgins legal row did not centre on false sex abuse allegations made against McCabe but rather a fabricated claim that his campaign to expose garda misconduct was motivated by a grudge. McCabe made a point of telling the Taoiseach that he had no issue with Frances Fitzgerald and did not believe she had any role in the legal strategy aimed at undermining his allegations. The whistleblower did not believe she should resign.

Back in the Dáil chamber, Fitzgerald endured a bruising hour-long debate that left the opposition with more questions than answers. The Tánaiste insisted she had nothing to hide and had merely failed to remember receiving the email that had been sent to her private secretary more than two years previous. The explanation was not entirely unreasonable, as ministers receive hundreds if not thousands of emails every week. However, the opposition parties would not accept it as plausible. Fianna Fáil wanted to know why the Tánaiste hadn't acted when she saw that the gardaí were once again trying to discredit Sergeant McCabe. Why had she not sought more information or called Commissioner O'Sullivan to ask why she was prepared to publicly back the whistleblower while attacking him, through her legal team, during a private inquiry. Sinn Féin upped the ante and threatened to table a motion of no confidence in the Tánaiste which would be debated the following week. All eyes turned to Fianna Fáil leader Micheál Martin, whose party was facilitating Varadkar's minority government. Fianna Fáil had spent months dancing around the question of whether they had confidence in the Tánaiste. The Sinn Féin motion, if formally put on the Dáil agenda, would now force their hand.

The following day, Wednesday 22 November, the Taoiseach put up a strong defence of Fitzgerald in the Dáil. But pressure was building around him to sack his no. 2. It was not the first time she had found herself in the opposition's cross-hairs and Fine Gael ministers had grown weary of the never-ending cycle of crises and controversies engulfing the justice system. The Taoiseach knew he had to act and he directed his ire at the Department of Justice for its failure to properly brief him. 'I am not satisfied with the fact that on a number of occasions – at least two in the past week – I have been given incomplete information from the Department of Justice and Equality,' Varadkar told the Dáil. 'My role is to account for the government to the House and it is not something I like to see happen.' But

Varadkar knew he had to match his harsh words with action. He instructed justice officials to complete a thorough trawl of department files to determine whether there was any other correspondence relating to the alleged plot to undermine McCabe. The affair continued to get murkier. The prospect of an election over the matter was now openly being discussed in political circles. It then emerged that justice officials had known about the email for a full week before contacting Fitzgerald. Flanagan, the serving Justice Minister, also had knowledge of the correspondence, though he wasn't aware of its significance. He had even known the email existed when he stood up in the Dáil and berated Alan Kelly for seeking the information from his department, accusing Kelly of running a smear campaign.

At 2.30 on Wednesday afternoon, Micheál Martin called Leo Varadkar directly on his personal mobile phone. He spoke in a calm and measured tone, signalling he meant business. Martin said Fianna Fáil's patience had worn thin and the party could no longer express confidence in Fitzgerald. The stakes had never been higher. The Sinn Féin motion, due to be debated within days, looked set to pass. Fianna Fáil was now even prepared to instigate its own motion of no confidence in Fitzgerald. The Taoiseach thanked Martin for his call and said he would endeavour to respond as soon as possible. He never called back.

On the same evening, Fianna Fáil held its weekly parliamentary party meeting in LH 2000, a building in the Leinster House complex. Anxious backbench TDs bundled into the meeting room on the fourth floor, eager to hear how the leader planned to win the showdown with Varadkar. But Martin was coy and told them nothing. He asked for time and space so he could handle the situation how he saw fit. He made no mention of his phone call with Varadkar. TDs left the meeting bemused and disappointed.

The next day, as speculation of an election spread like wildfire, Martin drove to Cork to attend constituency engagements. He expected to hear from the Taoiseach, but the call never came. Just after lunch, Sinn Féin submitted the motion of no confidence in the Tánaiste that the party had been threatening for days. By mid-afternoon, Martin had made up his mind. He phoned Fianna Fáil's justice spokesman Jim O'Callaghan and told him to pull the pin out of the grenade and publicly signal the party's withdrawal of support for Fitzgerald.

Martin's next phone call was to the Taoiseach. He told him O'Callaghan would be appearing on the RTÉ *Six One News*, where he would be announcing that Fianna Fáil no longer had confidence in the Tánaiste. The move was a clear breach of the confidence and supply arrangement between the two parties and would mean Varadkar had to either sack his Tánaiste or face a general election, just months into his tenure as Taoiseach.

Before O'Callaghan went on air, a group of Fianna Fáil TDs gathered in the members' bar in Leinster House. The news was being shown on a television set in the corner of the room. Fine Gael TDs watched as O'Callaghan prepared to follow the instructions handed down by his leader and withdraw support for Fitzgerald. Asked if Fianna Fáil still had confidence in the Tánaiste, O'Callaghan replied, 'She should go. We can no longer express confidence in the Tánaiste. I don't think anyone wants a general election.'

Inside the confines of the members' bar, some of the Fianna Fáil TDs cheered. Others banged the table, giddy and excited at seeing Fine Gael in trouble. The Fine Gael backbenchers looked on in disbelief. They could not believe it had come to this. And they were aghast that Fianna Fáil politicians would draw such pleasure from Fitzgerald's woes.

Shortly afterwards, several Fine Gael ministers, including the

Tánaiste, held an impromptu meeting in Government Buildings. The Taoiseach joined them. It was agreed unanimously by those present to hold firm. They would not be pushed around by Fianna Fáil, and the Tánaiste would not be forced to fall on her sword.

At around 10 p.m., the Taoiseach called an emergency meeting of the parliamentary party. He was firm in his belief that his long-time friend and political ally had not acted inappropriately. Fitzgerald would not be forced out in order to satisfy political gamesmanship, Varadkar told the meeting.

Fine Gael showed a united response that night. The meeting endorsed Varadkar's position, which was to face down Micheál Martin regardless of the consequences. The party unanimously passed a motion giving unwavering support to Fitzgerald. Even ministers who a day earlier had suggested she should be sacked now weighed in fully behind the Tánaiste. As far as Fine Gael was concerned, there would be no backing down.

The next morning, Martin also gathered his front bench to discuss their next move. He faced resistance from some of his senior TDs, who did not fancy the prospect of a Christmas election. Martin, now involved in a high-stakes game of poker with Varadkar, refused to budge.

On Friday afternoon, Fianna Fáil lodged their own motion of no confidence, which would be debated and voted upon the coming Tuesday. If a deal could not be agreed within seventy-two hours, the country was heading to the polls over a row that centred on a single email and the treatment of a whistleblower. Varadkar had just days to save the skin of the person who had given him his first introduction into politics.

Meanwhile, election preparations by all parties went into overdrive. Timetables for candidate selection conventions were fast-tracked and strategy committees were arranged to meet over the weekend. Election fever had well and truly gripped the country and it was hard to see how a national vote could be averted. Varadkar cancelled a planned mission to Africa the following day as he grappled to deal with his first crisis as Taoiseach. He was backed up by his Cabinet ministers. Foreign Affairs Minister Simon Coveney said Fianna Fáil's demand for a resignation was 'built on sand'. 'We are still not fully sure what she [Fitzgerald] is being accused of. This is Fianna Fáil and Sinn Féin competing with each other,' he said. The Taoiseach dismissed the charge against Fitzgerald as 'flimsy' and added that he would not be 'throwing a good woman under the bus for political expediency to save myself and my government'. 'If there is an election before Christmas it'll be because Fianna Fáil and Sinn Féin came together,' he added.

Moves were also made to persuade Sergeant McCabe to intervene and publicly state that he had confidence in Fitzgerald, according to government sources. The Taoiseach's advisers reached out to people close to McCabe in the hope of organising a meeting in Government Buildings on Friday afternoon. They hoped the whistleblower could save the Tánaiste with a statement absolving her of having any role in the alleged plot to discredit him. However, McCabe's team decided against meeting the Taoiseach or the Tánaiste and opted instead to remain silent as the political brinkmanship continued. During this period, Varadkar spoke to his Tánaiste and asked whether she was prepared to make a statement on the controversy. She said she would consider the matter but would not say anything that would compromise the outcome of the Disclosures Tribunal, which was separately investigating allegations of a garda-led conspiracy to undermine McCabe.

As tensions mounted, it was Micheál Martin who made the next move. For the first time since its signing, the Fianna Fáil leader invoked a clause in the confidence and supply agreement which stated that the two party leaders should meet if serious difficulties arose. Varadkar and his chief of staff Brian Murphy met Martin and his chef de cabinet Deirdre Gillane in a neutral venue in Leinster House. Martin dug in his heels. He insisted the Tánaiste would have to go and that serious reforms of the Department of Justice would also need to be introduced. Varadkar listened but insisted he would not be asking his minister to resign. He gave Martin a list of additional emails that had been identified as part of a thorough trawl of Department of Justice documents. The contents of the emails would soon follow.

At this point, Fianna Fáil and Fine Gael TDs had returned to their constituencies. After a week of chaos and excitement in Leinster House, they left on the Friday with the clear understanding that an election was on the cards. They were met by what one minister described as a cold winter chill from voters. The public did not want an election, TDs were told. People were not particularly exercised over the McCabe emails. It was a sobering experience and one that refocused minds.

On Saturday afternoon, Varadkar and Murphy made the short walk from Government Buildings to the Alexander Hotel in Dublin city centre. Martin and Gillane were already there. The Taoiseach presented to Fianna Fáil a file containing the additional emails exchanged between the Department of Justice and garda headquarters regarding the legal strategy used against McCabe. The chain of communication had been established in even further detail. The entire email trawl had not been completed but Martin could see from the correspondence given to him that he had the Taoiseach in a corner. 'Martin's view was that the emails were deeply damaging. It wasn't that the Tánaiste didn't remember the emails, it was that the content should have required a greater response and that was his view,' a well-placed source says. The two leaders agreed to accept an offer from Justice Peter Charleton, who was chairing the Disclosures Tribunal, to investigate the email controversy on behalf of the government.

At the meeting, Varadkar called Fitzgerald and told her she still had his confidence. But, as further trawls of emails took place, the Taoiseach and his advisers feared what would come next. With so much information already in the public domain, the Taoiseach's officials decided to refrain from releasing the emails given to Martin. 'What we feared entirely at that point was death by a thousand leaks,' says one senior source.

On Sunday, more detailed information emerged about a phone call the Garda Commissioner had made directly to the Department of Justice at around the same time as the email was sent about McCabe. The Tánaiste's spokesperson insisted she was not made aware of this call. Nonetheless, the additional information heightened the controversy and muddied the waters further. There were also phone calls, not just emails, that had been made between the garda force and the department. It only added to the suspicion about what exactly Fitzgerald knew about the garda legal strategy.

Martin spent Sunday afternoon watching his son playing for their local sports team in Cork. He was driven to Dublin after the match to hold a further meeting with the Taoiseach. Neither side blinked and the stalemate continued.

The email search was eventually completed before lunchtime on Monday and the final set of documents was given to the Fianna Fáil leader. It was expected that the emails would be published early in the afternoon, but the release was put back a few hours to allow Sergeant McCabe's legal team time to examine the documents.

The public mood, media commentary and party colleagues

were generally sympathetic towards the Tánaiste up to this point. But once the additional chain of emails was published at around 6 p.m., all that changed. The emails showed further exchanges between the minister, her officials and gardaí about the legal strategy. The new documents showed Fitzgerald had 'noted' the concerns raised about the garda force's aggressive legal strategy against the whistleblower. Once again, the emails showed she was specifically told that she was legally precluded from taking any action as minister. However, the opposition said the emails gave further proof of Fitzgerald's failure to intervene over a matter of grave concern. A citizen of the state was being wronged and the minister did not act. It was unacceptable and an abdication of her duties, the opposition argued.

News bulletins detailed the emails at length. Fine Gael TDs pulled out of television appearances and social media exploded with vitriol towards Fitzgerald. Emboldened Fianna Fáil and Sinn Féin deputies took to the airwaves to call for her resignation. The public mood had well and truly shifted.

Fine Gael TDs and the Taoiseach's advisers knew the game was up. 'We were in a difficult place from the start but by the end of the Monday evening it was clear the way things were going to end up,' a senior adviser says. Varadkar continued to fight on – even though he was facing the prospect of becoming the shortest-serving Taoiseach in the history of the state.

At their final meeting, Varadkar and Martin shared a calm and frank conversation. Both men knew what was at stake. Martin told the Taoiseach their talks had resulted in 'very good progress' on the issue of Department of Justice reform but inevitably the discussion returned to Fitzgerald's political future. 'It is not going to be possible to for us to abstain on a confidence vote,' Martin said at the meeting, signalling an end to the confidence and supply agreement.

According to a well-placed source, the Taoiseach told his counterpart he thought this was wrong and unfair. Varadkar wanted Fitzgerald to remain in place until after Justice Charleton's tribunal had investigated the email trail and the actions taken by Fitzgerald. She deserved due process, he insisted. If, in six months' time, the tribunal found she had acted inappropriately then he would cut her loose. Martin would not agree. He wanted her gone now and was not prepared to compromise.

The Tánaiste remained defiant, however, and issued a statement at 10.49 p.m. in which she insisted she could not interfere with the garda legal strategy and said the Disclosures Tribunal would 'objectively judge the appropriateness of my conduct'.

Fine Gael deputy leader Simon Coveney reinforced the government's stance on RTÉ's *Claire Byrne Live*. 'What is the problem with waiting six weeks for the tribunal and then making a judgement on what she did and didn't do and what was appropriate at the time?'

That night, Fitzgerald thought long and hard about the position she found herself in. She is a politician who believes in high standards and playing by the rules. Colleagues regularly criticise her for being overly cautious and relying too much on advice rather than instinct. But that has always been her style. In relation to the McCabe issue, Fitzgerald's officials had advised her not to act and she didn't. But, at the same time, she did not want to be responsible for a general election that the country did not want or need.

Fitzgerald arrived early at Government Buildings the next morning and was shown into the Taoiseach's office. At this point, backbench TDs in Fine Gael were sending text messages to each other discussing the prospect of calling on Fitzgerald to resign. In the Taoiseach's office, Fitzgerald and Varadkar spoke for more than an hour about the various scenarios the debacle had thrown up. Both agreed she had done nothing wrong, but they also knew the political and public tide of support was against them. The Taoiseach was not going to ask for her resignation, however. The decision rested with Fitzgerald, who, after much soul-searching, decided what she needed to do.

Fine Gael ministers gathered in the Sycamore Room in Government Buildings for their pre-Cabinet meeting. The only people missing were the Taoiseach and the Tánaiste. After some time, ministers were told the pre-Cabinet meeting was cancelled, which led most to believe the Tánaiste had decided to resign.

Once they concluded their conversation, Varadkar and Fitzgerald walked the short distance to the Cabinet Room together. They went through the entire Cabinet agenda before the Tánaiste had her turn to speak and officially announced her intention to step down. She insisted she had done nothing wrong and had not been afforded due process by Fianna Fáil. She said the Disclosures Tribunal would examine the totality of the evidence involved and she was confident it would clear her of any wrongdoing.

It was a poignant moment for many Fine Gael ministers. Most had worked with Fitzgerald their entire careers. She had mentored many of them, such as the Taoiseach and Minister for Health Simon Harris. But now she was gone. 'It is my strong view that a good woman is leaving office without getting a full and fair hearing. Deputy Fitzgerald has been an exemplary member of government and a loyal colleague,' the Taoiseach told the Dáil. 'In the past few days, a drip-drip of information may have made certain things seem greater than they are. There was a feeding frenzy and it became impossible for her to get a fair hearing based on the full facts. I hope that will change in the period ahead,' he added.

Leo Varadkar was shaken and upset. By refusing to seek Fitzgerald's resignation, he had brought the country agonisingly close to a general election. Within the Fine Gael party, Varadkar's handling of the affair had divided opinion. Some TDs felt he showed a lack of courage by refusing to ask her to step aside despite the revelations contained in the emails. But he had showed mettle too, deputies said, by resisting the efforts from Fianna Fáil to force her out.

Privately, Varadkar feared being labelled a 'misogynist' in the event of him throwing Fitzgerald under a bus. Helen McEntee, the Minister for European Affairs, believes the episode demonstrated Varadkar's true character. 'My own personal view is Frances was honest with him, said she hadn't done anything wrong, explained the situation and he said, "I'm not allowing a good woman to be thrown under the bus." To be honest, I think he was doing the right thing,' McEntee says. 'As it turned out, she went, and I think he is sorry that happened. I think he showed loyalty to the party but to the country as well because he did everything he could to make sure an election couldn't happen.'

Throughout the controversy, a much more serious crisis was developing. Varadkar was now preparing to lock horns with the British government over the UK's decision to leave the European Union.

CHAPTER 18

'THE MAFIA BROTHERS COME TO DUBLIN'

Mark Rutte, the Dutch Prime Minister, had a proposal for Leo Varadkar. Rutte had just become the latest in a string of European leaders to weigh in fully behind Ireland's position in the Brexit talks. Now, he wanted to send out the strongest possible message, showing that the Dutch and the Irish people shared the same values. After a short meeting with the Taoiseach in Government Buildings, Rutte suggested they take their staff to the nearest pub for a pint of Guinness. What better way to show solidarity with the Irish than downing a few pints of stout in a traditional bar, the Prime Minister asked. Rutte's proposal may well have fuelled Ireland's national stereotype as regular pub-goers – but Varadkar was only too happy to oblige. 'The Dutch were clear they wanted pictures in a pub or a social scene to send the message that these people were standing with Ireland,' says one senior member of Varadkar's team.

Rutte, like so many other EU leaders, had flown to Dublin specially in order to lend support to the government's stance on the Northern Ireland border. For senior government officials in

Dublin, the visit by Rutte on 6 December 2017 clearly signalled to Britain that the EU was in Ireland's corner when it came to protecting the border. However, Ireland's negotiating position had received its most important seal of approval a week earlier from President of the European Council Donald Tusk. Tusk had personally asked to visit Dublin so that he could publicly show solidarity with the government's point-blank opposition to a visible border between the Republic and the North. He had initially been due to meet Varadkar on the fringes of an EU–Africa summit in the Ivory Coast. But the Taoiseach was forced to cancel the trip to Africa amid fears the government would collapse over the garda whistleblower scandal. Varadkar's officials were briefed beforehand on Tusk's proposed speech – but, given his broken English, they weren't sure how effective the execution would be.

On the steps of Government Buildings, Tusk sent an emphatic warning to Downing Street. 'Let me say very clearly: if the UK offer is unacceptable for Ireland, it will also be unacceptable for the EU. I realise that for some British politicians this may be hard to understand,' Tusk said. 'This is why the key to the UK's future lies, in some ways, in Dublin, at least as long as Brexit negotiations continue.' Dublin's negotiating team was stunned and even emotional, as one figure close to Varadkar explains. 'There was this statement from Tusk which said, "We stand with you." For Leo, who would have been involved in the European People's Party, it was a big vindication.'

In similar fashion to Tusk, Rutte went much further than Irish officials had expected. And there were many more to come. From Michel Barnier to Angela Merkel, Varadkar's ability to secure high-profile endorsements was playing extremely well domestically. 'You had this situation where EU leader after EU leader were delivering speeches that went way beyond our aspirations,' says one senior official. 'Dublin wouldn't have written better scripts,' he adds.

A separate high-level source close to Varadkar recalls the show of support from the German politician and chairman of the European People's Party Manfred Weber. Weber joined colleagues in warning British Minister Theresa May that Ireland's opposition to a hard border was non-negotiable. The source says private conversations with Weber on Brexit made Leo feel he was talking to an Italian, not a German politician. 'Weber said, "These people need to understand you are in the family, they have left the family. We are family, we stand together." It was like we were Mafia brothers in New York. It was very powerful.'

It was back in July 2017, just weeks after his election as Taoiseach, that Varadkar began to carve out the initial strategy behind the government's Brexit negotiating position. After secret discussions with his new Foreign Affairs Minister Simon Coveney, it was agreed that they would adopt the most hardline stance possible in relation to the border. Ministers would be directed to constantly talk up the Good Friday Agreement – of which Ireland is a co-guarantor – and its benefits to both nationalist and unionist communities in the North. 'The Good Friday Agreement was the cornerstone of what we were about,' says a leading Brexit negotiator. The fact that Northern Ireland had voted to remain in the EU by a margin of 56 per cent should also be reinforced, strategists believed. Varadkar was advised that the Democratic Unionist Party (DUP), which had recently agreed a confidence and supply deal with the Tories, would seek to attack the government's stance. 'At every key juncture – the signing of the St Andrew's Agreement, the signing of the Good Friday Agreement – unionist politicians ramp up their attacks on us,' says one Varadkar aide.

Another figure involved in the Brexit talks says the July meeting has always underpinned Ireland's non-negotiable stance in relation to the prospect of a hard border. 'This was the meeting when Coveney and Leo decided to take a different tack to their predecessors,' the source says. 'They decided to play hard ball on the border and seek specific guarantees. Fine Gael was not prepared to allow the border to re-emerge.'

The advice given to Varadkar about the expected response from the DUP soon materialised in public. Just days after the meeting with Coveney, the DUP's deputy leader Nigel Dodds suggested 'confusion seems to be the order of the day' since the change of leadership in Fine Gael. 'Just what is going on in Dublin?' Dodds asked.

To understand Varadkar's approach to Brexit, one should go back to the decision in 2013 by the then Prime Minister David Cameron to signal an in/out referendum on EU membership. Varadkar, then Minister for Transport, immediately called on Ireland to capitalise on the uncertainty facing the UK. While insisting it was his preference for the UK to remain in the EU, he said investors could become more attracted to Ireland as a result of Cameron's gamble. 'In the short term, it could be used to our advantage,' Varadkar said in a newspaper article. 'The reality is that the uncertainty isn't good for Britain, precisely because investors will ask those questions,' he added. More than four years on from those remarks, Theresa May and her government found themselves asking whether Varadkar's stance could sink any chance of an exit deal.

May and Varadkar's relationship has always been cordial and professional. Varadkar is known to respect May deeply on a personal level and has expressed sympathy privately over her precarious position politically. Close aides of Varadkar say his most memorable encounter with May took place in Gothenburg on

17 November 2017. The two heads of state met on the fringes of a jobs summit. The meeting took place in a tiny Portakabin that could barely fit May, Varadkar and their respective teams. Cramped and uncomfortable, perhaps it represented the ideal setting for two sides that remained miles apart on the issue of the border. 'That was like a prison. It was a Portakabin that was done up. It was hilarious,' says one Irish figure who was one of six people who managed to squeeze inside. 'May said this as we went in. She said she was worried about closing the door because she thought it might lock and then someone made a comment about being locked out of Europe. It was very strange.' But the talks in Gothenburg themselves failed to produce results. 'We were getting nowhere,' the source says. '[May] doesn't genuinely believe you can square this circle: that you can have a free trade arrangement and at the same time have no borders. It doesn't work.'

As EU and UK negotiators worked towards signing off on Phase One of the negotiations, Varadkar found himself quickly becoming 'enemy no. 1' in the eyes of certain Brexiteers as well as Tory-leaning press outlets. Having recently described Brexit as the 'challenge of this generation' in a keynote speech in Belfast, Varadkar was accused of putting self-interest first. He was, according to some commentators, displaying complete naivety in relation to the talks process. And his hardline stance was motivated by his desire to boost his popularity at home, it was claimed in the UK media. In November, the UK edition of *The Sun* ran an 'exclusive' which claimed that the latest stand-off over the border was influenced by Fine Gael's fears of the rise of Sinn Féin. UK ministers briefed the newspaper to the effect that Leo felt threatened by the then Sinn Féin President Gerry Adams. Dublin was aghast and rubbished the claims. One minister close to Varadkar labelled the coverage in the UK press as 'complete and utter bullshit'. Just weeks later, Labour MP Kate Hoey – who had notoriously suggested that Ireland would have to pay for any hard border – accused Varadkar of trying to differentiate himself from his predecessor. 'It's about him being a new Taoiseach and wanting to exert his difference from Enda Kenny,' Hoey told the *Irish Times*. 'I mean, Enda Kenny was engaged very positively in a lot of these discussions. I think things might have been very different if he had stayed on,' she added.

Minister for European Affairs Helen McEntee took part in regular briefings with Varadkar during the onslaught from the UK press. In an interview for this book, McEntee said the clear instruction from Varadkar and other officials was to keep calm in the face of adversity. 'Nobody likes to be painted as an enemy. Leo would be no different,' McEntee said.

> His view was always 'That's not going to get us anywhere' and if we want the right outcome and the right result, we need to have calm heads, cool minds and that's just what he applied. Calling names and throwing shapes at people wasn't going to get us anywhere. All that does is create a divide among ourselves, among the party as well.

Throughout the early days of his tenure as Taoiseach, Leo Varadkar had one complaint for his colleagues: 'I need to get a few wins.' He would repeat the gripe over and over again, wondering when he would finally add some solid achievements to his name. Those close to Varadkar say that moment finally came on 8 December 2017.

Days of backchannelling had taken place between Ireland's lead Brexit negotiator, John Callinan, and his UK counterpart, Olly Robbins. A deal on the border was edging ever closer between the two parties, who were being supported by Michel

Barnier and his negotiating team. London was keen for Varadkar and May to have direct talks the weekend previous – but Dublin insisted the two governments had to work on some form of text. On Monday, that text emerged, and the Irish government felt – almost through a sense of disbelief – that its decision to hold firm had won out.

According to Dublin sources, moves were then made to run the text by the DUP. Heavyweights from May's government such as Damian Green and Defence Secretary Gavin Williamson were tasked with convincing the unionist leadership. All of a sudden, the deal was in jeopardy. 'There was some discussion about what was in a text but not the full text,' says a source in the Varadkar camp. 'The DUP blew up and [May] decided she would have to hold off.'

Over the coming days, negotiations went into overdrive. But on the morning of Friday 8 December, Varadkar's negotiating team went home to bed at around 6 a.m., knowing that he had finally got that win. A win not just for him, but also the country and the EU. 'It was probably the best speech I've seen Leo give. And he wrote the vast majority of it himself,' says one senior government source, referring to the speech Varadkar gave at 8 a.m. that day, in which he declared the commitments by the UK to avoid a hard border as 'cast-iron' and 'bulletproof'. Indeed, Varadkar may have got his win, as the talks moved towards the second stage. But his political reputation, through his own actions, had now been staked on there being no visible border on the island of Ireland.

* * *

Varadkar's first encounter with May had also been his first overseas engagement with another head of state since his election as

Taoiseach. And the meeting at 10 Downing Street only compounded the view held by his critics that he was more spin than substance. It was a charge that would hold firm during the early days of his tenure. During their press conference on 19 June 2017, Varadkar told May of his 'thrill' at being able to visit the location of the Richard Curtis romantic comedy *Love Actually*:

> It's my first time in this building so there's a little thrill in it as well. We spoke on the way in and I was reminded of that famous scene in *Love Actually* where Hugh Grant does his dance down the stairs. But apparently it wasn't actually filmed here so I didn't get a chance to see the stairs.

Varadkar's *Love Actually* quip caused government spin doctors to quiver. His defenders said his behaviour showed an endearing and vulnerable side. Those who know him insist it is merely illustrative of his sense of awkwardness and his ability to become starstruck a little too easily. But Varadkar's encounters with leaders on the world stage would feed into a narrative that would be used against him by the opposition at every opportunity: an obsession with public relations and his media image, rather than housing and healthcare. And these encounters would also lead to questions in the media as to who exactly the Irish people had as their Taoiseach.

The case in point involves Justin Trudeau. Just two months after his first overseas visit to meet a head of state in Downing Street, Varadkar welcomed the Canadian Prime Minister as his first official foreign visitor. The pair hit it off and Trudeau's visit quickly appeared more like a reunion with a childhood friend than a serious bilateral. Iconic images appeared in the Irish press of the two Prime Ministers running side by side wearing sunglasses in the Phoenix Park. The pair showed off their novelty coloured socks and took part in a game of hurling. Trudeau's visit to Ireland would be followed by a return leg to Montreal, where Varadkar and his partner Matt joined the Canadian Prime Minister in marching in the Montreal Gay Pride Parade. But, once again, it fed into the hands of Varadkar's detractors, who say he is simply too obsessed with image.

Varadkar has told colleagues that he feels at his most comfortable when holding meetings with other world leaders, some of whom he regularly texts. He has also struck up warm relationships with Germany's Angela Merkel, France's Emmanuel Macron, Hungary's Viktor Orbán, Estonia's Jüri Ratas and Luxembourg's Xavier Bettel. But, without doubt, it was his meeting with one particular world leader that would represent an early test for the young Taoiseach. Months after describing his remarks as 'dangerous' and 'racist', Varadkar prepared for his first encounter with Donald Trump.

CHAPTER 19

TRUMP'S AMERICA

On the eve of St Patrick's Day 2018, the Taoiseach invited a group of journalists to an upmarket French-style restaurant called Boucherie in Greenwich Village in New York City. It was coming to the end of a week-long trade mission to the United States that centred on Leo Varadkar's first meeting as Prime Minister with US President Donald Trump and Vice-President Mike Pence. The seven-day state visit was, at times, politically awkward. The leaders were, after all, cut from very different cloth. Varadkar, on the one hand, was a very modern Taoiseach who upon his election had told his people that they would live in a Republic that would be equal and where prejudice would have no hold. And yet, Varadkar was due to meet two notoriously conservative statesmen who believed in building walls and banning entire nations from visiting their shores. There was bound, too, to be a certain dynamic to meetings between one of the world's very few openly gay leaders and the likes of Trump and Pence, who had benefited from the support of America's influential evangelical voters. But for now, it was time to relax.

Since taking office, the Taoiseach has made a virtue out of wining and dining journalists who accompany him on international trade missions. Varadkar has a different relationship with journalists from that of his predecessors Enda Kenny and Brian Cowen and believes it is important to spend time with them socially. After the week-long trek around the United States, he decided it was time to down tools in one of New York City's culinary hot spots. More than twenty guests, who included journalists from print and broadcast media, joined the Taoiseach and foreign affairs officials for a five-course, three-hour-long meal. The Taoiseach's own advisers had sourced tickets for the highly sought-after Broadway musical *Hamilton* and did not join the party. Varadkar had tickets for another show, *The Book of Mormon*, the following evening and intended to bring his partner, Matt Barrett.

In the French restaurant, the Taoiseach insisted on drinking American red wine in recognition of his stateside trade mission. His guests devoured French onion soup, foie gras, filet mignon and mushroom ravioli dusted with black truffles. The Taoiseach talked openly and frankly about matters of state and international affairs. After several glasses of wine, the journalists were bundled into a waiting bus and brought to Fitzpatrick's Manhattan Hotel in Midtown. The Taoiseach arrived later with Matt, who had flown in from Chicago, where he was working as a cardiologist. The couple had not seen each other for some time and were openly affectionate.

The next morning, the couple would make history by becoming the first gay couple to lead the New York St Patrick's Day parade. It would be hugely symbolic for LGBT rights, considering that little more than five years previous, homosexuals were prohibited from marching in the parade. Earlier that evening, the Taoiseach visited the Stonewall National Monument in Greenwich Village. The statue of two gay and lesbian couples sits outside the Stonewall Inn, which was the scene of violent clashes between the police and members of the New York LGBT community in the 1960s. Varadkar drank a beer with gay activists in the Stonewall Inn and spoke with a barman, who told the Taoiseach he had been present in the bar at the time of the civil rights riots. Afterwards, Varadkar ventured outside and posed for photographs at the monument and happily took selfies with passers-by.

Throughout the trade mission, the Taoiseach was dogged by questions about whether he would raise the issue of gay rights with President Trump and Vice-President Pence. The focal point of Varadkar's state visit to the US was undoubtedly his meeting with President Trump in the White House, but there was also intrigue and anticipation surrounding what he would say, if anything, to conservative hardliner Pence. Pence spent most of his political career campaigning against gay rights and has been forced to deny that he supports discredited 'conversion therapies', which claim to be able to change a person's sexual orientation. He is unashamed, though, of his ultra-Christian views and adding him to the presidential ticket was seen as an attempt by Trump to reach out to the large evangelical voter base that spans the US.

The Taoiseach had avoided raising the tricky issue of gay rights with most of the Republican politicians he encountered on his US trip. In Austin, he held a short meeting with the Republican Governor of Texas Greg Abbott. Abbott was criticised in 2017 for introducing laws that allowed faith-based welfare agencies to discriminate against the LGBT community. He also opposed marriage equality rights, which were granted to same-sex couples following a US Supreme Court ruling. The Governor also sought to introduce a controversial 'Bathroom Bill' which would prevent transgender people from using public toilets aligned with their chosen identity. But, to some surprise back home, Varadkar failed to raise the issue of gay rights.

On the day of his meeting with Governor Abbott, the Taoiseach spoke on the topic of gay rights at the music and tech-
nology festival South by Southwest. In a room full of young
liberals and tech types, Varadkar said that he had always viewed
America as a 'beacon of freedom' and noted the country was
the home of the LGBT movement. 'This is the land of the free,
the home of the brave – this is where the gay rights movement began,' Varadkar told a packed hall. 'It's really tough to
see a country built on freedom, built on individual freedom,
not being a world leader in that space any more. I think the
majority of American people would agree with what I have to
say, even if the administration doesn't.'

The following day, the Taoiseach and his entourage drove to
Oklahoma to meet the Choctaw Nation. Along the way, they
held a brief meeting with Governor of Oklahoma Mary Fallin,
another staunchly conservative Republican politician who opposed marriage equality. But, yet again, the Taoiseach did not
use the meeting as an opportunity to tackle the issue.

In Washington, DC he shared a stage with Republican Congressman Peter King. King is an Irish American politician who
has opposed gay rights all his life and is credited with being
the brainchild behind President Trump's ban on people from
certain Muslim countries entering the US. The Congressman
also played an important role in negotiating the Good Friday
Agreement, which brought peace to Northern Ireland. At an
event marking the twentieth anniversary of the agreement,
King, despite sharing the stage with Varadkar, did not applaud
with the rest of the audience when the Taoiseach spoke about
attending a Gay Pride parade in Belfast.

The stage was now set for the two most anticipated meetings of the St Patrick's Day visit. Journalists covering the trip
directly asked Varadkar whether he would speak to Pence about

conversion therapy for gay people when they met. 'I'm told Vice-President Pence is not a supporter of conversion therapy even though some people have alleged he is,' Varadkar responded. 'But I imagine if I have the opportunity – I'm going to meet him over breakfast – so if I have the opportunity I'll certainly be mentioning the wider issue of equal rights and freedoms for LGBT,' he added.

The St Patrick's Day breakfast meeting between the Vice-President and the Taoiseach traditionally takes place early in the morning on the day of the official visit to the White House. However, Pence had decided to reschedule the breakfast event in his official residence, the United States Naval Observatory, for the day after Varadkar's meeting with Trump. The Vice-President's office also decided to break with tradition and banned the media from attending the event. It was a peculiar decision given that the previous year the media had been free to both attend and record the speeches by Pence and Enda Kenny.

The decision to ban the media from the event immediately set off alarm bells within the Taoiseach's entourage. Calls were made to Pence's office, but no explanation was given as to why reporters were not allowed to cover the annual event. Sources in the Varadkar camp said they were hugely disappointed by the decision and were suspicious of the reasons behind it. The decision was relayed to reporters in a briefing issued two days before the event. 'Please note that I have been informed this afternoon that the only media opportunity for the Vice-President's breakfast is the arrival shot. The remarks are not open to the press. Please let me know if that will affect your decision on whether or not to cover this event,' it read.

The press ban was front-page news in Ireland but got little, if any, coverage in the US. Further efforts were made by the Taoiseach's advisers and Department of Foreign Affairs staff to overturn the decision, but to no avail. The decision was final. A source in the Vice-President's office said it was not out of the ordinary for Pence to hold meetings with world leaders behind closed doors and insisted the previous five meetings with dignitaries were held in private. However, the decision to dramatically change traditional St Patrick's Day protocol ahead of a meeting with Ireland's first gay leader led most observers to suspect that Pence was seeking to avoid a potentially embarrassing showdown over gay rights.

On 15 March 2018, the Taoiseach and his handlers arrived at the White House for the much-anticipated meeting with President Trump. The two leaders posed awkwardly for photographs and questions in the Oval Office. Varadkar tried to speak to Trump prior to their private engagement, but the President seemed distracted by the baying mob of journalists throwing questions at him about his plans to visit Ireland and the poisoning of a former Russian spy and his daughter in the UK.

After the photo opportunity at the Oval Office, Varadkar, Trump and their closest advisers gathered in private to discuss trade, migration and the President's golf course in Doonbeg, Co. Clare. Trump's chief of staff John Kelly was there, as was Secretary of Commerce Wilbur Ross and director of the Office of Management and Budget Mick Mulvaney. Varadkar brought his own chief of staff Brian Murphy, press secretary Nick Miller, Secretary General at the Department of the Taoiseach Martin Fraser and Irish Envoy to the US John Deasy. Vice-President Pence was also in the room. He and Varadkar exchanged pleasantries but did not have the opportunity to speak at length.

During the press conference after the meeting, the Taoiseach told reporters his preference was that the meeting with Pence would be held in public but conceded that the ultimate decision rested with the Vice-President. 'I appreciate from a media point of view you'd like to be there, and we'd like you to be there too but it's their decision that it be closed,' Varadkar said. 'It allows us have maybe a frank conversation that we wouldn't be able to have if the media was present,' he added.

Later that day, the Taoiseach returned to the White House for the traditional Shamrock ceremony. In his speech before the ceremonial handover of the bowl of shamrock, the Taoiseach referenced the poem 'Old Ireland' by American poet and gay icon Walt Whitman. 'President Lincoln was memorialised in verse for all time by the poet of your national imagination, Walt Whitman. Whitman, writing about Ireland, described it as "an isle of wondrous beauty", and our people who were weathering a storm to cross the Atlantic,' the Taoiseach said. It was a subtle but pointed reference to the Taoiseach's own background and sexuality.

At the reception, Varadkar had a brief chat with Pence and his wife Karen. Pence asked why the Taoiseach's partner Matt had not accompanied him to the White House. Varadkar told Pence his partner was unable to get time off work in the busy hospital where he works in Chicago. Pence then told the Taoiseach that both men would be welcome in his home should they decide to return to Washington for next year's St Patrick's Day festivities. It was quite a step for a politician accused of supporting groups who believe in conversion therapy for gay people. The Taoiseach was surprised but graciously accepted the invitation.

The news of the invitation did not emerge until after the Taoiseach had attended the private breakfast meeting in the Vice-President's residency. Over spinach and mushroom omelettes and sliced avocado, Varadkar and Pence conversed warmly, joked and lavished each other's countries with praise. When he addressed the media about his meeting with Pence and his wife, the Taoiseach welcomed the invitation extended to him and his partner. 'They were very well-briefed,' he said. 'They knew about my personal story. They knew my partner is living in Chicago, and they said that both Matt and I would be very welcome to visit there in the future. It was a very nice gesture,' he added.

But, overall, Leo Varadkar's first official visit to the White House as Taoiseach will not be remembered for the strides he made for the gay community. Rather, the lasting memory for his advisers will be the unfortunate diplomatic gaffe he made at a lunch hosted by the Republican Speaker of the House of Representatives Paul Ryan.

During his morning meeting with Trump in the White House, the Taoiseach reminded the President that it was not the first time they had spoken. Some years back, when Varadkar was Minister for Transport, Sport and Tourism, his office had received a phone call from Trump about the proposed development of a wind farm near the businessman's golf club in Doonbeg, Co. Clare. Trump had asked Varadkar if there was anything he could do to prevent the construction of the renewable energy turbines, as he believed it would detract from the natural beauty of Doonbeg and potentially result in a loss of business.

Varadkar's advisers said the Taoiseach raised the matter with Trump at his White House meeting because they wanted to find a way to connect with the notoriously fickle President. They believed it would soften up the tough-talking business-man and make him more amenable to other topics of discussion, such as trade, immigration and tax reform. At the post-White House meeting press conference, Varadkar mentioned that they had discussed the President's golf course. This didn't raise any eyebrows, however, as Trump had already mentioned his Doonbeg resort during the Oval Office photo opportunity. But what happened next would prove deeply embarrassing and indeed damaging for Varadkar.

The full extent of their conversation and their previous encounter emerged just over an hour later, when the two leaders travelled to Capitol Hill for Speaker Ryan's lunch. In his speech, Trump welcomed the Taoiseach to Washington and said the two men had 'long experience'. He added that the Taoiseach would explain the story behind this when he addressed the meeting shortly. 'We actually knew each other from a different life and it was very successful,' Trump said. When Varadkar took to his feet, he recounted how he did not at first believe it when his assistant John Carroll told him Donald Trump had called his office. Varadkar said Trump had told him he had bought a 'beautiful golf resort called Doonbeg' but was disappointed to hear a company was seeking to build a wind farm near his hotel and golf club. Trump told Varadkar this would 'impact tourism and the beauty of the landscape'. With the ear of the room, the Taoiseach continued:

> So I endeavoured to do what I could do about it and I rang the county council and enquired about the planning permission and subsequently the planning permission was declined and the wind farm was never built – thus the landscape being preserved – and the President has very kindly given me credit for that, although I do think it probably would have been refused anyway.

The Taoiseach got a laugh from the assembled dignitaries and President Trump also smiled approvingly. But the press pack were immediately filing the comments to their news desk or posting them on Twitter.

Varadkar had previously mentioned the interaction with Trump over the wind energy farm in an interview with *Time* magazine but he had not gone so far as to say that he had lobbied a local authority on behalf of the businessman. The remarks immediately gave way to the suggestion that Trump had asked Varadkar to intervene in a planning application. And, as reported immediately afterwards, the then minister obliged and the proposed wind farm was rejected.

The story made headline news in Ireland and was blasted across television and radio bulletins. Such a gaffe was considered more typical of Enda Kenny than the media-savvy Leo Varadkar. The Taoiseach's advisers went into panic mode. Desperate phone calls were made to journalists seeking to downplay the significance of the Taoiseach's remarks. Advisers insisted it was just a light-hearted joke aimed at winning over the President's affections. They stressed that Varadkar had acted entirely appropriately and no planning laws were contravened. But it was too late: the damage was done.

Opposition leaders sitting at home in Ireland pounced on the faux pas. Statements were issued calling on the Taoiseach to clarify what action he had taken on Trump's behalf. And things were about to get worse. Following a barrage of media queries, Clare County Council, the local authority responsible for planning decisions at Doonbeg, issued a statement insisting they had no record of any correspondence or phone call from Mr Varadkar or his officials. The company behind the renewable energy project also published a statement saying the firm was disappointed that the former minister had 'interfered' in the planning process and said it would review the matter. Despite the escalating controversy, the Taoiseach's aides continued to dismiss the opposition's uproar over his involvement in the planning application as a 'ball of smoke'. But pressure was building. The Taoiseach had to address the matter and provide some reassurance that he had not acted inappropriately at Trump's behest. Outside an arts centre in New York the following afternoon, the Taoiseach admitted that he had not actually contacted Clare County Council at all. His memory of events had been incorrect, he revealed.

After the phone call from Trump, the Taoiseach instead emailed Shaun Quinn, the then chief executive of the state's tourism agency, Fáilte Ireland, writing:

> I took a call from Donald Trump last Friday. He is concerned about plans to build very large wind farms near Doonbeg. I don't want to get into the nitty gritty of it but I did commit to asking Fáilte to review the planning applications or development plan for Clare as appropriate with a view to making observations if the agency shared his concerns about the impact on landscapes and tourism.

Fáilte Ireland followed up with an explanatory note issued to journalists explaining the action the agency took following the call. The controversy soon subsided as opposition politicians backtracked from their earlier indignation.

When the Taoiseach returned from his first US trade mission, there was little said in the Dáil about the gaffe. However, the embarrassing incident did give him a greater appreciation of the various cock-ups that had landed Enda Kenny in hot water when he was in the Taoiseach's office.

EPILOGUE

IRELAND'S 'SECOND CHANCE'

As Leo Varadkar walked through the corridors of Government Buildings on his way to the weekly Cabinet meeting on Tuesday morning, his phone vibrated in his pocket. It was a text message from his mother, Miriam. 'It is always the woman's right to choose,' she said. She knew her son was facing the political battle of his career as he prepared to stage the first referendum on abortion in thirty-five years.

In a matter of weeks, the Irish people would be asked to remove Article 40.3.3, otherwise known as the Eighth Amendment, from the constitution. The 1983 provision, which gives equal right to the life of the mother and the unborn child, has served as a potent symbol of division in Ireland for over three decades. Those who campaigned to insert the Eighth Amendment into the constitution say it underpins Ireland's Catholic values – a desire to protect the unborn child. Opponents, however, insist the amendment has forced thousands of vulnerable women to take lonely boat trips or plane journeys to England because abortion services were outlawed in Ireland.

Varadkar believed he was part of a majority who felt, deep down, that the lifespan of the Eighth Amendment had reached its conclusion a long time ago. Ireland's abortion laws were, in his view, too restrictive and needed to be liberalised. They were the cause of so much hurt to the lives of families who, in many cases, had already been dealt the cruellest of hands.

Varadkar believed, like his mother Miriam, that it was time to allow women the right to choose. But less than a year into his premiership, the relatively inexperienced Taoiseach was faced with a judgement call over a piece of law that was introduced before he was in primary school. The question on the ballot paper needed to be carefully considered; otherwise, the status quo on abortion would remain for years to come. Indeed, any miscalculation could also have devastating consequences politically for the government and for the Fine Gael leader personally.

The text message from Miriam weighed heavily on Varadkar's mind as he prepared to convene one of the most important Cabinet meetings of his career. His mother, although always extremely supportive of her son, rarely offers her own political insight. So, when she does, Leo tends to listen.

Miriam and her husband Ashok always considered themselves socially liberal. In India, Ashok's country of birth, abortion had been legal for decades. The couple had also spent their lives working in hospitals and had seen first-hand the realities of crisis pregnancies. Their daughters, Sonia and Sophie, have always been pro-choice and have many friends who have experienced crisis pregnancies.

Varadkar's own approach to the abortion issue had been far from liberal for most his career. He was part of a group within Young Fine Gael that called for the liberalisation of abortion laws as far back as 1997. However, in the years that followed, Varadkar's views on the subject became deeply conservative. He was opposed to abortion in most circumstances, even expressing unease about providing terminations for women who had been raped. While serving in opposition, he drew a comparison between women travelling overseas to access abortion services with people who visit Amsterdam in order to experience the drug culture.

As a young TD, Varadkar watched with great sadness and regret as some of his closest friends in Fine Gael lost the whip after opposing the party's stance on the Protection of Life During Pregnancy Bill. But, like many others in Irish politics, his views were shaped by the outcome of the work of the Citizens' Assembly, as well as the Oireachtas Committee on the Eighth Amendment, which proposed an unrestricted abortion regime of up to twelve weeks.

For Varadkar, the abortion referendum was about presenting the Irish people with a second chance to change the state's abortion laws. He tasked his Health Minister Simon Harris with drafting the legislation that would pave the way for a historic public vote on 25 May 2018. After reappointing him to Cabinet, Varadkar briefed Harris on his three objectives: 1) to hold the referendum; 2) to win it; and 3) not to split the party over the issue.

But weeks before the legislation could be brought before Cabinet, Varadkar realised that keeping the party together was not going to be so straightforward. And it was his Tánaiste, Simon Coveney, the very man who had challenged him in the leadership contest, who posed the most serious threat.

* * *

After weathering his first big crisis as Taoiseach over the garda whistleblower scandal, Varadkar knew that the first half of 2018 would be dominated by the abortion issue. Behind the scenes, he discussed with his key advisers how best to publicly outline his own position and his plans to campaign in favour of the twelve-week proposal. The Taoiseach knew that concessions would have to be made in order to ensure the proposals from the Oireachtas committee were palatable – not only to the public but also to the Fine Gael party. It quickly became clear that there was a sizeable number of Fine Gael TDs who felt the twelve-week proposal went too far.

The issue was also causing division within Fianna Fáil and Sinn Féin. Just months earlier, Fianna Fáil grassroots members had passed a motion at the party's Ard Fheis calling for the Eighth Amendment to be retained. The position of many of the party's conservative TDs was absolute: there should be no change to the status quo. Sinn Féin, under its new leader Mary Lou McDonald, was also facing the prospect of losing two of its own TDs – Peadar Tóibín and Carol Nolan – over the party's stance in favour of repeal.

Before the Cabinet could take a position on the abortion issue, Varadkar consulted some of his own conservative-leaning ministers who had deep reservations about the journey ahead. There were plenty of ministers, such as Regina Doherty, Paschal Donohoe, Eoghan Murphy, Josepha Madigan, Mary Mitchell O'Connor and Helen McEntee, who, alongside Simon Harris, were prepared to vigorously campaign for a Yes vote. This group would soon be joined by several others, including Charlie Flanagan and Richard Bruton. But a number of rural-based ministers, including Simon Coveney, Michael Creed, Michael Ring and Heather Humphreys, were wavering over the twelve-week proposal.

In an interview for this book, Varadkar reveals for the first time the options explored with his team of officials in order to prevent a split in his party. The Taoiseach considered the idea of holding two referendums on the same day, after coming under pressure from Coveney and Creed. The first would be a straight yes or no to the question of whether to repeal the Eighth Amendment. The second, in the form of a plebiscite, would ask whether people agreed with the idea of unrestricted access to abortions up to twelve weeks. 'We were genuinely worried the referendum would be defeated because of the twelve-week [proposal],' Varadkar says.

> That would have been a disaster. That would have been the worst-case scenario where people actually voted to change nothing because we asked the wrong question. So we considered a second question, which was the plebiscite option. If people voted for the twelve weeks, fine, that would be in the legislation. If they didn't, we would do something more restrictive.

Holding a constitutional vote alongside a non-binding plebiscite was described by Varadkar as a 'national referendum'. It has never happened before in the history of the state. Varadkar soon found out why.

As the prospect of a national referendum was being actively considered, Varadkar's team was informed by the Attorney General of a little-known veto clause in the constitution contained in Article 47. If the national referendum option had been pursued, the result of the plebiscite would have been based on the full electorate and not just the number of people that turned out to vote. The article also states that the proposal will be vetoed if one third of those on the register of electors vote against the question. It was a minefield – untested, far too complex and deeply unpredictable. 'We went up all these rabbit holes all these times,' Varadkar says of the various options explored.

With the media piling pressure on all ministers to lay out their positions, Varadkar held several secret conversations with his Tánaiste. Varadkar discussed with Coveney his plans to introduce measures that were not proposed by the Oireachtas committee. For example, ensuring the legislation provided for a 72-hour reflection period between the time of certification and the termination of the pregnancy. This would allow for a period of counselling to take place if agreeable by the mother.

Other safeguards were also thrashed out between Varadkar and Coveney ahead of the publication of the bill. An original proposal by the committee for a 'GP-led' service was changed to a 'doctor-led' service. But Coveney told Varadkar that he was deeply torn over the twelve-week proposal.

The prospect of the Tánaiste campaigning on the other side to the Taoiseach would have created an extraordinary dilemma for Fine Gael. 'Simon genuinely wrestled with the issue,' Varadkar says.

> We spoke about it on a number of occasions. He was genuinely wrestling with the issue as a public policy question and he was also genuinely wrestling with the issue of not wanting to be a deputy leader and a Tánaiste who was going against what the government was trying to do and what I was trying to do.

But before Coveney could publicly declare his position, another leading Cork politician caused considerable surprise in political circles. Micheál Martin, without warning to even some of his closest supporters in Fianna Fáil, entered the Dáil chamber and delivered an impassioned and considered speech on the Eighth Amendment. Having previously opposed any substantial change to Ireland's abortion laws, the Fianna Fáil leader backed the twelve-week proposal. 'If a family is told of a fatal abnormality during a pregnancy, the law, as it stands and as it is required to be under the Eighth Amendment, says that they can do nothing,' Martin said. 'Under threat of a criminal sentence they must carry the pregnancy to its term irrespective of the potentially devastating impact it will have.'

The decision by the leader of the opposition came as a major boost to Varadkar's bid to secure a Yes vote. Varadkar knew Martin, like Mary Lou McDonald, would be an asset to the Yes campaign. He has a particular appeal to rural and conservative voters and his backing was warmly welcomed in government circles.

Just days after Martin's intervention, Coveney set out his stall. In an interview with RTÉ broadcaster Sean O'Rourke, the Foreign Affairs Minister said he would support a repeal of the Eighth Amendment. But, crucially, he said he could not back unrestricted access up to twelve weeks. 'The circumstances of an abortion or terminating a pregnancy needs to be justified if it is going to happen in order to protect women as opposed to having unrestricted access or no protection in law at all for an unborn child,' Coveney said. 'Which is what is being proposed by some in the case of unrestricted access for the first twelve weeks to abortion services in Ireland,' he added.

Coveney's stance was confusing and untenable in the eyes of a number of Fine Gael ministers. But the Varadkar camp knew that the Tánaiste's position would, at worst, prove to be an unhelpful distraction rather than a destabilising force on the referendum itself.

On the evening of 29 January, the Taoiseach concluded a historic Cabinet meeting and made his way to the press centre in Government Buildings. Flanked by Simon Harris and

Children's Minister Katherine Zappone, Varadkar formally announced plans for a summer referendum. He also confirmed his intention to campaign for a Yes vote. 'However difficult, I believe the time has come for the people to make this decision,' Varadkar told reporters. 'The question has to be a yes or no one. Do we reform our abortion laws or leave them as they are? For my part I will advocate a Yes vote; my own views have evolved over time. Life experience does that.'

Just three weeks later, the Cabinet agreed the formal wording that would be put to the people on 25 May. Thirty-five years after introducing the Eighth Amendment into the constitution, the voters of 2018 would be asked whether 'Provision may be made by law for the regulation of termination of pregnancies'.

But shortly before the campaign itself kicked off, Varadkar was handed another surprise boost. Just weeks after declaring his opposition to the twelve-week proposal, Simon Coveney changed his mind again. In an opinion piece published in the *Irish Independent*, the Tánaiste switched to the government's side:

> I will say at Cabinet tomorrow that I could support a law that allows access to such medication up to twelve weeks' gestation, effectively 10 weeks of pregnancy, if it is coupled with strict medical guidelines – resulting in a 'clinical protocol' to be followed in every case when an abortion is requested.

Varadkar and Harris had now met the first and third of their three objectives. The referendum was scheduled to take place on 25 May and the prospect of a party split had been abated. All that was left to do was win the vote.

* * *

As with the marriage equality referendum three years earlier, it was the powerful testimony of women and men affected by abortion that set the tone of the campaign. Women who had endured horrendous ordeals bravely put their own personal accounts on public display. These were stories that, for too long, been kept secret. So many other women went to their graves having lived for years chained by silence and shame. The No side was at all stages on the back foot. They were up against extremely well-organised opponents, led by the effective 'Together for Yes'.

Varadkar did not play an instrumental role publicly in the campaign itself and refused to take part in any of the televised debates. He had the luxury of leaving that to his Cabinet, most notably Simon Harris, who won plaudits across the political spectrum for his role in the campaign.

However, attempts to depoliticise the referendum were not always successful. At one stage, pro-choice campaigners proposed arranging a public event that would be attended by Varadkar and the other party leaders. But Fine Gael backed off when it emerged that the event would be attended by just Varadkar and Mary Lou McDonald. 'We thought that was unwise, to have a joint Fine Gael–Sinn Féin [event],' Varadkar admits.

Addressing his parliamentary party just days before polling, Varadkar urged against the sort of celebrations that had taken place when Ireland said yes to gay marriage. This was different. Regardless of the result, people were going to be upset. Varadkar knew that so many people who had decided to vote Yes had, like him, reached that conclusion with considerable difficulty. The people Varadkar was considering were those who belong to 'Middle Ireland'. And they hold the key to any politician seeking power.

For Varadkar, 25 May was not about lauding the start of a new chapter for modern-day Ireland. Instead, it was about closing the door on another chapter – a chapter that the generation of today, Varadkar's generation, never had a say in writing.

As polling day approached, the Taoiseach considered the potential implications of a No vote. 'I think it would have been damaging. It would have been seen as a big failure,' he told the authors in an interview for this book. 'A lot of people in civil society groups and campaign groups who think we did a good job today would have blamed us. "The government didn't do this, didn't do that, didn't explain, didn't campaign hard enough."'

Around 10 p.m. on 25 May, an exit poll was published by the *Irish Times*, suggesting that voters had backed repeal of the Eighth Amendment in dramatic fashion. When the results came in the following day, the exit poll was confirmed: the final tally was 66.4 per cent Yes versus 33.6 per cent No. Thirty-nine out of the country's forty constituencies backed repeal. Ireland, for so long wrapped in the straitjacket of the Catholic Church, had broken free.

* * *

As Leo Varadkar arrived at Dublin Castle, he thought about the text message his mother had sent him months previously. The women referred to by Miriam Varadkar had been given that choice that they had so long sought. Many of them were present at Dublin Castle on that historic day. The tears of joy rolling down their faces told the world exactly what the vote meant to them and their families.

'A quiet revolution has taken place,' Leo said. 'I believe everyone deserves a second chance. This is Ireland's second chance.'

ACKNOWLEDGEMENTS

Firstly, we would like to thank the dozens of politicians, friends, officials, supporters and critics of Leo Varadkar who entrusted us with their time and insight.

A special mention goes to Independent News and Media, particularly journalists Des Gibson, Kevin Doyle, Cormac Bourke, Fionnan Sheahan, Stephen Rae, John Downing, Ken Foy and Robin Schiller for their tremendous support and advice.

Our publishers, Biteback Publishing, in particular Olivia Beattie and Iain Dale, are owed a huge deal of gratitude. Thank you for taking a chance on us and for your constant professionalism and guidance.

Others who lent support along the way, including Dan O'Connor, Pat Byrne (RIP), Paul Kehoe and Alan Kinsella.

Our most important acknowledgements go to the Ryan and O'Connor families, and indeed our close friends, whose love and patience will never be forgotten. Thank you for always believing in us.

Finally, we would like to thank Leo Varadkar and his family.

Philip Ryan and Niall O'Connor

ABOUT THE AUTHORS

PHILIP RYAN is an award-winning journalist working for Ireland's biggest newspaper group, Independent News and Media (INM). Philip is a political correspondent across all of the group's titles, including the *Sunday Independent*, *Irish Independent*, *The Herald* and Independent.ie. He has previously worked as an investigative journalist for the *Irish Mail on Sunday* and the *Irish Daily Mail*.

NIALL O'CONNOR is Ireland's 'Young Journalist of the Year 2017/18' and has written extensively about politics and current affairs for the *Irish Independent* and *Herald* newspapers. The Wicklow native was recently appointed special adviser to Ireland's minister with responsibility for defence.

INDEX

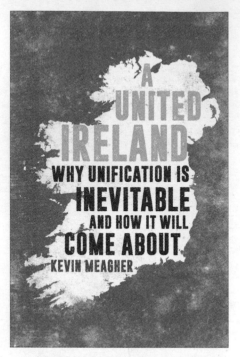

256PP HARDBACK, £12.99

For over two centuries, the 'Irish Question' has dogged British politics in one form or another – Northern Ireland's 'Troubles' being perhaps the bloodiest manifestation. And although the past twenty years have seen intensive efforts to secure a devolved local settlement via the Good Friday Agreement, its principle of consent – which holds that the country cannot leave the UK without a majority vote – has meant that the constitutional status of Northern Ireland remains moot.

Remote from the UK mainland in terms of its politics, economy and societal attitudes, Northern Ireland is placed, in effect, in an antechamber – subject to shifting demographic trends which are eroding the once-dominant Protestant Unionist majority, making a future referendum on the province's status a racing certainty. Indeed, in the light of Brexit and a highly probable second independence referendum in Scotland, the reunification of Ireland is not a question of 'if', but 'when' – and 'how'.

In *A United Ireland*, Kevin Meagher argues that a reasoned, pragmatic discussion about Britain's relationship with its nearest neighbour is now long overdue, and questions that have remained unasked (and perhaps unthought) must now be answered.

— AVAILABLE FROM ALL GOOD BOOKSHOPS —